UCLA FORUM IN MEDICAL SCIENCES

UNIVERSITY OF CALIFORNIA LOS ANGELES

BRAIN FUNCTION

VOLUME II

RNA AND BRAIN FUNCTION
MEMORY AND LEARNING

UCLA FORUM IN MEDICAL SCIENCES

NUMBER 2

BRAIN FUNCTION

VOLUME II

Proceedings of the Second Conference, 1962

RNA AND BRAIN FUNCTION
MEMORY AND LEARNING

Sponsored by the Brain Research Institute, University of California Los Angeles,
in collaboration with the American Institute of Biological Sciences
and with the support of the U.S. Air Force Office of Scientific Research

EDITOR

MARY A. B. BRAZIER

UNIVERSITY OF CALIFORNIA PRESS

BERKELEY AND LOS ANGELES

1964

EDITORIAL NOTE

The present volume contains the proceedings of the second in a series of conferences on Brain Function, supported by grants made to Dr. H. W. Magoun of the Brain Research Institute of the University of California Los Angeles. The American Institute of Biological Sciences acted as co-sponsor.

The first conference of the series, on Cortical Excitability and Steady Potentials, was published as UCLA Forum in Medical Sciences No. 1. The third conference, on Speech, Language and Communication, held November 1963, will appear as UCLA Forum in Medical Sciences No. 3. The fourth conference, dealing with the Learning Process and Education was held in November 1964.

CITATION FORM

Brazier, M. A. B. (Ed.), *Brain Function, Vol. II: RNA and Brain Function; Memory and Learning*. UCLA Forum Med. Sci. No. 2, Univ. of California Press, Los Angeles, 1964

University of California Press
Berkeley and Los Angeles, California

Cambridge University Press
London, England

Library of Congress Catalog Card Number: 64-22268
Printed in the United States of America

PARTICIPANTS IN THE CONFERENCE

H. W. MAGOUN, *Co-Chairman*
Brain Research Institute, University of California Los Angeles
Los Angeles, California

F. FREMONT-SMITH, *Co-Chairman**
American Institute of Biological Sciences
Time and Life Building, Rockefeller Center
New York, New York

M. A. B. BRAZIER, *Editor*
Brain Research Institute, University of California Los Angeles
Los Angeles, California

W. R. ADEY
Brain Research Institute, University of California Los Angeles
Los Angeles, California

P. K. ANOKHIN†
Laboratory of Neurophysiology, Academy of Medical Sciences
Moscow, USSR

R. E. BELLEVILLE
Behavioral Biology Program
National Aeronautics and Space Administration
Washington, D. C.

S. BENZER
Department of Biological Sciences, Purdue University
Lafayette, Indiana

R. G. BICKFORD
Mayo Clinic
Rochester, Minnesota

---

* Present address: Interdisciplinary Communications Program
  New York Academy of Sciences
  New York, New York
† Not present.

M. Calvin
Department of Chemistry, University of California
Berkeley, California

J. A. Deutsch
Department of Psychology, Stanford University
Stanford, California

W. Feindel
Montreal Neurological Institute
Montreal, Canada

S. W. Fox
Institute for Space Biosciences
Florida State University
Tallahassee, Florida

J. D. French
Brain Research Institute, University of California Los Angeles
Los Angeles, California

D. A. Glaser
Department of Physics, University of California
Berkeley, California

J. D. Green
Brain Research Institute, University of California Los Angeles
Los Angeles, California

J. Henry
Department of Physiology, University of Southern California
Los Angeles, California

A. W. Hetherington
Headquarters Air Force Systems Command
Andrews Air Force Base
Washington, D.C.

W. Hild
Department of Anatomy, The University of Texas
Galveston, Texas

H. Hydén
Institute of Neurobiology, Faculty of Medicine
University of Göteborg
Göteborg, Sweden

E. R. John*
Center for Brain Research, University of Rochester
Rochester, New York

* Present address: Brain Research Laboratory
New York Medical School
New York, New York

A. B. Kogan*
Chair of Human and Animal Physiology
Scientific Research Institute of Biology, The Rostov State University
Rostov-on-Don, USSR

J. V. Luco
Laboratorio de Neurofisiología, Universidad Católica de Chile
Santiago, Chile

J. V. McConnell
Department of Psychology, University of Michigan
Ann Arbor, Michigan

M. Mishkin
National Institute of Mental Health
National Institutes of Health
Bethesda, Maryland

W. F. H. M. Mommaerts
Department of Physiology, University of California Los Angeles
Los Angeles, California

F. Morrell
Department of Neurology
Stanford University School of Medicine
Palo Alto, California

M. W. Nirenberg
National Heart Institute
National Institutes of Health
Bethesda, Maryland

S. L. Palay
Department of Anatomy, Harvard Medical School
Boston, Massachusetts

G. D. Pappas
College of Physicians and Surgeons, Columbia University
New York, New York

O. E. Reynolds
Bioscience Programs, Office of Space Sciences
National Aeronautics and Space Administration
Washington, D. C.

R. Sinsheimer
Division of Biology, California Institute of Technology
Pasadena, California

---

* Not present.

G. Svaetichin[*]
Departamento de Fisiología
Instituto Venezolano de Investigaciones Científicas
Caracas, Venezuela

R. Thompson[†]
Neuropsychiatric Institute, University of California Los Angeles
Los Angeles, California

M. Victor
Cleveland Metropolitan General Hospital
Cleveland, Ohio

L. Weiskrantz
Psychological Laboratory, University of Cambridge
Cambridge, England

---

[*] Not present.
[†] Present address: Department of Psychology, Louisiana State University
Baton Rouge, Louisiana

1664-1964

The year 1964 marks the three hundredth anniversary of the publication of Thomas Willis' celebrated *Cerebri Anatome*, the most complete and accurate description of the nervous system to appear up to that time. His observations on the relation of brain and memory are of particular interest as background for the present volume. The following is an excerpt* from this famous book:

"The ancients offered nothing on the general function and use of the cerebellum worthy of its craftsmanship or suited to its structure. Some have decided that it is another cerebrum and performs the same actions as that; but if anyone were to be provided with a fool's soft cerebrum, I very much doubt that he would become wise if he were to obtain a harder and more solid cerebellum. Some locate memory in this place, supposing the cerebellum to be like a chest or repository in which the idea or image of things already recognized may be preserved separately from newly entering appearances; but it is far more likely that this faculty resides in the cortical gyri of the cerebellum (as we demonstrated elsewhere), for as often as we attempt to remember something long past we rub our temples and the forepart of our head; we arouse the cerebrum and stir up the indwelling spirits as if busily seeking to pluck out something lying hidden there; meanwhile we attempt nothing at the rear of the head, nor are we conscious of any movement there. Furthermore, we have demonstrated that phantasy and imagination act in the cerebrum, but memory so depends upon imagination that its action seems to be reflective or inverted. Therefore it is necessary that memory be located in the same cloister, that is, in the cerebrum, for it is very clear that there is no direct communication between the cerebrum and cerebellum."

---

* Translated by Professor C. D. O'Malley from the first edition of: WILLIS, THOMAS, *Cerebri Anatome: cui accessit nervorum descriptio et usus*. Studio . . . Londini, Typis Tho. Roycraft, impensis Jo. Martyn & Ja. Allestry, 1664.

THOMAS WILLIS

1621-1675

Author of *Cerebri Anatome* (1664), which has the first accurate drawing
of the temporal lobes. In modern times this part of the brain has been implicated as important for the function of memory.

(From the portrait commissioned in 1742 by his grandson, Browne Willis.)

CONTENTS

APPENDIX

INTRODUCTION

H. W. MAGOUN
Chairman

This conference is one of a series designed to explore the brain mechanisms underlying various phenomena usually subsumed under behavioral fields. An earlier conference has examined factors influencing cortical excitability. This one is concerned with the phenomena of learning and memory. Because of suggestions that analogies might be drawn between information storage in genetic and in memory processes, exponents of both these fields have been invited to join in the interchange of data and views.

In the great scientific advances of this present age, achievements in nuclear physics have been followed closely by those in molecular biology. Outstanding among the latter has been the accumulated knowledge of the role of DNA in the genetic code. While a century ago biologists repudiated vitalistic factors and sought understanding of life processes in scientific terms, only currently does the prospect seem feasible for gaining real insight into the information storage and control mechanisms of the cell. The genetically coded nucleotide sequences of the DNA macromolecules of the nucleus are being found to constitute the blueprint of heredity, through RNA control of cytoplasmic protein and enzyme production.

In a recent symposium on *Scientific Change*, at Oxford, Bentley Glass (2) pointed out: "Within the past decade geneticists far and wide have come to accept what is not infrequently called the dogma of the holy trinity, DNA . . . , RNA . . . , and protein. The dogma . . . takes the following form: in all organisms . . . the ultimate story of genetic information which is replicated and passed on from generation to generation lies in the DNA of the chromosomes contained within the nucleus of each cell. DNA not only replicates itself, but also passes on to RNA a code of information in the chemical form of a specific sequence of the nucleotides making up the nucleic acid molecule. RNA moves from the nucleus into the cytoplasm and there presides over the synthesis of protein molecules, in such a way that a specific sequence of nucleotides in the RNA molecule becomes translated into a specific sequence of amino acids in a polypeptide molecule; and polypeptides are combined into protein molecules of specific sorts."

There are a number of investigators today who propose that nature has not been profligate enough to have evolved more than a single process for

1

information coding and storage in biology. Current research is exploring the possibility that the unique organ of the body, devoted chiefly to the storage and retrieval of information and to control, namely the brain, may depend for its learning and memory functions upon modification of neuronal RNA, of which the ubiquitous Nissl substance of the nerve cell has been found to be composed. Such specified and replicated RNA is proposed, in turn, to provide the template for elaboration of neural transmitter substances, responsible for consequent patterns of postsynaptic firing or inhibition.

In a recent conference on *Information Storage and Neural Control* at Houston, Ralph Gerard (1) has remarked: "The environment normally does not alter the DNA molecules, although it is ultimately responsible for the rare and random genetic mutations. Rather, it selects one or another set of these molecules in terms of the phenotypes produced and of the relative degree of their adaptation to the environment. This is Darwinian evolution—natural selection of certain molecules from an array of possible DNA molecules or groups of molecules. But when a given DNA molecule starts to operate in a given organism, it produces messenger RNA and ribosome RNA and proteins and enzymes and all the rest; and somehow or other this sequence is under pretty direct control of the environment. Indeed, it looks as if there is here a Lamarckian kind of influence by the environment. . . . Just where in the sequence it acts, we do not know; but a reasonable guess would be that it operates on the messenger RNA, which is small in amount and relatively unstable, to modify it in kind or amount or distribution."

Earlier explanations of the memory process rested heavily upon the maintenance of nerve impulses in reverberating circuits, along with plastic changes at synapses, involving swelling, outgrowth, or multiplication of presynaptic terminals. More recently, Holger Hydén, who reports here directly, has summarized some of his thinking about the establishment of memory traces as follows:* "The modulated frequency [of nerve impulses] generated in a neurone by a specific stimulation is supposed to affect the RNA molecule and to induce a new sequence of nucleotide residues along the backbone of the molecule. This new distribution of components will then remain: the RNA has been specified. This leads also to a specification of the protein being formed through the mediation of this RNA.

"By a combination of this specific protein with the complementary molecule, the transmitter substance at the points of contact with the next neurone at the synapsis is activated. This allows the coded information to pass on to this next neurone in the chain. The reason for the response of this next neurone is that the protein which had once been specified through a modulated frequency now responds to the same type of electrical pattern whenever it is repeated. The specific RNA and protein are constantly

* As cited by H. Hoagland (3).

produced in the neurone. From a statistical point of view, the molecules can be estimated to furnish the necessary permutation possibilities to store the memory experience of a lifetime."

Since the planning stage of this present conference, we have learned of a lecture series organized by Frank Schmitt, given in the 1961 Spring term at the Massachusetts Institute of Technology, and brought together in a volume titled *Macromolecular Specificity and Biological Memory* (4). In his introduction, Schmitt points out:

"Also of interest is the mechanism by which the nerve impulse activates the innervated structure by liberation of potent transmitter hormones, such as acetylcholine and noradrenaline, but it seems improbable that transmitters are involved in the memory coding process as such.

"The ultrastructure of neurons, like that of exocrine gland cells, reflects high biosynthetic activity involving principally RNA (Nissl substance) and protein (of which the only type thus far characterized in any detail is that comprising neurofilaments). The biosynthesized neuroplasm appears to be conveyed down the axon [Weiss and Hiscoe, 1948] at a rate suggesting that a volume several times that of the neuronal cell body might be produced per day [Weiss, 1961]. The fate of this neuroplasm is unknown. The high metabolic activity of neurons may reflect the requirement not only for materials to maintain the integrity of the axon, whose length may be large compared with the cell diameter, and for enzymes and transmitters necessary to sustain impulse propagation along the axon and across synapses [as suggested by Weiss, 1961] but also for the production of a constant and sufficient supply of engram components. Indeed it is possible that cytodifferentiation of neuroblasts into neurons simultaneously achieves: suppression of ability to divide (thus avoiding the chaos that neuronal mitosis would produce in the fully formed brain); ability to form the neuroplasm needed for outgrowth and regeneration of the sometimes lengthy axon; and ability to form an ample and constant supply of engram components (to make possible memory, learning, and other cognitive processes). . . .

"It has been postulated that fixation of sensory information is produced by transduction of modulated frequency ion flux inputs from impulses coming into centers over sensory nerves into specifically structured macromolecules, probably RNA. . . ."

Schmitt goes on to remark, however, "Question may be raised as to whether the electrical energy in the ionic fluxes representing the informational input from sensory nerve fibers would suffice for the transduction to specific chemical synthesis as hypothesized."

This present conference in Los Angeles provides a fitting sequel to the MIT lecture series of a year ago, since it has been designed to review the state of nucleic acid coding in genetics, re-examine some of the earlier attempts to identify such a nucleic acid base for information storage and retrieval in the nervous system, and to attempt a current evaluation as to whether or not it is justifiable to carry over to the processes of learning and memory some of the advances established for genetic coding.

REFERENCES

1. GERARD, R. W., Summary and general discussion. In: *Information Storage and Neural Control* (W. S. Fields and W. Abbott, Eds.). Thomas, Springfield, 1963: 353-376.
2. GLASS, B., The establishment of modern genetical theory as an example of the interaction of different models, techniques, and inferences. In: *Scientific Change* (A. C. Crombie, Ed.). Heinemann, London, 1963: 521-541.
3. HOAGLAND, H., Potentialities in the control of behaviour. In: *Man and His Future* (G. Wolstenholme, Ed.). Churchill, London, 1963: 299-314.
4. SCHMITT, F. O. (Ed.), *Macromolecular Specificity and Biological Memory*. M.I.T. Press, Cambridge, 1962.

NUCLEIC ACIDS IN RELATION TO THE CODING OF GENETIC INFORMATION

MARSHALL W. NIRENBERG
National Institutes of Health
Bethesda

One of the truisms of comparative biochemistry is that the apparent diversity and complexity of living things often masks basic similarities in metabolism. Many enzymic pathways found in mammalian tissues resemble very closely pathways which occur in bacteria. For example, the general pattern of coding genetic information and synthesizing nucleic acids and proteins seems similar, for the most part, in the relatively few bacterial and mammalian systems which have been examined thus far. Since genetic coding in brain tissue has not been investigated, discussion will center predominantly around basic findings and concepts which have emerged from studies of the code in *E. coli.*

The terms "genetic memory" and "psychic memory" shall be used to describe different phenomena, and the molecular mechanism of one may bear no relation whatsoever to that of the other. The data available at this time are too limited to warrant extrapolations from one to the other.

Many types of biochemical memory depend upon recognition of one molecule by another. For example, with marked specificity enzymes recognize substrates, antibodies interact with antigens, cells recognize other cells, and so forth. The basis of genetic memory is similar, for it depends upon complimentary recognition of one nucleotide by another via highly specific hydrogen-bonding. Genetic memory, which is specified by nucleotide sequences in DNA is a relatively stable memory and usually is passed from one generation to the next with little error. However, temporary genetic memory also occurs, but this perhaps depends upon mechanisms permitting the selective reading or functioning of genes. For example, certain segments of DNA (genes or cistrons) may function only when a cell is exposed to a particular environment.

Calvin: Is there some easy operational definition for "cistron"?

Nirenberg: It is the smallest functional segment of DNA which can direct the synthesis of a protein molecule. Dr. Benzer coined the term, so he is eminently qualified to describe it.

Benzer: I do not think we should go into great detail. The idea is that a cistron represents the segment of DNA which carries the information to determine the sequence of amino acids of a particular protein molecule, thereby constituting a genetic unit of function in the organism. I think that is enough. From what is known there may be a correlation between length of cistron and the length of the protein, but very few cases have actually been tested.

The hypothesis is as follows: DNA contains a definite sequence of nucleotides. This sequence is translated into a corresponding stretch of RNA with specific nucleotide sequence. That sequence is further transcribed into a sequence of amino acids, making one single polypeptide chain. A given enzyme may be composed of more than one such polypeptide chain, so it can require more than one cistron.

Nirenberg: One of the major findings that have emerged during the last few years is that a gene may consist of more than one cistron.

The point which should be emphasized is that genetic memory is relatively permanent, but that temporary learning also may be present. Such temporary memory has been termed enzyme induction or repression. Although the molecular aspects of these phenomena remain to be clarified, the available evidence suggests that in some cases selective readout of genetic information may be possible.

In order to discuss the molecular basis of the genetic code, the structure of DNA and the process of protein synthesis must be reviewed briefly.

In a double-stranded helix of DNA the bases pair in a complementary manner, via hydrogen-bonding, C (cytidine) with G (guanine), and A (adenine) with T (thymine). The overall process of protein synthesis is as follows:

$$DNA \longrightarrow RNA \longrightarrow Protein$$

The base sequence in DNA specifies the base sequence of a class of RNA termed template or messenger RNA (mRNA) which, in turn, specifies the sequence of amino acids in protein.

An enzyme, RNA polymerase, catalyzes the synthesis of RNA. The bases A, G, C and T in DNA are transcribed into U (uracil), C, G and A, respectively, in RNA. Recent evidence suggests that only one of the two DNA strands or double helix is transcribed into a complementary mRNA strand able to code for protein. The function of the other DNA strands remains to be clarified.

RNA may be synthesized in other ways also. Under conditions which probably do not occur *in vivo,* purified RNA polymerase preparations have been found to copy RNA rather than DNA templates. In addition, recent studies have demonstrated that infection of some bacterial and mammalian cells with certain RNA-containing viruses results in the production of similar enzymes (termed RNA synthetases) which copy RNA only.

Another enzyme, polynucleotide phosphorylase, was shown by Grunberg-Manago & Ochoa (12) to catalyze the synthesis of randomly-ordered RNA from nucleotide diphosphate substrates. This enzyme does not copy nucleic acid templates, and the reaction is reversible. Although its physiological role *in vivo* has not been defined completely, it may degrade rather than synthesize RNA.

Bickford: Is this a random way of getting into the kinetics?

Sinsheimer: It would be wrong to leave the impression that this enzyme was a way of introducing new genetic elements into a cell.

Nirenberg: Yes. The equilibrium of the reaction is such that nucleic acid can be degraded very easily by this enzyme. Although *in vivo* the enzyme most probably does not function to introduce new genetic elements, I do not know of definitive experiments which would rule this out.

Cells contain three classes of RNA: mRNA, ribosomal RNA, and soluble or transfer RNA (sRNA). The mRNA fraction constitutes only about 5-10 per cent of the total *E. coli* RNA. Messenger RNA serves as templates for protein synthesis.

The ribosomal or microsomal RNA fraction represents about 80 per cent of the total cellular RNA, and occurs as sedimentable ribonucleoprotein particles upon which protein is synthesized. The function of this RNA fraction is unknown.

Soluble RNA, the third fraction, constitutes 10-15 per cent of the total cellular RNA. Each cell contains many different species of sRNA and one or more species correspond to each amino acid. The molecular weight of sRNA is relatively low; each molecule contains about 75 bases. Soluble RNA molecules function as adaptors which carry activated amino acids to specific sites on ribosomes in the sequences specified by mRNA.

Although direct recognition of messenger RNA codewords by transfer RNA molecules has not been demonstrated, it is clear that these molecules perform at least part of the job of placing amino acids in the proper position in the protein chain. When the amino acids arrive at the proper site in the chain, they are linked to each other by enzymic processes that are only partly understood. The linking is accomplished by the formation of a peptide bond. The process requires a transfer enzyme, at least one other enzyme and a cofactor, guanosine triphosphate (GTP). Molecules of protein are synthesized by incorporation of amino acids, one at a time, starting at the end of the chain carrying an amino group and proceeding toward the end that terminates with a carboxyl group.

The process of protein synthesis can be studied conveniently in cell-free extracts of *E. coli*. Bacteria are harvested, washed and then are gently disrupted by grinding them with finely powdered alumina. The contents of the cells may be extracted with buffer and removed from the alumina by centrifugation. Such extracts contain ribosomes, activating enzymes, sRNA, DNA, and other necessary components. When fortified with ATP and an ATP-generating system, they readily incorporate C^{14}-amino acids into protein.

Independently, Tissières et al. (36), Kameyama & Novelli (15), and Nisman & Fukuhara (27) had reported an inhibition of amino acid incorporation by DNase. J. H. Matthaei and I confirmed these observations and studied the characteristics of this inhibition (21), for here appeared to be a cell-free system in which DNA directed the synthesis of protein. DNase completely inhibited incorporation of C^{14}-amino acids occurring in the reaction mixtures after 30 minutes of incubation at 37°C. (23, 24). This type of experiment suggested that the DNase-inhibited system might be dependent upon the availability of mRNA. Crude mRNA fractions were found to stimulate amino acid incorporation and proved to be a requirement for cell-free protein syntheses (23, 24). This technique afforded a highly sensitive, cell-free assay for mRNA, and provided the rationale for all of our subsequent work.

We obtained mRNA fractions from various natural sources, including an RNA-containing virus, tobacco mosaic virus, and found that many fractions, including the viral RNA, were highly active in directing C^{14}-amino acids into protein.

Fremont-Smith: Does this suggest RNA is taking the place of the DNA in this instance?

Nirenberg: In one sense, yes, DNA directs the synthesis of mRNA. In *E. coli* extracts dependent upon DNA for protein synthesis, the requirement for DNA can be replaced by mRNA.

The sensitivity of the mRNA assay was greatly increased by first hydrolyzing the DNA with DNase and then incubating extracts at 37°C. for a short time, under optimal conditions for protein synthesis. Seemingly, endogenous mRNA was depleted and some partially finished peptide chains may have been completed.

Chemically defined synthetic RNA preparations prepared with polynucleotide phosphorylase were also assayed for template activity. Polyuridylic acid (poly U) markedly stimulated the incorporation of C^{14}-phenylalanine; polycytidylic acid (poly C) stimulated C^{14}-proline incorporation. Thus a series of uridylic acid residues in poly U appeared to be the RNA codeword corresponding to phenylalanine, and a series of cytidylic acid residues in poly C the RNA codeword corresponding to proline. This cell-free system capable of synthesizing protein under the direction of chemically defined preparations of RNA provided a relatively simple means of determining characteristics of RNA and of translating the genetic code.

Current experiments on the synthesis of polynucleotides and proteins seem to emphasize the functional importance of polynucleotide secondary structure. Thus, for example, the highly ordered double-helical structure of DNA readily leads to ideas concerning RNA replication. As described previously, our notions concerning the secondary structure of the various types of RNA are much less precise; however, it does appear that RNA molecules are primarily single-stranded and contain varying degrees of helical content. Poly U in solution at room temperature has very little secondary structure. When poly U is mixed with poly A, double- and triple-stranded helices are formed which are completely inactive in directing phenylalanine synthesis (23, 26). The stability of such helices is influenced strongly by the chain-length of each component. Longer oligonucleotides form more stable helices than shorter ones. In agreement, we found a greater inhibition of polyphenylalanine synthesis by longer oligo A preparations than by shorter ones (octa A > hexa A > tetra A > tri A). In addition, Singer et al. (32), have shown that guanine-rich polymers containing a high degree of ordered secondary structure are also inactive as templates for protein synthesis. Thus, single-strandedness and lack of extensive intra-molecular hydrogen-bonding appear to be requisite for mRNA activity. Recently we have found that poly U-poly A helices do not bind to ribosomes, and it would seem probable that such inability to attach to ribosomes would prevent protein synthesis.

Another factor influencing the messenger efficiency of synthetic poly-nucleotide is the molecular weight of the RNA. In *E. coli* extracts, poly U containing more than 200 uridylic acid residues per chain clearly has greater template activity than smaller chains (20). Nonetheless, oligo A fractions containing as few as nine or ten adenylic acid residues per chain have been found by Jones et al. (14) to direct polylysine synthesis and, in yeast extracts, oligo U of average chain length 11 has been shown to direct phenylalanine incorporation (19). Since oligonucleotides may appear to be less efficient as templates for protein synthesis, RNA chain-length should be considered when comparing template activities of different RNA fractions.

Does each molecule of mRNA function only once or many times in directing the synthesis of protein? We found that 90 per cent of the poly U added to the reaction mixtures was degraded to mononucleotides before it was able to function as mRNA (1). Nevertheless, only about 1.5 uridylic acid residues poly U were required to direct the incorporation of one molecule of phenylalanine into protein. Spyrides & Lipmann (35) have reported that only about 0.75 U residues are required to code for one molecule of phenylalanine. Assuming that the RNA codeword corresponding to phenyl-alanine contains 3 U residues, it seems probable that each poly U molecule directs the synthesis of more than one molecule of polyphenylalanine. Similar results have been obtained *in vivo*. Messenger RNA synthesis was inhibited in a bacterium, *B. subtilis*, with an antibiotic, actinomycin, and each mRNA molecule present at the time messenger synthesis was turned off was found to direct the synthesis of ten to twenty molecules of protein (18).

Fremont-Smith: If it could function ten to twenty times, why not thirty to forty? Theoretically, would it stop? Does it become degraded?

Nirenberg: The question you raise is an important one, but not enough data are available to answer it completely. Probably in different tissues the rate of synthesis and/or breakdown of mRNA corresponding to one protein will be found to differ from that of another. Many laboratories are working on this problem, for it may relate to enzyme induction and repression.

To investigate this question, Dr. Barondes and I synthesized H^3-poly U, added it to our reaction mixtures and determined its fate during incubation. After three minutes of incubation at 37°C., approximately 90 per cent of the H^3-poly U became alcohol-soluble and could be recovered as mononucleotides. The rest of the poly U became associated with a polydisperse peak of ribosomes which sedimented faster than 70S ribosomes. Several nucleases known to occur in *E. coli* might catalyze such rapid breakdown of mRNA.

Fremont-Smith: You are suggesting it acts semi-catalytically.

Nirenberg: Yes. The results obtained both in *E. coli* and *B. subtilis* strongly suggest a limited catalytic activity of mRNA. However, one should not extrapolate these results to mRNA function in other tissues. The data that I cited were obtained very recently, and more information is needed.

The coding problem centers around the question: "How can a four-letter alphabet (the bases A, G, C and T) specify a twenty-word dictionary (each word corresponding to an amino acid)?" In 1954 George Gamow (10) predicted that each codeword in such a dictionary might contain three bases. It is obvious that only four codewords can be formed if the words are only one letter in length. With two letters, 4×4, or 16, codewords can be formed. And with three letters, $4 \times 4 \times 4$, or 64, codewords become available. This would be more than enough information to code specifically the twenty amino acids.

The ease with which synthetic polynucleotides direct cell-free amino acid incorporation afforded a reasonable experimental approach to this problem. Polynucleotides containing all base combinations now have been used by both Ochoa and his colleagues and by ourselves to direct protein synthesis in *E. coli* extracts (2, 13, 17, 20, 22, 23, 24, 28, 33, 34). A qualitative summary of these data is presented in Table 1. Only those polynucleotides containing the minimum bases necessary to direct an amino acid into protein are shown. For example, phenylalanine is directed into protein by poly U as well as other U-containing polymers; however, since other bases are not required, phenylalanine is listed only under poly U. Poly U, poly A, and poly C direct into protein phenylalanine, lysine, and proline, respectively.

Polylysine synthesized under the direction of poly A has been found to contain 3-15 lysine residues per chain (14). No messenger activity has been demonstrated for poly G (20), but the highly ordered structure of poly G might mask template activity. However, a polynucleotide composed only of hypoxanthine (poly I) with less secondary structure than poly G, still has not been found to direct amino acids into protein. Since hypoxanthine can replace G in RNA codewords, the 2-amino group of G does not appear to be essential for coding (13).

TABLE 1

Summary of Coding Data

Poly	U	A	C	G			
	PHE	LYS	PRO	—			
Poly	UA	UC	UG	AC	AG	CG	UAG
	TYR	LEU	LEU	HIS	ARG	ARG	MET
	LEU	SER	VAL	ASP-NH₂	GLU	ALA	ASP
	ILEU		CYSH	GLU-NH₂	GLU-NH₂	SER	
	ASP-NH₂		TRY	THR	—	—	

Each polynucleotide composed of two different bases has eight triplets, but no polymer has been found to direct more than six different amino acids into protein. Poly UC is unique in that it codes for only four amino acids. It is important to note also that polynucleotides containing only two different bases direct with great specificity almost all amino acids into protein. These findings undoubtedly reflect basic molecular characteristics of both the recognition process and the general nature of the code.

Benzer: Is there any indication of stimulation of phenylalanine by non-U containing polynucleotides?

Nirenberg: Absolutely none.

Benzer: You always tested?

Nirenberg: We have tested polynucleotides containing almost every base permutation. I think the negative data are extremely important.

With only two kinds of nucleotides, it is possible to make six varieties of RNA polymer: poly AC, poly AG, poly AU, poly CG, poly CU and poly GU. If the ratio of the bases is adjusted with care, each variety can be shown to code with great specificity for different sets of amino acids. The relative amount of one amino acid directed into protein compared with another depends upon the ratio of bases in the RNA. Assuming a random sequence of bases in the RNA, the theoretical probabilities of finding particular sequences of two, three or more bases can be calculated easily if the base ratio is known. For example, if poly UC contains 70 per cent U and 30 per cent C, the probability of the occurrence of the triplet sequence UUU is $0.7 \times 0.7 \times 0.7$, or 0.34. That is, 34 per cent of the triplets in the polymer are expected to be UUU. The probability of obtaining the sequence UUC is $0.7 \times 0.7 \times 0.3$, or 0.147. Thus, 14.7 per cent of the triplets in such a polymer are expected to be UUC.

Recently, Dr. Jones and I synthesized a series of poly AC and poly UC preparations with different proportions of bases and determined their activities in stimulating cell-free amino acid incorporation. By making the calculations just described, one can compare the relative frequency of amino acid incorporation to the theoretical frequency of triplet or doublet codewords in polynucleotide preparations, and can demonstrate experimentally the quantitative relationships between codewords in mRNA and amino acids incorporated into protein. Phenylalanine, proline, leucine, serine and threonine were found to be coded either by two triplets in a polymer or by a doublet—the data do not allow us to distinguish between these possibilities. Our experiments strongly suggest that histidine, asparagine, glutamine and lysine are coded by triplet words. These data demonstrate that at least part of the RNA code is composed of triplets. In accord, the available and genetic evidence suggests that codewords are either triplets or multiples of triplets (5).

Fox: In a system such as this, are you using only the amino acid represented or just measuring these?

Nirenberg: Each reaction mixture contains one C^{14}-amino acid and nineteen C^{12}-amino acids.

Calvin: In the series in which you varied the base ratio, did you have any control over the molecular size?

Nirenberg: We determine the sedimentation constant of most polynucleotide preparations. However, every polynucleotide preparation appears to be polydisperse. We are now using, on a routine basis, a fractionation technique which separates oligonucleotides from molecules of higher chain length. Nonetheless, the RNA fractions of high molecular weight still are polydisperse.

It is difficult to compare directly the messenger efficiencies of different polynucleotide preparations because the efficiency is modified by molecular size and secondary structure. However, if the average chain length and secondary structure of different RNA preparations are assumed to be approximately equal, our experiments suggest that nucleotide compositions may not influence greatly the overall template efficiency of mRNA (assuming random sequence). Poly U, poly UC, poly ACG and poly UAGG contain 1, 8, 27 and 64 triplets respectively, and recently we have found that they will direct 1, 4, 9 and 18-20 amino acids, respectively, into protein. The essential point is that approximately the same total quantity of amino acids were directed into protein by each polynucleotide. Although these data must be interpreted with care because the same factor may not limit the incorporation rate of each amino acid, the data suggest that each polynucleotide preparation may have approximately equal template efficiency and that most nucleotide sequences may be able to code for amino acids. Although genetic evidence suggests that nonsense codewords may exist, thus far none have been demonstrated definitively in this cell-free system.

A surprising conclusion drawn from the incorporation data shown in Table 1 is that almost every amino acid tested can be coded by a polynucleotide containing only two kinds of bases. The data of Table 1 also demonstrate that certain amino acids, such as leucine, are coded by more than one qualitatively different codeword. Thus, the genetic code appears to be a degenerate code.

TABLE 2

SUMMARY OF RNA CODEWORDS

Amino Acid	RNA codewords (arbitrary nucleotide sequence)			
Alanine	CCG	UCG*	ACG*	
Arginine	CGC	AGA	UGC*	CGA*
Asparagine	ACA	AUA	ACU*	
Aspartic Acid	GUA	GCA*	GAA*	
Cysteine	UUG			
Glutamic Acid	GAA	GAU*	GAC*	
Glutamine	AAC	AGA	ACU*	
Glycine	UGG	AGG	CGG	
Histidine	ACC	ACU*		
Isoleucine	UAU	UAA		
Leucine	UUG	UUC	UCC	UUA (UUU)
Lysine	AAA	AAU		
Methionine	UGA			
Phenylalanine	UUU	CUU		
Proline	CCC	CCU	CGA	CCG*
Serine	UGU	UCC	UCG*	ACG
Threonine	CAC	CAA		
Tryptophan	GGU			
Tyrosine	AUU			
Valine	UGU	UGA*		

* Probable.

Assuming for the present that all amino acids are coded by triplets, current approximations of RNA codewords may be summarized as shown in Table 2. Nucleotide sequence is arbitrary. Fifty of the 64 possible triplets have been assigned. Since polynucleotides containing three bases direct protein synthesis as efficiently as polymers containing only two bases, it seems probable that most three-base words are recognized. Tentative assignments are given for such words.

It seems clear that most amino acids are coded by multiple words. Furthermore, multiple words corresponding to one amino acid often differ in base composition by only one nucleotide. These observations suggest that nucleotide sequences in multiple words often may be identical. A triplet code may be constructed wherein either correct hydrogen-bonding between two out of three nucleotide pairs may in some cases suffice for coding, or a base at one position in the triplet sometimes may pair optionally and correctly with two or more bases. It should be noted that such triplet codes in some respects would bear superficial resemblances to a doublet code and would be in accord with all of the data available.

The coding data obtained thus far clearly indicate that most nucleotide sequences can code for amino acids with great specificity. Only one codeword has been found which seems, under special conditions, to direct more than one amino acid into protein. This is termed an ambiguity. Poly U directs small amounts of leucine into protein, in addition to phenylalanine. However we find that in the absence of phenylalanine, poly U codes about half as well for leucine as it would for phenylalanine. The molecular basis for this ambiguity has not been clarified fully. Nor is it known if such dual coding exists in living systems as well as in cell-free systems.

A molecular explanation of degeneracy has been provided recently by Weisblum, Benzer & Holley (37). Two different species of sRNA capable of recognizing leucine had been found in a bacterium; Weisblum and his co-workers separated the two sRNA species and assayed each in the cell-free E. coli system. They found that one of the sRNA species recognized poly UC more easily than poly UG, whereas the other species recognized poly UG more easily than poly UC.

The number of sRNA species per cell is unknown, and one wonders whether each sRNA species recognizes a different codeword or whether coding can occur on occasion via *correct* pairing between two out of three bases. It is important to emphasize the possibility that randomly-ordered synthetic polynucleotides may test the cell's potential to recognize code-words, and that the entire potential may not be utilized *in vivo*, except perhaps during mutation. Thus mRNA synthesized by a cell may not contain as many codewords as randomly-ordered polynucleotides.

Still not completely understood is the manner in which a given amino acid finds its way to the proper site in a protein chain. Although sRNA was found to be required for the synthesis of polyphenylalanine, the possibility remained that the amino acid rather than the sRNA recognized the code-word.

To distinguish between these alternative possibilities, the following experiment was performed by Chapeville and associates (4). Cysteine is transported by one species of sRNA and alanine by another. Those workers attached C^{14}-cysteine to cysteine sRNA and then reduced the cysteine with Raney Nickel, which converted it to alanine without detaching it from cysteine sRNA. They then asked the question, "Will the labeled alanine be coded as if it were alanine or cysteine?" They found that it was coded by UUG, just as though it were cysteine. This experiment showed that the amino acid lost its identity after combining with sRNA and was carried, willy-nilly, to the codeword recognized by the sRNA.

The question of a universal code also may be raised. Does each species have its own code, or is essentially the same code used by all species? Preliminary evidence suggests that most species may have similar codes. A number of laboratories have recently found that synthetic polynucleotides code the same way in mammalian cell-free systems as they do in bacterial systems. Approximately six to eight RNA codewords have been determined thus far in mammalian systems, and in every case the words were identical to those found in E. coli. Nevertheless, it seems probable that some differences may be found in the future. Since most amino acids appear to be coded by multiple words, it is entirely possible that one species may prefer to use one word, whereas other species may prefer a different but synonymous word.

John: In the synthesis with C^{14} you have one labeled amino acid. I gather there are nineteen others which are C^{12}. What is the effect of changing the relative concentrations of the remainder?

Nirenberg: The concentration of amino acids in the reaction mixtures is higher than that required for incorporation into protein. We have tested this aspect carefully. Dr. Matthaei and I also determined the effects of omitting one or more amino acids from reaction mixtures. Omission of an amino acid normally coded by a polynucleotide lowered the incorporation of the other amino acids also coded by that polynucleotide. However, such experiments are difficult to perform because, in spite of extensive dialysis, one cannot obtain extracts completely free of endogenous amino acids. Also, during incubation of reaction mixtures, amino acids may be formed from protein due to endogenous proteolysis. For this reason we have not performed extensive studies of competition among amino acids for coding sites.

John: Does the nature of the code depend to any extent on the composition of the mix?

Nirenberg: Of the amino acid composition? If one were to distort the concentration of the amino acids drastically, mistakes due to competition between amino acids might be expected.

John: A paper by a Russian named Bresler and his associates (3) has appeared on protein resynthesis under pressure. It will take a moment to summarize, but I think it is relevant. After horse serum albumin was degraded with a specific enzyme such as trypsin, it was dialyzed, and the dialysis products were subjected to ultracentrifugation. Particle size determinations were made. It was established these were about the size of single amino acid residues. They were then subjected to high atmospheric pressure, in the presence of the enzyme previously used.

In ultracentrifuge studies of this mixture under pressure, particle size determinations showed a very large macromolecule of essentially 1,000,000 molecular weight being assembled. The distribution also showed a large content of particles about the size of single amino acids. No particles of intermediate molecular weight appeared in the distribution. Finally, the large macromolecule which was assembled under pressure was dialyzed away from the amino acids, and it was found to be horse serum albumin.

The effect of introducing amino acid mixtures obtained from the degradation of other proteins was checked, and it was found that the introduction of such amino acids, checked by dialysis and ultracentrifugation, interfered with the synthesis. The implication of this study was that the composition of the mix somehow affected the ability of the mix to undergo a particular kind of polymerization.

Nirenberg: I think that marked distortion of the ratio of one amino acid to another certainly will, in certain cases, give erroneous results.

Benzer: In the case of leucine and phenylalanine, there is a competition for poly U.

Nirenberg: This is the only ambiguity we are aware of.

Benzer: I think others have not been completely ruled out.

Fox: I wonder if you have done anything with N- terminal amino acid analyses?

Nirenberg: Yes, we are trying to. Dr. Sidney Pestka, in our laboratory, has performed both C- and N- terminal analyses on polypeptide products synthesized in these reaction mixtures. It is technically difficult, though, to perform such analyses on polyphenylalanine, and thus we have studied predominantly peptides synthesized due to the addition of randomly mixed polynucleotides containing lower amounts of U or containing bases other than U. Dr. Pestka does find radioactivity in N- and C- terminal positions. However, we do not know whether polypeptide chains can be initiated in this system, for the ratio of C- terminal to N- terminal radioactivity is much greater than one. I should emphasize that these data are preliminary and that all technical difficulties have not been overcome in performing the analyses.

Benzer: Can you be sure they are not long chains broken in the middle?

Nirenberg: No, I would expect some degradation.

Benzer: But it is very small in comparison to the number of peptide chains?

Nirenberg: Although we have attempted to measure the extent of degradation, our data are too preliminary to allow conclusions to be drawn.

Benzer: The question is whether it is much smaller than one N- terminal group per chain.

Nirenberg: We must do more work before this question can be answered with any sort of certainty.

John: Has any work been done on the effects of electrolyte concentration in the synthesis situation?

Nirenberg: Yes, the ionic strength has to be adjusted with care. Optimal amino acid incorporation is obtained only under carefully controlled conditions.

Calvin: What is the optimum concentration?

Fox: Precisely what do you mean by "cell-free", free of the outer membrane?

Nirenberg: The cells are disrupted by grinding packed cells with alumina in a mortar. Intact cells and debris are removed by repeated centrifugations at 30,000 G. The pellet is discarded and the supernatant fluid is treated with DNase, "preincubated" under conditions optimal for protein synthesis, and then dialyzed. Many times, ribosomes are sedimented by centrifugation at 100,000 G, and the supernatant solution and ribosome suspension are stored separately. Intact cells or protoplasts, if present, would be found in the ribosomal pellet. Negligible contamination by intact cells or protoplasts is strongly suggested, for ribosomes alone or 100,000 G supernatant solutions alone incorporate only negligible amounts of amino acids into protein. Both are required for active incorporation. In addition, polynucleotide-dependent C^{14}-amino acid incorporation is obtained starting with C^{14}-amino acyl-sRNA in the presence of a large pool of free C^{12}-amino acids.

Fox: There is still much uncharacterized material?

Nirenberg: Yes. A great deal of fractionation and purification remains to be done. However, some purification has been achieved already, for in re-action mixtures containing C^{14}-amino acyl-sRNA, washed ribosomes, puri-fied transfer enzyme, GTP and mRNA, C^{14}-amino acid incorporation has been obtained (25). Transfer enzyme, purified about tenfold, will replace the 100,000 G supernatant solution. However, the transfer enzyme must be purified further, for the available evidence suggests that at least two en-zymes are required. In addition, ribosome purification seems necessary, for only 5 to 15 per cent of the ribosomes actively support protein synthesis when poly U is added.

Sinsheimer: It is really surprising to be able to code for so many amino acids, using groups of polymers, with only two nucleotides at a time. As-suming a three-letter code, this would give you 32 possible code words. That is half of the total possible number.

Nirenberg: Yes, I have thought about this but not enough data are avail-able to warrant favoring one coding scheme over many others which are equally plausible. I think we may be testing the *coding potential* of cells. By coding potential, I mean the *capability* of the cells under abnormal con-ditions to read random nucleotide sequences—either *in vitro* when synthetic polynucleotides direct cell-free protein synthesis, or *in vivo*, due to nucleo-tide substitutions in codewords which may occur via mutation. We find that randomly ordered polynucleotides can be read with minimal error. However, serious consideration must be given to the possibility that all codewords which a cell *can* recognize (that is, the coding potential) may not be utilized to the same extent *in vivo*. The genetic code is highly degenerate and most amino acids seem to be coded by multiple words, but a cell may prefer a more monotonous language which minimizes misunderstanding and error. Cells may employ certain codewords much more frequently than synony-mous words.

Luco: They would be able to learn?

Nirenberg: Perhaps through trial and error words read with least misun-derstanding would be selected. Certainly, the cell's capacity to read alternate words eventually would be tested via mutation.

Bickford: I wondered if you could extrapolate to multicellular organisms. We are still quite a long way from the brain. You have told us much about the very beautiful mechanisms at this level. What I am puzzled about is why these cannot be used in engineering changes in the growing organism. What is the snag there?

Nirenberg: I do not know whether "psychic memory" is directly related to "genetic memory". Thinking about this question is very stimulating, but I had better defer speculation and finish summarizing what we know about the general nature of the genetic code, and what we clearly do not know.

Very probably DNA is read starting from fixed positions, three nucleotides at a time. The direction of reading (polarity), the mechanisms which specify the beginning and end of a message, and also the phase of reading have not been clarified. The nucleotide compositions of about fifty RNA codewords have been determined, but base sequences of most are still unknown. The problem is reminiscent of an anagram, for the letters of words have been deciphered but are scrambled and now must be placed in proper sequence.

Both the specificity and the efficiency of RNA codewords appear to be high. Error in ordering amino acids into proper sequence during protein synthesis probably has been minimized through billions of years of trial and error. Although the evolution of the code is largely unknown, the few highly organized species examined thus far seem to code for amino acids in much the same way as more primitive species. Most amino acids appear to be coded by multiple words, but it is not known whether cells employ certain alternate words more frequently than others. It would seem probable that different groups of triplet pairs have evolved which code for each amino acid with minimal error. Further study is needed to determine whether certain triplet pairs are employed more often than alternate triplet pairs.

Messenger mRNA with much secondary structure codes poorly or not at all. In addition, polynucleotide chain-length must be considered when interpreting the results of cell-free amino acid incorporation studies.

Although I do not know whether the mechanisms of genetic coding are related directly to the mechanisms of psychic memory, the phenomenon of temporary genetic memory deserves emphasis. As described earlier, enzyme induction and repression are terms relating to the specific and selective retrieval of genetic information. Thus, two cells of identical genetic constitution may differ, for certain genes may function in one cell and not in another. The expression of these genes seems to depend upon the presence of small molecules which usually are chemically similar to the substrate or product of the enzyme whose synthesis is directed by the gene. The possible relation of such phenomena to differentiation is apparent. Antibody synthesis is another example of adaptive or learned memory.

Specific questions may be asked in order to determine whether psychic memory depends directly upon enzyme induction or repression. For example, the question may be posed as to whether the learning process requires RNA and/or protein synthesis. Does memory entail the synthesis of molecules, and if so, how many different kinds of molecules are formed?

Biochemists often find that the study of primitive as well as highly organized cell types is advantageous. Perhaps it would be easier, initially, to study certain processes in bacteria rather than in higher organisms. For example, the question of how cells perceive certain stimuli might be pursued on the molecular level by studying chemotaxis in bacteria. Similarly, the recognition of bacteria by bacterial viruses or the recognition of one bacterium by another during mating might provide model systems for studying fundamental questions related to cellular interactions.

Benzer: You might conclude from the observations on universality that the messages in bacteria could be read by the brain of a higher organism.

Nirenberg: The genetic message?

Benzer: The memories of bacteriahood.

Nirenberg: How can any cell forget the stories told during billions of years of trial and error.

Morrell: You noted that ionic strength was crucial. What are the effects of altering the concentration of specific electrolytes?

Nirenberg: Inorganic ions have a marked effect upon many enzymatic reactions. Many reactions are dependent upon particular salts, and salt concentrations must be adjusted carefully.

John: Can you elaborate on the effects of potassium and magnesium?

Nirenberg: Ribosomes aggregate in the presence of magnesium, and both magnesium and potassium appear to be required for protein synthesis. The effects of these ions are complex in this system and have not been defined fully. Organic cations such as spermidine and putrescine may also play roles in protein synthesis in certain bacterial species.

John: Rudenberg & Tobias (29) have reported that calcium is bonded to RNA in axoplasm. Are there any data on the effect of calcium in the system you mentioned?

Nirenberg: I am sure that the addition of calcium ions would result in ribosomal aggregation.

Benzer: The system is complex. There are several reactions. There are different activating enzymes for the various amino acids, each of which has its own response to ionic strength. You want to get all of these to work, plus the transfer reactions from sRNA to the polypeptide. It is not surprising that there should be a sharp, tuned concentration.

John: I wonder if there is any possibility that the electrolytes might function as coenzymes capable of altering the activity of the RNA. Since electrolyte flux in nerve cells alters radically with discharge of the cell, this might constitute a functional coupling between processes of cell discharge and processes of macromolecule synthesis.

Nirenberg: Certainly a flux of ions or change in the ionic strength of the medium will affect the activity of many enzymes.

Green: Of what order of magnitude are the concentration changes that might produce some effect? A nerve fiber can fire perhaps 100,000 times before its potassium is so depleted it cannot fire any more. Even then, there is a lot of potassium left in the nerve fiber.

Nirenberg: This is a difficult question to answer because ion concentration at one intracellular site might differ markedly from that at a different site.

Benzer: I think I can give the order of magnitude observed in the cell-free mixture. Given a maximum rate at, say 0.015 molar magnesium concentration, if the concentration is increased by one-third, the rate of protein synthesis will drop to about half. If it is decreased by one-third, it will also drop half. It is quite sharp. This would agree with your observation. It is conceivable that a nerve might control RNA synthesis by changing the ionic environment.

Nirenberg: What is the change in intracellular potassium levels after a neuron has fired?

Green: After one action potential, I should not think there is anything detectable at all.

Feindel: You are suggesting it has to be absolute loss. There could be a shift that might be considerable and also influence the protein synthesis.

Green: I suppose so. At what distance from the membrane can synthesis occur? In other words, are we limited to a few hundred angstroms, as seems quite likely?

Palay: One of the calculations showed that the exchange of ions could take place in the 100-angstrom thickness of the membrane, so you would see no change at all in anything you could measure, considering the volume of the nerve fiber.

Calvin: I would like to ask a general question. I do not know whether Dr. Nirenberg will want to answer it; if not, perhaps somebody else will. In one of the overall schemes he presented, every information transfer molecular process but one involved a base pairing complementarity. The exception was that in which the activated amino acid is hung at the side of RNA. In that case there is not a base pairing, at least not an obvious base pairing mechanism for recognition or for transfer. The transfer would involve going from a protein to the nucleic acid at that point. Do you have any ideas about how that might be accomplished?

Sinsheimer: The enzyme should be able to recognize a pattern of hydrogen bonds.

Nirenberg: Certainly the activating enzyme protein recognizes the amino acid, ATP, and sRNA with great specificity. One wonders whether recognition occurs also between the amino acid adenylate and sRNA. It would be extremely important to investigate the latter possibility.

Calvin: It would have to be the protein recognizing a rather large chunk of the soluble RNA effect.

Benzer: Ribonuclease recognizes only particular sequences.

Calvin: It has to recognize that part which corresponds to the amino acid.

Sinsheimer: It may not be the same part as is used for coding.

Benzer: It has to recognize both the RNA and the amino acid.

Calvin: That is right. That is the problem.

Benzer: We do know that these enzymes change from one species to another, and so does the sRNA. For instance, the arginine attaching enzyme from yeast will not attach arginine to coli sRNA, or vice versa. Nevertheless, if you take yeast arginine sRNA, plus the yeast enzyme, and hook arginine onto the yeast arginine sRNA, and then put it in Dr. Nirenberg's *E. coli* system, to measure the transfer of the arginine into protein, the response to polymers is exactly the same as it would be if the arginine had been attached to coli sRNA. In other words, the coding end of the molecule stays the same in the different species, in spite of the fact that the end of the molecule which interacts with the amino acid may change.

Bickford: I am still not clear on the implications of the findings for the multimolecular situation. If you had a tissue culture with dividing cells, is it possible to manipulate RNA factors, so that the outcome will be altered?

Nirenberg: Enzyme induction and repression phenomena in mammalian cells growing in tissue culture have been found. Many different laboratories are studying these processes currently. However, it is not known whether the alteration in enzyme activity which has been demonstrated is the result of manipulating RNA.

The unity and simplicity of metabolism throughout nature, which is masked by the apparent diversity of living things, again should be emphasized. Without doubt, gene function can be altered temporarily by environmental factors in reproducible and specific ways, but the mechanisms which control gene function have not been clarified fully. An immense amount of work remains to be done.

I have tried to describe in general terms the current status of the genetic coding problem, nucleic acid and protein synthesis, enzyme induction and repression. Although I have emphasized the limitations of the data available at this time, it seems probable that similar phenomena will be found in species and tissues which have not yet been studied. Currently, this area of research is being investigated intensively in many laboratories, and in the future the rate of acquisition of knowledge should be even higher than it is now.

A Model of Abiogenesis and the Origin of Memory at the Molecular Level

Fox: [*] I hope to be able to clarify the relevance of such a topic to a conference on RNA and Brain Function. I am doubtful that the relevance is obvious, in the usual ways of regarding this quality. Understanding of evo-

[*] The research described here has been aided by grants from the National Science Foundation, the Public Health Service, the General Foods Corporation, and the National Aeronautics and Space Administration.

lutionary origins of any given phenomenon is, however, often illuminating. I am going to ask you, in your considerations, to descend through the bottom of the phyletic scale into the area of molecular evolution. Then we will try to work our way back up conceptually.

In 1950, one of our participants, Dr. Calvin (11), ushered in the experimental era which has become known as *origin-of-life* research. This took the place of the nineteenth century experimental era of what was called spontaneous generation. In the light of Darwin's theory, it is now clearly evident that experiments aimed at production of maggots, microbes and little men were doomed to failure. The emphasis should have been on the first primitive organism.

I would like to present what, within the area that we can refer to as molecular evolution, is generally agreed would constitute the subareas that must be understood in order to comprehend the total process of conversion from the simplest inorganic compounds to those that compose living organisms as we know them.

The organic micromolecules which are our first concern would be the small molecules: amino acids, vitamins, monosaccharides, and the like. The first step is the spontaneous generation of such substances from simple compounds, mostly inorganic, like carbon dioxide, ammonia, methane (an organic compound), water, etc. From this point, it becomes essential to understand the origin of macromolecules. We are concerned particularly with the proteins, the nucleic acids, and we need also to include the polysaccharides. Third, in such a conceptualization it becomes necessary to understand the continuing generation of compounds of both the small and the large types. This is, then, concerned with the origin of metabolism. We can now see a unique relationship to the subject matter of the conference, for the understanding of the origin of metabolism requires that we understand a mechanism for a remembering of the first metabolic sequences.

There, then, would be memory at the most primitive or molecular level. If we once understand that, I think we would have a beachhead on the understanding of the memory process, at a level more rudimentary or fundamental than psychological memory or genetic memory. Lastly, in the sequence of abiogenetic steps, a spontaneous organization of precellular forms must also be understood.

Although the chemical era of experimental studies of origins is now just over a decade old, we can find examples of each one of these stages in terms of experimental parallelism. From these can be constructed a relatively comprehensive model of origins of biochemical and cellular systems. What we do not have available is an accurate assessment of the exact relevance of these processes to occurrences of two billion years ago. The processes must be good any place, any time, but the necessary conditions and their occurrences represent a kind of question that still requires much investigation, as do some of the other individual points within the processes involved in a comprehensively integrated model.

The kind of experiment that our laboratory has been concerned with is the heating of amino acids to yield polymers having many of the properties of protein. This was suggested by studies of the origin of protein from the standpoint of Darwinian evolution, at the molecular level.

If one heats amino acids, the usual expectation is that the result will be a dark tarry mass (6). Chemists and biochemists have known this for decades.

The studies of molecular evolution in organisms indicated that there is a relatively high proportion of aspartic acid and glutamic acid in virtually all proteins. This fact suggested that a relatively high proportion of aspartic acid and glutamic acid characterized the first protein molecules which might have generated spontaneously, and that this, in turn, required a relatively high proportion of these amino acids in the chemical matrix from which such protein emerged.

If this clue from the evolutionary analysis is followed, and one starts with dry amino acids, one can then heat to such otherwise brutal temperatures as 170°C. for several hours and obtain therefrom a light amber-colored product; this may then be further purified from aqueous solution, as by precipitation with ammonium sulfate (which is a classical procedure for the purification of proteins themselves). In moving from the tarry mass to the clean one I am ignoring many man-years of effort, but this latter material contains all of the amino acids common to protein. If one starts with the 18 known amino acids, a sufficient proportion of aspartic acid, and heats dry, one gets not just 18 amino acids, but 19 or 20, due to the amide formation of two amino acids during the reactions. The wide variety and range of polymers of this sort, referred to as *proteinoids*, have been extensively characterized (7, 8).

A couple of heresies are involved in this heating, other than that of heating amino acids in the first place. One of those is that the chemist tends to relate simple compounds to simple processes, complicated compounds to complicated processes. These are very complicated materials but the processes or the preparation are very simple. Perhaps the most salient contribution of this work is that now it is possible to visualize the production of very complicated molecules and units by relatively simple processes. Another heresy concerns the question of how one even dare hope to obtain materials like proteins when one knows that heat is one of the most dependable of agents for denaturing or, in part, destroying the native configuration of proteins. The key here, again, is the participation of water in the process. A few scientists, food technologists in particular, knew that if proteins were heated in the absence of water, they could be heated to remarkably high temperatures. One can, for example, maintain them at 160° C. Some enzymes lose their enzymatic activity slowly at 160° C., provided they are dry to begin with.

Quantitative evaluation of the amino acid contents of the proteinoids has been made. One feature of this is the fact that there are practically no amino acids other than those that were in the reaction, except for one unknown peak. Otherwise we are dealing with a profile which is remarkably like that of any natural protein as observed after hydrolysis by the amino acid analyzer.

Aspartic acid content is relatively high compared to natural proteins, and two amino acids, threonine and serine, do not survive such heating treatment very well, although more recently we have found ways of protecting them in simpler systems. These combinations are rigidly controlled by internal factors. Such syntheses have been carried out in four other laboratories that I know of, and the products have been analyzed in six other laboratories of which I am aware. The fact that synthesis in different laboratories will give similar analyses is documented in a paper in *Nature* by Krampitz & Knappen (16).

The yields of these protein-like materials are typically 10 to 30 per cent. Higher yields are obtained when ATP or polyphosphoric acid is added. Under those conditions, the temperature can be lowered to values as low as 65° C. This is of interest because it suggests a bridge between the presumed prebiological chemistry represented here and biological chemistry itself, due to the function of polyphosphate in the biochemical systems.

It is also true that, instead of using a considerable proportion of aspartic acid in the reaction, one can use another non-neutral amino acid, lysine—lysine being a basic amino acid—and get about the same qualitative results. All of the amino acids are obtained in polymers from either aspartic acid or lysine.

Benzer: Is their composition dependent upon the starting material?

Fox: Quantitatively, it is dependent. Qualitatively, one obtains in each case all the amino acids included in the reaction. The proportions in the aspartic acid proteinoid are quantitatively different from those in the lysine proteinoid. Each composition is of itself quantitatively highly repeatable in replicate experiments.

I would like to present some data from Krampitz's* laboratory, which he has given me permission to use. The data illustrate the fact that these materials have a kind of structure which is disruptable.

In this case, a proteinoid is made and then is subjected to the action of pepsin; the kinds of fragments obtained are chromatographed and stained with ninhydrin. There is some breakdown, but not very much.

If the proteinoid is heated at 80° C. for one minute in aqueous solution, and then subjected to the same treatment, fragmentation is found. A great deal of splitting of this synthetic polymer following the kind of treatment which is comparable to denaturation of proteins is observed, however. In heated substrate material, without the action of the enzyme, there is no such opening at all.

---

* G. Krampitz, University of Bonn, Germany.

These results, taken in conjunction with others of another sort, on catalytic activity, which we have reported earlier (8), indicate that it is possible to obtain by dry heat very complicated molecules which are disrupted by wet heat.

We have also looked at the terminal residues, that is, the kind of amino acid at each end of these chains. Some of these polymers have an average molecular weight of 10,000. This involved C- terminal analysis and N-terminal analysis. What the studies tell us, in essence, is the relative proportion of each of 18 types of amino acids at the ends of the proteinoid chains.

Quite a disparity from the total composition has been found, which suggests there is internal ordering in these molecules, due merely to the interaction of the reacting amino acids. This is not in any sense to be construed as a downgrading of the importance of nucleic acids of contemporary organisms, but, if one questions the extent to which we are dealing here with a valid model of the origin of protein, it does indicate that some of the order could have been introduced by the reaction of the amino acids alone. This question has been raised and that is why I refer to it here.

This kind of emphasis has led recently to reports of the possibility of polymerizing mononucleotides in a similar fashion. Schramm (30), using exactly our conditions but different material, an ethyl polyphosphate instead of polyphosphoric acid, recently reported that he can polymerize mononucleotides to polynucleotides. Some of the work in our laboratory which, in essence, is a modification resulting from the suggestion from Schramm's work, indicates that under our exact conditions, at 65° C. in the presence of polyphosphoric acid and urea, one can obtain polymers of cytidylic acid.

This is unfinished work, but we find hyperchromicity comparable to that found in polycytidylic acid made in other ways. The alkaline shift and the absorption spectrum which characterized such material are present. The elemental analyses are in quite good agreement except for the nitrogen, which is low. Studies of ribonuclease are just getting under way (31).

The thermal model is *in toto* more comprehensive than what I have presented (6). The aspects most clearly germane to this conference have however been presented and are:

a) the theoretical position of the most primitive memory mechanism (9),

b) the fact that molecules approximately as complex as proteins could arise in a simple spontaneous polymerization, as demonstrated in the laboratory under geologically plausible conditions,

c) the fact that some of the chemical information of (*b*) is being applied quite directly, with so far partial success, in converting mononucleotides to RNA-like polymers, and

d) these processes arise in a continuum which upon experimental test additionally suggests a total outline of abiogenesis.

REFERENCES

1. BARONDES, S. H., and NIRENBERG, M. W., Fate of a synthetic polynucleotide directing cell-free protein synthesis. I. Characteristics of degradation. *Science*, 1962, **138**: 810-813.

2. BASILIO, C., WAHBA, A. J., LENGYEL, P., SPEYER, J. F., and OCHOA, S., Synthetic polynucleotides and the amino acid code. *Proc. Nat. Acad. Sci. USA*, 1962, **48**: 613-616.

3. BRESLER, S. YE., GLIKINA, M. V., SELEZNEVA, N. A., and FINOGENOV, P. A., Investigation of the resynthesis of proteins under pressure. *Biokhimiya*, 1952, **17**: 44-55 (in Russian).

4. CHAPEVILLE, F., LIPMANN, F., VON EHRENSTEIN, G., WEISBLUM, B., RAY, JR., W. J., and BENZER, S., On the role of soluble ribonucleic acid in coding for amino acids. *Proc. Nat. Acad. Sci. USA*, 1962, **48**: 1086-1092.

5. CRICK, F. H. C., BARNETT, L., BRENNER, S., and WATTS-TOBIN, R. J., General nature of the genetic code for proteins. *Nature*, 1961, **192**: 1227-1232.

6. FOX, S. W., How did life begin? *Science*, 1960, **132**: 200-208.

7. FOX, S. W., and HARADA, K., The thermal copolymerization of amino acids common to protein. *J. Am. Chem. Soc.*, 1960, **82**: 3745-3751.

8. FOX, S. W., HARADA, K., and ROHLFING, D. L., The thermal copolymerization of α-amino acids. In: *Polyamino Acids, Polypeptides, and Proteins* (M. A. Stahmann, Ed.). Univ. of Wisconsin Press, Madison, 1962: 47-53.

9. FOX, S. W., VEGOTSKY, A., HARADA, K., and HOAGLAND, P. D., Spontaneous generation of anabolic pathways, protein, and nucleic acid. *Ann. New York Acad. Sci.*, 1957, **69**: 328-337.

10. GAMOW, G., Possible relation between deoxyribonucleic acid and protein structures. *Nature*, 1954, **173**: 318.

11. GARRISON, W. M., MORRISON, D. C., HAMILTON, J. G., BENSON, A. A., and CALVIN, M., Reduction of carbon dioxide in aqueous solutions by ionizing radiation. *Science*, 1951, **114**: 416-418.

12. GRUNBERG-MANAGO, M., and OCHOA, S., Enzymatic synthesis and breakdown of polynucleotides; polynucleotide phosphorylase. *J. Am. Chem. Soc.*, 1955, **77**: 3165-3166.

13. JONES, O. W., and NIRENBERG, M. W., Qualitative survey of RNA codewords. *Proc. Nat. Acad. Sci. USA*, 1962, **48**: 2115-2123.

14. JONES, O. W., TOWNSEND, E. E., SOBER, H. A., and HEPPEL, L. A., Effect of chain length on the template activity of polyribonucleotides. *Biochemistry*, 1964, **3**: 238-246.

15. KAMEYAMA, T., and NOVELLI, G. D., The cell-free synthesis of β-galactosidase by *Escherichia coli*. *Biochem. Biophys. Res. Commun.*, 1960, **2**: 393-396.

16. KRAMPITZ, G., and KNAPPEN, F., Thermal copolymerization of protein hydrolyzates containing ^{35}S amino acids and distribution of radioactive sulphur after application of ^{35}S-labelled amino-acid copolymers in the rat. *Nature*, 1962, **195**: 385-387.

17. LENGYEL, P., SPEYER, J. F., BASILIO, C., and OCHOA, S., Synthetic polynucleotides and the amino acid code, III. *Proc. Nat. Acad. Sci. USA*, 1962, **48**: 282-284.

18. LEVINTHAL, C., KEYNAN, A., and HIGA, A., Messenger RNA turnover and

protein synthesis in *B. subtilis* inhibited by actinomycin D. *Proc. Nat. Acad. Sci. USA*, 1962, **48**: 1631-1638.

19. MARCUS, L., BRETTHAUER, R. K., BOCK, R. M., and HALVORSON, H. O., The effect of poly U size on the incorporation of phenylalanine in the cell-free yeast system. *Proc. Nat. Acad. Sci. USA*, 1963, **50**: 782-789.

20. MATTHAEI, J. H., JONES, O. W., MARTIN, R. G., and NIRENBERG, M. W., Characteristics and composition of RNA coding units. *Proc. Nat. Acad. Sci. USA*, 1962, **48**: 666-677.

21. MATTHAEI, J. H., and NIRENBERG, M. W., Characteristics and stabilization of DNAase-sensitive protein synthesis in E. coli extracts. *Proc. Nat. Acad. Sci. USA*, 1961, **47**: 1580-1588.

22. NIRENBERG, M. W., and JONES, JR., O. W., The current status of the RNA code. In: *Informational Macromolecules* (H. J. Vogel, V. Bryson and J. O. Lampen, Eds.). Academic Press, New York, 1963: 451-465.

23. NIRENBERG, M. W., and MATTHAEI, J. H., The dependence of cell-free protein synthesis in E. coli upon naturally occurring or synthetic polyribonucleotides. *Proc. Nat. Acad. Sci. USA*, 1961, **47**: 1588-1602.

24. ————, The dependence of cell-free protein synthesis in *E. coli* upon naturally occurring or synthetic template RNA. In: *Biological Structure and Function at the Molecular Level* (V. A. Engelhardt, Ed.). Vol. I. of Proc. Fifth Int. Cong. Biochem., Moscow, 1961. Pergamon, Oxford, 1963: 184-195.

25. NIRENBERG, M. W., MATTHAEI, J. H., and JONES, O. W., An intermediate in the biosynthesis of polyphenylalanine directed by synthetic template RNA. *Proc. Nat. Acad. Sci. USA*, 1962, **48**: 104-109.

26. NIRENBERG, M. W., MATTHAEI, J. H., JONES, O. W., MARTIN, R. G., and BARONDES, S. H., Approximation of genetic code via cell-free protein synthesis directed by template RNA. *Fed. Proc. Symp.*, 1963, **22**: 55-61.

27. NISMAN, B., and FUKUHARA, H., Incorporation des acides aminés et synthèse de la β-galactosidase par les fractions enzymatiques de *Escherichia coli*. *C. R. Acad. Sci.* (Paris), 1959, **249**: 2240-2242.

28. OCHOA, S., Synthetic polynucleotides and the genetic code. In: *Informational Macromolecules* (H. J. Vogel, V. Bryson and J. O. Lampen, Eds.). Academic Press, New York, 1963: 437-449.

29. RUDENBERG, F. H., and TOBIAS, J. M., The effect of ribonuclease on the dialysis of calcium from homogenates of lobster nerve and the binding of sodium in the homogenates. *J. Cell. Comp. Physiol.*, 1960, **55**: 149-157.

30. SCHRAMM, G., GRÖTSCH, H., and POLLMANN, W., Non-enzymatic synthesis of polysaccharides, nucleosides and nucleic acids and the origin of self-reproducing systems. *Angew. Chem. Intern.* (Engl. Ed.), 1962, **1**: 1-7.

31. SCHWARTZ, A., and FOX, S. W., Thermal synthesis of internucleotide phosphodiester linkages. *Biochim. Biophys. Acta*, 1964, **87**: 694-696.

32. SINGER, M. F., JONES, O. W., and NIRENBERG, M. W., The effect of secondary structure on the template activity of polyribonucleotides. *Proc. Nat. Acad. Sci. USA*, 1963, **49**: 392-399.

33. SPEYER, J. F., LENGYEL, P., BASILIO, C., and OCHOA, S., Synthetic polynucleotides and the amino acid code, II. *Proc. Nat. Acad. Sci. USA*, 1962, **48**: 63-68.

34. SPEYER, J. F., LENGYEL, P., BASILIO, C., and OCHOA, S., Synthetic polynucleotides and the amino acid code, IV. *Proc. Nat. Acad. Sci. USA*, 1962, **48**: 441-448.

35. SPYRIDES, G. J., and LIPMANN, F., Polypeptide synthesis with sucrose gradient fractions of E. coli ribosomes. *Proc. Nat. Acad. Sci. USA*, 1962, **48**: 1977-1983.

36. TISSIÈRES, A., SCHLESSINGER, D., and GROS, F., Amino acid incorporation into proteins by *Escherichia coli* ribosomes. *Proc. Nat. Acad. Sci. USA*, 1960, **46**: 1450-1463.

37. WEISBLUM, B., BENZER, S., and HOLLEY, R. W., A physical basis for degeneracy in the amino acid code. *Proc. Nat. Acad. Sci. USA*, 1962, **48**: 1449-1454.

RNA—A FUNCTIONAL CHARACTERISTIC
OF THE NEURON AND ITS GLIA[*]

HOLGER HYDÉN[†]
Institute of Neurobiology
University of Göteborg
Sweden

Characteristic for the central nervous system is the complicated three-dimensional structure composed of non-dividing neurons and of neuroglia. An obvious feature of the integrated function of the brain is the capacity to perceive the outer world and to store, recall and utilize the information for immediate action or for abstraction.

Characteristic of the neurons is their capacity to produce, among other substances, great amounts of RNA and proteins (22). This is an outstanding feature and the more interesting when viewed against the background of evolution and the development of the human brain during the relatively short period of 500 million years, and especially when one considers the probable key role in evolution of polymers with the inherent capacity of autonomous replication, such as DNA and RNA (36). In the rapidly moving field of nucleic acid research, the findings of the role played by messenger RNA in protein synthesis has placed the *ribosomal RNA* and its function as a question mark. In the large neurons of mammals, the amount of DNA is 8-10 μμg per nucleus. In contrast, the amount of cytoplasmic RNA, the main part of which is ribosomal RNA, reaches values up to 2000 μμg. A pertinent question, therefore, is whether the main part of the ribosomal RNA of the neuron is an inert but necessary framework of the cell, with only a small fraction of ribosomal RNA serving the messenger RNA at their precise mediation of amino acid polymerization (as is indicated by the studies of bacterial systems). Is the great amount of RNA in neurons only a reflection of the extent to which protein synthesis proceeds in these cells? Does the bulk of the neuronal RNA comprise a specialized RNA system serving the nervous function?

[*] The studies reported here have been supported by grants from the Swedish Medical Research Council, the Air Force Office of Scientific Research of the Air Research and Development Command, United States Air Force, through its European Office, and by the National Multiple Sclerosis Society, New York.

[†] The Editor regrets that limit of time at the Conference prevented those present from hearing all the material Dr. Hydén came prepared to present. Readers of this volume are referred to Dr. Hydén's other published works included in the reference list.

At the present time the characterization of neuronal and glial RNA using cell-free systems remains to be done. In the experiments to be described, the main emphasis has been on the compartmentalization of brain RNA, quantitative aspects and base composition characterization, even of fractions of nerve cells.

As Dr. Nirenberg has pointed out, the definition of brain RNA leaves much to be desired; there is one main reason for this, and that is that, in the intricate compartments where the RNA is to be found, the three-dimensional structure of the central nervous system is composed of nondividing neurons and of glia. The large neurons have few competitors as RNA producers. I would like to say that this production of RNA in the neurons is as characteristic as the production of bioelectrical potentials.

Therefore, the distribution of the brain RNA will be discussed, and some characteristics of the neuronal RNA and glial RNA during stimulation and during a learning experiment. Changes will be demonstrated in the neuronal and the glial RNA composition. This leads to a discussion of the functional aspect of the brain RNA and the relationship between the neuron and its glia.

To study the content of RNA in the different structural compartments, the only successful way proved to be an isolation of the structures. Figures 1 to 6 give examples of isolated nerve cells and glia samples and cell details prepared for analysis with microchemical methods (3, 8, 9, 10, 14, 15, 25, 30, 31). Nerve cells, isolated by free-hand technique under a stereomicroscope at 80 to 120 times magnification, have been cultured without resultant

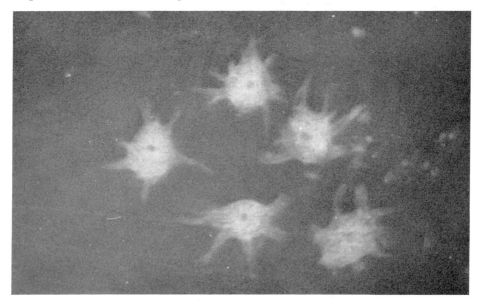

Figure 1. Deiters' nerve cells of rabbit, isolated from the glia and photographed in incident light. × 80

structural changes, and they show respiration for several months. Only cell material rapidly removed from the animal and isolated within five to ten minutes has been used in the experiments to be discussed.

Figure 1 shows some cells from the lateral vestibular nucleus, the so-called Deiters' cells. These cells are swimming in isotonic solution. They have been taken out by free-hand dissection with very simple instruments made from stainless steel wires 15 mμ in diameter.

In Figure 2 the nucleus and the first part of the dendrites can be seen. The dendrites become very thin and break off at the dissection. But these are completely free from glia, as can be noted. They have been lightly stained with methylene blue to bring out the synaptic knobs which can be faintly seen at the edges. One question is, what error may be introduced by breaking off the rest of the dendrites? We have tried to compute that. It is an error which, anyhow, is lower than the sensitivity of the methods, for many reasons. There are no appreciable amounts of RNA in these dendritic tips, for example. The concentration of organic substances is very low, and they are very thin.

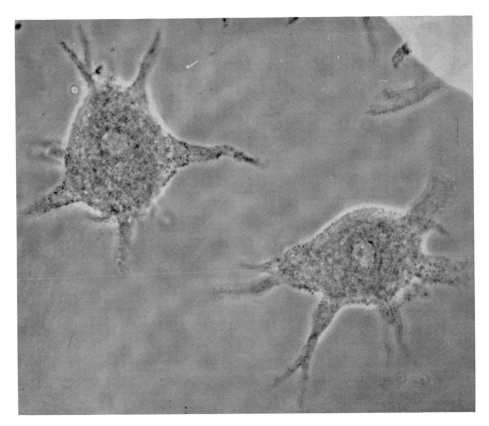

Figure 2. Two of the Deiters' nerve cells in Figure 1 photographed in the phase contrast microscope. Note the synaptic knobs focused at the surface of the cells. × 850

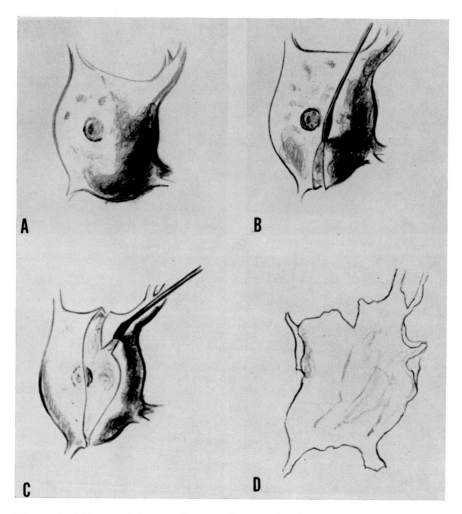

Figure 3. Microsurgical procedure to obtain isolated nerve cell membrane. A: Whole nerve cell; B: initial cut; C: cut along dendrite; D: prepared membrane. (From Hydén, 24.)

It is possible to perform analysis on parts of cells if the methods are sensitive enough. Figure 3 demonstrates the procedure we have used. This is an isolated cell and by means of a small stainless steel knife—the blade here is around 10 mμ—a cut is made on the surface of the cell and out in one of the dendrites, and a few other cuts are made, too. The flaps are folded back toward the surface, and the content of the cell is removed. That leaves a membrane. This membrane we have measured: it is around 2500 Å thick. It is made up of the double layer seen in the electron microscope and also of another layer, adjacent to the membrane, which has a slightly denser consistency than the rest of the components of the cell. It is impossible to obtain these membranes by mechanical means. We have tried ultrasound without success.

Hild: Do you mean to say that the cytoplasm is of a different viscosity than the cell membrane, and that you actually can isolate the two components mechanically?

Hydén: We open the cell, and then with a small micropipette we direct a jet of solution to the middle of the open cell where the flaps are folded. So, by that means, we take away most of the content of the cell. I used to take a very soft instrument and scrape very cautiously inside it. It is impossible to obtain thinner membranes by such means, they only break and crumple up. The values obtained have been between 2500 and 2900 Å.

Hild: I am asking because this is such a surprising fact for me, since I am working with living nerve cells in culture, though not with fresh cells. Whenever I pierce a membrane, the cell disintegrates *in toto;* there is no membrane left; there are no contents left. It just flows away and disappears. Any type of cell, glia or neuron, present in the cultures behaves in the same manner.

Hydén: They disintegrate in the culture, when you pierce the membrane?

Hild: Yes. I have published photographs of this phenomenon in my article in von Möllendorff's *Handbuch der mikroskopischen Anatomie des Menschen* (19).

Hydén: I have not observed the phenomenon you speak of. One difference is that I am not working with cells in cultures. Our cells are taken directly from the brain. We use different kinds of media for these cells. One simple medium is an isotonic mixture of sucrose, in some cases fortified with glucose, ATP and some ions. The cells do not go to pieces in this type of solution.

Fremont-Smith: Do nerve cells divide in culture?

Hild: Neurons do not divide and reproduce *in vitro,* just as they do not divide and reproduce *in vivo* once they are differentiated. Glial cells *in vitro* can be seen to divide just as well as they do *in vivo.* However, their mitotic rate is not sufficient to increase the cell population *in vitro;* it is not even sufficient to maintain the mass of the explant. One must keep in mind that during the time of preparation of the explants many cells are injured to such a degree that they will not survive. The majority of nerve cells within a fresh explant about 1 mm³ in size are irreversibly damaged by amputation of cell processes and mechanical mishandling, and it is surprising that some of them do survive and regenerate at all. However, cells becoming established *in vitro* are actually living, as evidenced by the regrowth of cell processes, their participation in myelin formation, the reconstitution of a typical Nissl pattern, their measurable electrical activities, their metabolic activities, etc. I like to contrast them in this respect with freshly isolated cells which may not be viable at all. The living cell as we observe it *in vitro* will die and disintegrate within a few minutes if the cell membrane is ruptured by a microinstrument. I wanted to emphasize that living cells in these preparations are not firm enough to be manipulated mechanically.

Fremont-Smith: Dr. Hydén, how long after your cells have been removed from the Deiters' nucleus do you make your observation?

Hydén: I would say between three and five minutes. We have measured the oxygen consumption and the level of ATP when they have adjusted to the environment. But we get different measurements of enzymatic activities when they are presented with a substrate for different enzymes. Evidently there is an important difference in these properties when the cells are taken immediately for observation and manipulation from when they are kept in such a medium, living and respiring for a certain period of time.

French: Dr. Hild, how long after you remove the cells from the preparation do you examine them?

Hild: It takes several days before the cells are visible under the microscope. This is due to the gradual flattening of the explants. Only in thin layers of cells can morphological details be observed with the phase contrast microscope. I want to add something to an earlier remark: by just looking at a neuron under the microscope one cannot always be sure whether it is living or not. In 1958 I observed in one culture that three or four cells which appeared normal at first glance, and which I tried to impale with microelectrodes, were impenetrable for some unknown reason. They were so firm that they were torn loose from their surroundings. In the effort to penetrate them they were moved around before the tip of the electrode. All this manipulation did not in the least distort these cells. This strange phenomenon could only be explained by the assumption that they were dead cells that for one reason or another somehow were gelated. This, however, was the only instance in which a cell did not disintegrate when it was handled by a microinstrument.

It could be that immediately after isolation the cells may have different physical properties.

Luco: If an axon is cut, will it regrow?

Hild: If the axon of a neuron *in vitro* is cut or injured fairly close to the perikaryon, the cell will die just as if the cell body were injured. The same is true for cells the dendrites of which are injured. The surprising fact is this: when the explants are prepared and pieces of central nervous tissue are cut to a size of about 1 mm^3, innumerable neurons are mutilated by amputation of axons to such a degree that they will die. Yet there are still quite a number of cells that will survive and regenerate their axons. Already around the tenth to fifteenth day of incubation I have seen and measured axons 15 to 20 mm long. This indicates a great viability and regenerative power in some neurons. However, if the cell body or one of the major processes close to the cell body is injured *in vitro*, the cell disintegrates very rapidly.

Hydén: We have been working with this type of material, I would say, since 1956. One main thing for us in the procedure is to work rapidly. From the moment the animal is killed until the cells are clean (and we usually use between five and ten cells for each analysis) it should take no more than five to ten minutes. If you put them in the medium right away, you can manipulate the cells, and clean them from the glia; yet the cells do not burst. You can work on them in this way for about four hours after isolation, or something like that. But, evidently, if you put them in a medium and cultivate them, something must change.

Hild: I have thought about this problem a long time. I have tried many times to repeat experiments reported by De Rényi (5, 6, 7). He investigated the physical properties of freshly isolated nerve cells and fibers which were suspended in a "physiological" NaCl solution. According to De Rényi, the viscosity of nerve cells is so high that they could be broken into pieces which showed definite fracture lines and which kept their shapes so that they could be fitted together again by means of a micromanipulator. He also reported that the degree of viscosity is different in anterior horn cells and dorsal root ganglion cells. In contrast to these results, whenever I injured a neuron soma or one of its major processes with a microneedle or a micropipette, I observed a total disintegration of the whole cell. Of course, my cells are not freshly isolated and suspended in NaCl but have been living for various periods of time *in vitro*.

Hydén: I would say a good test would be to measure the oxygen consumption, following the culture from the very beginning. Have you done this?

Hild: No, I have not measured oxygen consumption. However, I have sufficient evidence that cultures of CNS tissue require a fair amount of air for survival. In roller tubes of 15 ml volume only 2 ml are taken up by nutrient fluid medium, the rest is air. In these conditions the cultures can be well maintained. As soon as the air space is taken away, i.e., when the cultures are removed from the roller tube and mounted in a closed chamber for microscopic observation, they will degenerate in this chamber in a few hours. Such closed chambers contain about 0.8 ml fluid but no air space.

Hydén: We have, during the last month, worked with a computation of the endogenous respiration. We have isolated the cells as soon as possible, so that only a few minutes pass before the cells are in a medium consisting of an isotonic solution. Then we have measured the oxygen consumption for the nerve cells (I am not speaking about the glia but the nerve cells) by the microdiver technique. The first values are below zero, which is possible in the diver technique but, within five or ten minutes, the oxygen consumption rises rapidly, and then it falls off. What is interesting, with respect to what you say, is the rapidly rising phase. We interpret it as a sort of cell shock to begin with, when the cells have been rapidly taken out of their environment and isolated from the glia. Before they adjust to the new environment, which is a foreign one of course, it takes a certain time. This is around ten minutes.

This is endogenous respiration, nothing added to it—but in a culture, if the cells receive substances which they can utilize as energy sources, it is known that the potassium begins to increase; so the cells can evidently adjust. I was not aware of the membrane phenomena.

Adey: May I draw attention to what I think is a quite relevant fact, namely that there are very substantial differences in the fragility of the nerve cell membranes in different parts of the central nervous system. The anterior horn cell, for instance, can be repeatedly penetrated from different directions by micropipette and maintain a substantial proportion of its membrane potential, and does not appear to be damaged thereby. But I think most of us would agree that an attempt to penetrate the cells of the brain, in almost any cortical or subcortical region, is indeed an extremely delicate procedure, and that to record for more than a few seconds, let alone for minutes or hours, requires extreme attention to this problem of total rupture of the membrane and disintegration of the cell.

In fact, there are very few people who have succeeded in recording consistently from inside brain cells, whereas it is virtually an easy task to record from inside one of the anterior horn cells. The anterior horn cells appear to have membrane almost like leather. Thus the extensive extrapolations made about its functions and the generalizations drawn therefrom about the neuraxis in general and intracellular organization in particular would appear to be relatively unwarranted.

In connection with what has been said by Dr. Hydén and Dr. Hild, we might expect, apart from the differences in the culture preparations as opposed to the whole brain, these differences in regional functions and regional organization in nerve cell membrane. This may, of course, relate quite importantly to the RNA mechanisms which are presumed to be organized adjacent to the membrane in a variety of ways discussed by Dr. Hydén.

Green: Might I ask Dr. Hild a question? In the case of your tissue culture cells, are they covered with synaptic knobs as Dr. Hydén's are? This may make a difference to the mechanical stability.

Hild: No, they are not. Boutons terminaux around neurons *in vitro*—at least in my preparations—apparently are lost very soon. They were never observed. Those cells are essentially naked. They are, of course, touched in many places by surrounding cells but these contacts apparently are not of a functional nature.

Once the cells are isolated and freed of their synaptic coverings there still must be a difference between Dr. Hydén's and my material.

Hydén: Dr. Green has an important point. We computed that one such Deiters' cell, including the main part of the dendrite, must be covered by at least ten thousand synaptic knobs. That might be a significant factor.

Magoun: Could we hear from the electron microscopists about the pre-synaptic contribution to the synaptic or the junctional membrane structure? You made reference to the postsynaptic membrane of the nerve cell. What presynaptic layers might provide an increment here, that would add to the stability of the membrane?

Palay: There are structures which resemble attachment plaques that might be concerned in stabilizing the membrane.

Fremont-Smith: Could this be a species difference?

Hild: We use rat and kitten material. Mouse and rabbit tissue—in our hands—is not very useful. Several years ago I had good luck with dog brain, too. However, there may be the important factor of the nature of nutrient media involved, so that it is quite difficult to explain the different behavior of explants from different species.

Calvin: Why do you find it so surprising that the stability of the membrane of the cell should change in four days, or however long it is kept out of the animal? I do not find this mysterious; I am surprised cells can be kept for four days without disintegrating.

Hild: It takes at least four days or so for the explants to flatten out enough—in some areas—to permit recognition of single cells under the microscope.

Weiskrantz: Do you find cells other than Deiters' cells are more difficult to manipulate, or simply that the Deiters' cells are larger?

Hydén: The hypoglossal cells from the rat, with which we struggled for some months, differ a little.

Benzer: Did you use Deiters' cells because they are large and easy to take out?

Hydén: Not only that, but it is easy to use them in a physiological experiment. Also, they are regular in size. With respect to the content of RNA, for example, it is surprising how constant they are. The coefficient of variation in the values is very small.

Benzer: How many Deiters' cells would there be in one brain?

Hydén: Between 500 and 600 large Deiters' cells on each side. So, 1100 or 1200, something like that, in the rabbit.

Luco: Following up Dr. Magoun's question, in your preparation you probably have no presynaptic membrane covering the subsynaptic membrane. It is well known that when the presynaptic membrane is removed, as in the experiments of Birks, Katz & Miledi (1), the glial cells cover the subsynaptic membrane of the muscle system. If there are no glial cells to cover the isolated portion of subsynaptic membrane because the presynaptic membrane has been removed, there may be a locus of lowered resistance for keeping the whole structure normal.

Hild: That is a very good point. It has to be explored.

Feindel: I am not quite clear from your comments, Dr. Hydén, whether your experience with dissecting nerve cells and removing the interior has been in all types of nerve cells examined. Could you tell us what other kinds of nerve cells, other than Deiters' nucleus, you have studied?

Hydén: We started with spinal ganglion cells several years ago. We have used anterior horn cells. We have used hypoglossal cells and supraopticus. We have used cells from the descending nucleus of the trigeminus, and of the reticular formation.

Figure 4 shows a Deiters' cell again. Notice particularly the shape of the dendrites; the picture on the right shows the membrane prepared from this cell. The shape of the dendrites can be recognized. All the dots in this photograph are synaptic knobs.

Feindel: How do you know they are synaptic knobs?

Hydén: We have made a number of experiments with the silver stains and with other types of stains. Dr. Ekholm of the Anatomy Department at Göteborg has been kind enough to help us with some electron micrographs.

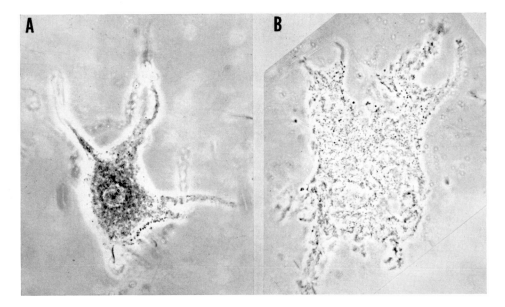

Figure 4. A: Isolated Deiters' nerve cell in phase contrast (note the synaptic knobs at the cell periphery); B: the isolated membrane of the cell in phase contrast (note density of synaptic knobs). The cell was stained with diluted methylene blue solution. (Reproduced in part from Hydén, 24.)

When such cells, not within the tissue but isolated, are processed in all the solutions needed to prepare them for electron micrography, the result was not very satisfactory but at least it assured us that the dots were synaptic knobs. Morphologically, they had the appearance of synaptic knobs.

Figure 5 shows one important procedure we have used, the results of which I shall discuss later on. These are two cells which were isolated cleanly from the glia and then were precipitated by means of phenol-saturated water, cold ethanol and chloroform. The nucleus was then removed. The hole can be seen and, above each cell, the nucleus which was removed from it. To begin with, we had tried the Harris procedure, going back to biochemical methods to neutralize RNA. We found that this was not satisfactory from the chemical point of view. Therefore, the only remaining

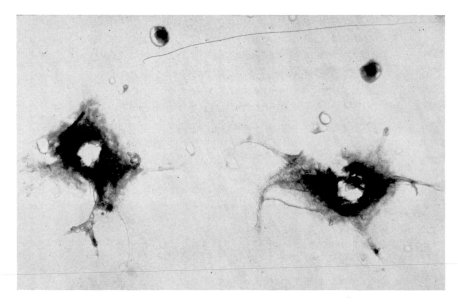

Figure 5. Two isolated Deiters' nerve cells, cleaned from glia and treated with phenol-water. The nucleus from each has been removed and is placed above its respective nerve cell, in the center of which is seen the corresponding hole. Photographed at 2570 Å. (From Hydén & Egyházi, 25.)   × 400

procedure was to take out the nuclei; we pull twenty of them for each analysis.

Figure 6 shows three Deiters' cells and the clusters of glial cells that had previously surrounded each (pressed onto the glass for the photograph). Their volume was measured, their dry weight was determined by X-ray microradiography at 8 to 10 Å, and the radiograms were scanned with a computer. The weight of these cells from the rabbit averaged 20,000 μμg; the glia surrounding the cells had the same dry weight per volume unit. These results were obtained biochemically, and this routine procedure has proved satisfactory.

Feindel: Would it be fair to say, from looking briefly at the glial cells in Figure 6, that they too showed synaptic knobs? Could you distinguish those from the ones you make out on the nerve cells? The morphological appearance, if you are using that as an indicator, is not very dissimilar in the two cases.

Hydén: Those synaptic knobs are so small that from the point of view of the results they can be of no significance. These are visible on the electron microscopic level. We have not been studying some of the more crucial substances for which even a small volume should be a matter of concern.

Feindel: If you have 10,000 synaptic knobs on a cell membrane, as you mentioned, is that not significant?

Hydén: It depends. If you are determining RNA, it is of no significance. If you are determining the total amount of protein, it can be of no significance because it still must be below the sensitivity of the methods. So, over the years, we have worked out a number of methods with sufficient accuracy to deal with substances at the level of 20 to 1000 μμg or, for example, the oxygen consumption of microliters times 10^{-4} per cell per hour. I will not go into the methods but, instead, will discuss the distribution of RNA and some results which might be of interest.

As pointed out, the large neurons have no competitors among somatic cells as RNA producers, and the amount depends on the size of the cells. When the mass of RNA and the amount of proteins are taken into consideration, a large neuron has the characteristics of an enormous gland cell.

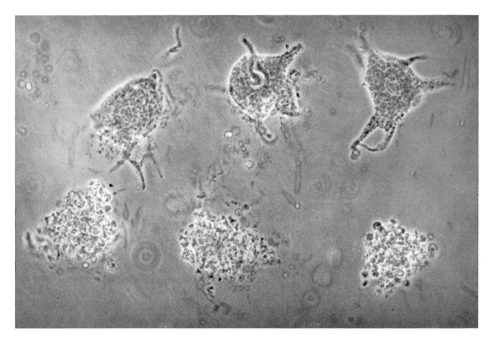

Figure 6. Above are shown three isolated Deiters' cells. Below each cell is a cluster of neuronal glia of the same volume as that of the nerve cell, i.e., around 90,000 μ³, and with the same weight, 20,000 μμg. (From Hydén & Pigon, 32.)   × 170

Table 3 shows how much the RNA content varies. Retinal ganglion cells have 45 μμg/cell. Spinal cells vary enormously. Hypoglossal cells have around 200, and Deiters' giant cells, 1550.

In other species, there may be still more RNA per cell. The extreme example is one which Edström recently described (12), the Mauthner cell in the fish. Every fish and some amphibians have just one pair of these cells. Motor cells of fish contain as much as 4000 μμg/cell body (24). Mauthner nerve cells from growing fishes have been found to contain 10,000 μμg per neuron, 8,000 μμg of which was in the axon (12).

In mammalian neurons, the *nuclear RNA* constitutes only around five per cent of the total RNA, e.g., 30 μμg in the giant Deiters' neurons (25). Of the nuclear RNA, 30 to 50 per cent can be calculated to belong to the nucleolus. Quantitatively, in man, as shown in Figure 7, the amount of RNA

TABLE 3

RNA Content in Different Types of Nerve Cells

Type of nerve cell	RNA ($\mu\mu$g/cell)
Retinal ganglion cells, rabbit	45
Nerve cells of the supraoptic nucleus, rabbit	70
Spinal ganglion cells, rabbit	1070
Hypoglossal cells, rabbit	200
Anterior horn cells, rabbit	530
Anterior horn cells, man, 40–50 years	670
Anterior horn cells, man, 60–70 years	540
Deiters' giant cells, rabbit	1550
Deiters' nucleus medium-size cells	885

per anterior motor horn cell increases significantly up to the age of 40, remains at a steady level until 60, and decreases significantly after this age (23).

Benzer: As there are no points in the curve, it is hard to tell how much scatter there is. The difference between the maximum and the lowest values here is only 50 per cent. Would you expect that much variation from one individual to another?

Hydén: I would expect that, yes. The curve in Figure 7 is from approximately 40 cases. They vary quite a bit. This is the general trend, and that is what I wanted to present, rather than placing the emphasis on small variations. There is no doubt that there is the tendency shown in this curve.

Feindel: Is there any chance that the type of death here, being accidental, would affect your value?

Hydén: I do not know. The only thing I can say is that we have taken out pieces of brain and let them remain in room temperature for up to 14 hours, with no difference in the amount of RNA per cell. That was done in order to see whether or not it would be possible to utilize autopsy material. I cannot comment on the question of accidental death.

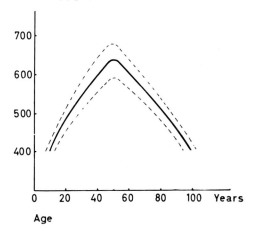

Figure 7. The amount of RNA per anterior horn cell of man increases up to the age of 40 and decreases rapidly after 60 years of age.

TABLE 4

NERVE CELL RNA, BASE COMPOSITION

(Molar proportions in % of the sum)

	N. Deiters rabbit	N. Supraopt. rat	N. Deiters rat	F. Reticul. rat	Glob. Pall. man
Adenine	19.7	18.9	20.7	19.5	17.1
Guanine	33.5	36.0	33.3	30.0	29.8
Cytosine	28.8	26.9	27.5	34.0	37.0
Uracil	18.0	18.2	18.5	16.5	16.1

Feindel: Was there a fairly uniform interval between death and your examination of the tissue in these cases, or did it vary?

Hydén: It varied between 5 and 15 hours, I would say, during the years.

In reference to Table 3, I should add that the electron micrographs of different types of neurons have demonstrated a well developed system of ribosomes belonging to the endoplasmic reticulum. Therefore, it is reasonable to assume that the main part of the high molecular RNA as determined with the microchemical method in μμg/cell is made up of ribosomal RNA. In the following the term *cytoplasmic RNA* will be used.

By analogy from electrophysiological studies, there has also been a tendency to consider nerve cells as "black boxes" from a biochemical point of view. That this is not so is demonstrated by the base ratio composition of RNA of neurons from different areas. The values in Table 4 are based on a large number of analyses of mammalian materials, and show that the cytosine values of nerve cells from globus pallidus and from the reticular formation are higher than the guanine values. The reverse is true for the cytosine and guanine values of nerve cells from Deiters' nucleus, the nucleus supraopticus and also from the spinal cord.

The question then arises of different types of nerve cell producing a different population of proteins. This seems likely, but cannot be proven at the present time.

As seen from Table 5, the base ratios of the nuclear RNA differ from the cytoplasmic RNA in having higher adenine and uracil values. There is a

TABLE 5

COMPOSITION OF RNA IN DEITERS' NERVE CELLS FROM CONTROL RABBITS: WHOLE NERVE CELLS AND THEIR NUCLEI

	Whole nerve cells		Nuclei		P
	Molar proportions	Variation coefficient	Molar proportions	Variation coefficient	
Adenine	19.7 ± 0.37	4.2	21.3 ± 0.42	4.9	0.02
Guanine	33.5 ± 0.39	2.6	26.6 ± 0.27	2.5	0.001
Cytosine	28.8 ± 0.36	2.8	30.8 ± 0.38	3.0	0.01
Uracil	18.0 ± 0.18	2.3	21.3 ± 0.43	5.0	0.001

trend to complementarity, but the nuclear RNA composition does not agree with that of the DNA.

The morphological relation between neuron and glia is most complicated. The thin, folded multimembranes of the glia cover every part of the neuronal surface which is not covered by synaptic knobs. The oligodendroglia which mainly constitute the immediate surround of the neuron are characterized by mitochondria in considerable numbers and are filled by electron-dense small particles, as seen with the electron microscope. In the following, the term *neuronal glia* will be used. Whereas 20 per cent of the dry organic substance of the neuron consists of lipids, removable with

TABLE 6

THE COMPOSITION OF THE RNA IN CONTROL DEITERS' NERVE CELLS
AND THEIR OLIGODENDROGLIAL CELLS IN RABBITS

(Microelectrophoretic Analysis of the RNA)

Nerve cell: 1550 $\mu\mu$g of RNA per cell; average dry weight: 20,000 $\mu\mu$g. Glia: 125 $\mu\mu$g of RNA per sample; average dry weight: 20,000 $\mu\mu$g. Purine and pyrimidine bases as molar proportions in percentages of the sum
Number of animals: 5
Number of analyses: 49

	Nerve Cell		Glia Mean		P
	Mean	V	Mean	V	
Adenine	19.7 ±0.37	4.2	20.8 ±0.28	3.0	
Guanine	33.5 ±0.39	2.6	28.8 ±0.64	5.0	0.001
Cytosine	28.8 ±0.36	2.8	31.8 ±0.27	2.0	0.001
Uracil	18.0 ±0.18	2.3	18.6 ±0.55	6.7	0.001

$$V = \text{the coefficient of variation}, \frac{S \times 100}{\text{Mean}}. \quad P = \text{probability after t-test.}$$

chloroform-methanol, this is the case with almost 80 per cent of the neuronal glia material (2). Quantitatively, the glia contain only one tenth the amount of RNA per dry weight unit as does the neuron which the glia surround (32). The large Deiters' nerve cells contain, on an average, 1550 $\mu\mu$g of RNA per cell, and the neuronal glia 125 $\mu\mu$g of RNA computed per the same weight and volume, 20,000 $\mu\mu$g and 90,000 μ^3 respectively.

Qualitatively, there exists a significant difference in the RNA composition of the neuron and the glia (15). The neuronal RNA contains more guanine than cytosine and the glial RNA more cytosine than guanine, as is shown in Table 6. Neurons and their glia are both derivatives of the neuroepithelium. The guanine-cytosine values suggest a complementarity, as if during ontogenesis their cytoplasmic RNA had been duplicated, each one from one strand of DNA. Thus the neuron and its surrounding glia synthesize different populations of RNA.

Axons and myelin sheath from growing Mauthner neurons have been shown to have an RNA concentration which is 0.1 per cent of that found in the cell body (12). The axonal RNA shows higher adenine and guanine values than does the cytoplasmic RNA, which has the usual high guanine and cytosine contents. The myelin sheath RNA shows an unusual and variable composition.

I would now like to demonstrate some differences in behavior between the neurons and the associated glia of these vestibular nerve cells when the animals are subjected to stimulation.

In a number of experiments on motor and sensory nerve cells, a graded physiological stimulation has been found to be followed by an increase of RNA per nerve cell (13, 20, 21, 22). A prolongation of the stimulation can cause a decrease in the RNA concentration and in the content per nerve cell. The decrease proved to be reversible within hours.

In Figure 8 are given in a schematic form two examples of the effect of stimulation and increased activity. The results demonstrated in this figure were based on approximately 1800 analyses carried out between 1957 and 1962 (18, 32). Rabbits were stimulated for 25 minutes per day for one to seven days by slow rotation back and forth through 120° horizontally and

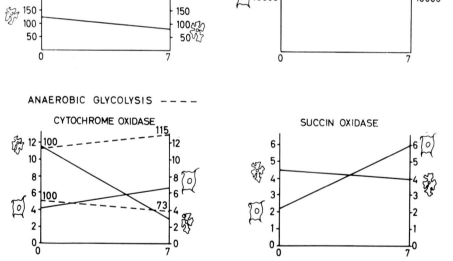

Figure 8. Diagrammatic representation of metabolic and chemical changes in Deiters' nerve cells and their glia as a function of physiological stimulation. (From Hydén & Pigon, 32.)

30° vertically. Such a stimulation has been shown to produce an increased depolarization pressure in the lateral vestibular nucleus, the large Deiters' nerve cells of which were used in our study (16).

As is demonstrated by the diagrams in Figure 8, the amount of neuronal RNA and proteins *increased*. The changes were significant (P = 0.01). In contrast, the glial RNA per same dry weight *decreased* significantly (P = 0.001).

The data summarized in Figure 8 also indicated a metabolic linkage between the neuron and its glia (18, 28, 32). At the increased activity and RNA and protein production of the vestibular Deiters' nerve cells, their respiratory enzyme activities rose, indicating a production of enzyme proteins. A kinetic study (29) showed that the neurons increased the capacity of the electron transport system as a function of the stimulation. The glia, in contrast, showed no such behavior and the respiratory enzyme activities fell, as did the content of RNA. The anaerobic glycolysis fell by 25 per cent in the neurons, simulating a Pasteur effect, and rose by 15 per cent in the glia, suggesting a Crabtree effect (18). From these and other studies (4) there seems to be no doubt that the neuron and its glia, reacting as a unit, are linked in an energy system, the units of which can swing between two positions, giving a great stability to the system from a cybernetic point of view. The neuron has priority in utilizing the easily available energy generated by the respiratory chain. If need be, the glia then partly resorts to anaerobic glycolysis.

Deutsch: I am not quite clear about the procedure. Was the rabbit's head fixed when it was being rotated? And how was it situated during the 23 hours of the day when it was not being rotated?

Hydén: The rabbit was placed in a tailor-made box, with the head out towards the periphery, but the head was not fixed separately. It could compensate, but the head also went slowly up and down through 30° with each turn and horizontally 120°, slowly, back and forth. Between tests the animal was kept in the cage, free to sit and move its head.

Benzer: What about the glial proteins?

Hydén: I did not study them. I did not want to introduce a possible error in these quantitative results by making a determination of proteins in the glia samples. The computer used in this X-ray microradiographic method has difficulty in discerning between the border, the background, and the slightly ripe borders in the glial clusters. The computer, however, easily discerns between the border of the cell and the background. In this case, the computer divides the sample into small areas, 3 μ^2 each, and then every fiftieth of a second it takes a value which gives the amount of dry weight per this area in two figures, from 00 to 99. It is easy to use cells with definable boundaries. Analyses of the glia were not performed because of these technical difficulties.

Benzer: If there were points on the curve in Figure 8, would each one represent an average of five rabbits, or ten cells?

Hydén: These represent 1800 analyses. There must be three or four hundred animals or more.

Feindel: In Figure 8 on the left, where you show the RNA change, there is a change of 100 units, from 1500 to 1600. Is that seven per cent increase significant in terms of the other variables, such as age, which you presented in Figure 7? Do you think there is any chance it could still lie within the range of variation when you compare this with the tables which you showed before?

Hydén: In the paper we published (32), we were careful to give all the values which showed that it was statistically significant. The values I showed before in discussing this problem were with respect to anterior horn cells, mostly. I pointed out the great variation in anterior horn cells. I have seen studies made during recent years where anterior horn cells clearly should not have been used because of their variation.

Deutsch: By a simple calculation, the experimental experience of rotation took something like a fiftieth of the time each day, and some of the differences seem rather large for that.

Hydén: Why do you think they are large? Have you something to compare them with?

Deutsch: There would probably be a large amount of random fluctuation of vestibular stimulation in the rest of the rabbits' daily experience; the animals would hop around the cage to different degrees. I should expect even a small percentage fluctuation to wash out any difference due to this fiftieth of the time you take, by the variance so produced. I wondered if you controlled for the amount eaten by the animals, the amount of activity, and so forth.

Hydén: The cages are the usual rabbit cages, not very large. You know a rabbit is not apt to make gymnastic movements very often during the day. They all had the same amount of diet composed of the same weighed amount of vegetables containing water. So, these variables, I think, would not affect the result. I would regard the rotation as raising the level of stimulation because in this way the whole vestibular apparatus is, in fact, stimulated. That was our purpose. If a rotational stimulus is always used in the same direction, an habituation is produced. We made it go back and forth and also up and down, slowly, to be sure that it would be a real stimulation.

The main point is that stimulation and increase in activity is followed by an increase in RNA which can be followed over a period of time.

Feindel: Do you compare an increase in the Deiters' neurons with some other control nerve cells during the same series of experiments? If this is a specific reaction to the vestibular stimulation you should, with reason, have some non-vestibular cell to compare against it, one which did not show an increase.

Hydén: We have used hypoglossal cells for that, which did not show any increase in the amount of RNA.

Feindel: This control occurred experimentally in each of your cases? That is, you analyzed the hypoglossal cells in the same rabbit?

Hydén: Yes. They all fall within the control values.

Luco: If I understand correctly, your idea was to stimulate the vestibular system and to observe some alteration of the RNA concentration of the cells due to activity.

The rabbits are eating all day, or perhaps four times a day, and that means that the hypoglossal nuclei are active for that many times a day, and if the activity is the reason for the modification of the biochemical process, you should have observed this alteration at the hypoglossal nuclei. For this reason, the cells of the hypoglossal nuclei are not a good control.

Glaser: I was going to ask if you had any measurements that indicated whether the rabbits were happy or unhappy, or had a strange physiological state during this experience which would have made it physiologically an important part of every twenty-four hours? Did the heartbeat go up, and so on?

Hydén: No, I must say that we have not followed it physiologically. We have followed the weight: there was no drastic change in weight compared with the control animals we had at the same time. If it was a severe stress it ought to show up at least in the weight of the animal.

McConnell: Are your animals group-housed before they are put through the experiments? Do you have them in group cages, and then put them in individual cages? Some Dutch experimenters have reported that animals housed in individual cages show a much higher RNA content than those that are group-housed (35).

Hydén: Our animals are kept in individual cages from one week to ten days. If the Dutch report is correct, our control values should give higher results. I am really interested to know how they performed the measurement of the RNA.*

Bickford: I wondered why you chose a relatively short stimulation period during the day. If you wanted to establish a relation with vestibular stimulation, why did you not apply it for a relatively longer time or even, on occasions, all day? Maybe it is not justifiable to do this to the animal. What factors influenced you in this choice of stimulation period?

Hydén: The choice was based on our experience with other types of ex-

---

* *Added by Dr. McConnell after the Conference:* The Dutch experimenters were estimating the nucleic acid content of slices of cerebral cortex (35). Richard Santen, working in B. W. Agranoff's laboratory at the University of Michigan's Mental Health Research Institute, and Margaret Clay and I in the Department of Psychology, have recently obtained results which differ significantly from the findings of Noach et al. (35). Rats were taken 21 days after birth and divided in two groups. Group I animals were housed individually in bare metal cages with cheesecloth over the fronts to minimize external stimulation. Group II animals were raised in large wooden boxes holding three or four rats. The boxes had shavings on the floor, paintings on the wall, various "playtoys" and gymnasium equipment, and an open wire mesh covering the top of the box. When the animals were approximately 60 days old, they were sacrificed and the nucleic acid content of their whole brains was estimated by a new and quite accurate technique which Santen & Agranoff (37) have recently devised. No differences whatsoever were found, either for RNA or for DNA, between the rats raised in individual, deprived environments and those raised in group, enriched environments.

periments on motor activity. If you impose a short period of motor activity
and then let the animals rest for a time, and then repeat the test, you see a
rise in the level of RNA, and also in the amount of protein and enzyme
activities. Therefore, based on our experience with other types of cells, we
used this short vestibular stimulation instead of a longer one. Also, we were
afraid of habituation.

Reynolds: Is not the significant difference between this particular stimulation and either random movements of the head or eating, that this is a new
experience to the animal and, therefore, one to which he has not become
adjusted in the past? Perhaps the changes that are being discussed, such as
changes in the hypoglossal nucleus, would occur at an early stage in the
life of the animal when eating was a new experience, for example. In other
words, is that the distinction between this type of stimulation and the type
of stimulation of the vestibular system which occurs with random movement?

TABLE 7

AMOUNT OF RNA IN $\mu\mu$g PER ANTERIOR HORN CELL, BARRACUDA, 60 CM, IN CONTROLS,
IN EXHAUSTED AND IN RESTING ANIMALS

Controls	Exhausted	Resting				
		1 Hour	2 Hours	3 Hours	4 Hours	5 Hours
3244 ± 113	3416 ± 97	3637 ± 118	3658 ± 77	3723 ± 78	4029 ± 87	4019 ± 86

Hydén: It is certainly a completely new experience for the animal.

Weiskrantz: There is another logical possibility. There may be a difference between activation to certain units when the activation is initiated by
the organism itself and when the activation is imposed upon them from
outside. In the case of moving the eyes voluntarily in the ordinary way, for
example, the world does not appear to move. If the eyes are prodded by the
fingers, it does move. These are examples of two different kinds of excitation
leading to quite different results. Similarly, whether or not excitation of the
vestibular system is self-produced or externally produced may make an important difference.

Hydén: As an example of motor activity, Table 7 demonstrates quantitative changes in motor cells from the spinal cord of barracuda fishes which
were exhausted by swimming. These fish are characterized by their capacity
to exert an intense muscular activity for a short time. On the other hand,
they are easily fatigued. This intense swimming for 20 to 30 minutes made
barracudas 60 cm long completely exhausted.

Table 7 demonstrates a successive increase of the amount of RNA per
nerve cell following the enhanced motor activity. On resting up to five hours

there was synthesis of RNA, which overshot the original RNA values by 25 per cent (from 3220 μμg to 4020 μμg).

Using constant and flickering light in a study of the frog's retina, Utina and collaborators (38) found that the increase in RNA coincided with the state of excitation recorded electrophysiologically. The most direct evidence for increased RNA metabolism in the brain cortex caused by stimulation has been obtained by Geiger (17) and co-workers using macrochemical methods.

Summarizing a great many data from ours and other laboratories on the relation between the amount of RNA per mammalian nerve cell (in the adult and excluding regeneration) and the functional state, I would like to make the following generalization: *an increased amount of RNA per nerve cell measured during a period of time can be taken as an indicator of increased neuronal function.* One reservation may be the case where an increased RNA synthesis is not observable in quantitative terms. Further information can be expected when a radioactive technique adaptable on a cyto-scale becomes available.

I would now like to discuss nuclear RNA and glial RNA changes in learning experiments.

A main problem is the specific function of this elaborate system of RNA and protein in the nerve cell as related to nervous function, and the significance of the glial RNA changes. Molecular and biological properties make the RNA a probable substrate for intraneuronal molecular storage of information.

In experiments on rats, the learning of a motor skill was studied for its effect on the RNA in nerve cells active during the learning period (26). This is an unorthodox type of learning experiment in view of the current trend in experimental psychology; the reason for the experimental design is that conditioning experiments involving discrimination are complicated processes encompassing "shaping up" of the animals. Processes in cortical areas and basal ganglia are subjects of interest in such experiments. On the basis of present physiological data, it would be impossible to choose some special type of nerve cell suitable for microchemical analyses and primarily involved in the reflex, and we therefore excluded learning experiments of the conditioning type. We also wanted to exclude the complicated cortex with its multitude of small nerve cells and instead take a phylogenetically old type of cells.

We therefore chose learning of a motor skill, which involved, as the second or third neuron, the large Deiters' nerve cells of the lateral vestibular nucleus. As one control, vestibular stimulation of the same area was used. In both these cases, as will be shown below, a significant increase of the amount of RNA per nerve cell was found. By definition, therefore, referring to the results quoted in the previous section, the increase of the amount of RNA per cell is an indicator that there had occurred a stimulation of these vestibular nerve cells in both the learning and the control rats. An important difference is that in the learning experiment the animals are *active*, in the control experiment *passive*.

This is rather important for us to keep in mind, and to state firmly with respect to the following learning experiments.

The experimental design was as follows. A 95 × 45 cm wooden box was used. On one of the end walls, one meter above the floor, was a small platform with a feeding cup. The size of the platform exceeded that of the feeding cup by only a small area. A 1 m long, 1.5 mm thick steel wire from the floor to the platform was strung at a 45° angle. Young rats, of the Sprague-Dawley strain, weighing 150-200 g were used. All rats used, including the controls, were kept hungry, with 4 g of food daily and free access to water. They were kept in single cages, 19.5 × 19.5 × 21.5 cm, during the experiment and during one day preceding the experiment. The only way the rats could satisfy their hunger was to learn how to balance on the wire leading up to the feeding cup (see Figure 9). This is an exceedingly difficult task but clearly within the capacity of the species. The learning experiment lasted for eight days on the average. Every day the rats were allowed 45 minutes of training. On the first day they succeeded in balancing a certain number of centimeters up the wire; on the second day a few more centimeters before they lost their equilibrium, swung round on the wire and jumped down to the floor. On the fourth day, on the average, the rats succeeded in balancing both up and down the wire.

Figure 9 shows a rat on its way up. No signs of stress in the form of squealing or increased frequency of defecation were observed during these experiments. On the fourth (or fifth) day the rats balanced up to the platform three to five times, on the sixth day around ten times, and on the seventh and eighth day around fifteen times, during the hour allotted to them. The loss in weight per animal was on an average 12 per cent. The animals were killed on the eighth day and the material immediately taken for analysis.

It is an acute learning experience. They have the motivation of hunger, and they keep on trying.

With respect to the stress, I am sure some of you could comment on whether the stress factor would be of any consequence or not. We have not been able to find a physiological or biochemical method which was sufficiently accurate to be used as an objective sign of stress.

Calvin: Could you say a few words about what the rats do during the learning period? How do they proceed to learn?

Hydén: When they first come in, they have to be accustomed to the environment, so they have to have a look at the box, and so on, before the experiment starts. Then they run around a little on the floor, and they smell the food up in the feeding cup. Then they gradually begin to jump up on the wire and try to climb it. On the first day they usually try three to five

times. It is exceedingly hard and they have to place their paws very carefully, one before the other. But then some of them are successful and they
continue to train and climb up. Some of them, when they have reached the
middle of the wire, turn down with the head upside down, and some continue to climb in this position.

It takes them four days, on the average, to learn how to balance (see
Figure 10). Then we allow them about four further days, one hour per day,
before we sacrifice them.

John: Could you describe the early part of this eight-day period, telling
how the animal looks?

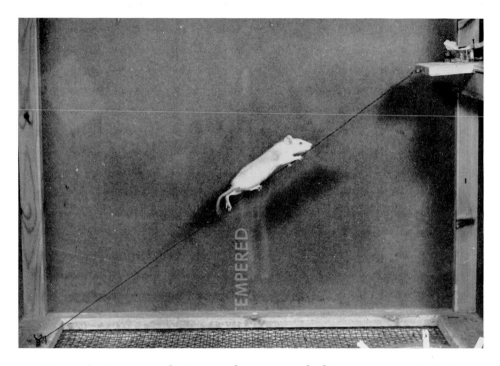

Figure 9. Experimental situation showing rat climbing wire to reach food.

Based on the rat and cat conditioning I have done, in comparable situations, I feel that early in such a situation the animal shows a number of
signs of excitability. For example, there is a tendency to defecate on the
part of the rat; occasionally there is squealing, and so forth. Could you
describe what the rat does when it climbs up the wire and falls down? Is
there a tendency to vocalize when this happens? Does it look agitated?

Hydén: No, the rat does not scream or vocalize in any way. When it has
jumped down, it runs around a little along the edges of the box, and sniffs,
and so on; it stops, and then resumes its movements, usually going around
the box.

Now, the question is, does that really involve learning in the usual sense of the word, or is it something else? If we stop the experiment and transfer the animals to their cages, they become clumsy and have to be retrained. This is done very easily but, as a matter of fact, they do have to be retrained. Therefore, we considered that it is a learning experiment of a trial and error type.

Feindel: What is the interval they can remain in their cages without having to be retrained, a matter of a day or two? Have you determined that period at all?

Hydén: No; we have kept them caged four, five, six, seven days.

Deutsch: This seems very strange to me because, in general, when rats have learned something—I have had this happen quite frequently—they seem to remember it with very little decrement over a period of months.

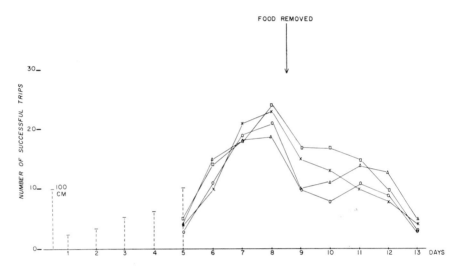

Figure 10. Chart showing the number of successful trips to the food tray made each day by each of four different rats. Note the decrease when the food reward is removed.

This raises the question, what kind of a deprivation schedule did you have these animals on before they entered the situation?

Hydén: I think there is another factor going into this. This is a motor skill.

Deutsch: That is much more resistant to forgetting.

Hydén: Yes. By now we are very much interested in this question because of the chemical results we found. I will come to that because it involves a technical question which is hard to solve.

John: You said that on the first day they perform about five trips up the wire. Do they continue their unsuccessful efforts to climb the wire throughout this time, or do they only try a few times during the hour?

Hydén: Once they have been up and have fed, they do not go up again immediately; they walk around a little on the floor, and suddenly they go up again.

John: When they run up three to five times an hour, are they capable of making it to the top each time they start up, or do they fall down a good part of the time?

Hydén: No; once they manage it they always succeed, almost without exception.

John: Does the frequency of trips they make up the wire or their ability to balance on the wire increase during the four-day period?

Hydén: Not once they are trained. We have to discern between the training period and the four-day period during which they can manage to reach the top. So, we have divided the results into those two periods.

Green: As influences on RNA content, have you done anything to distinguish between activity of the neurons and learning? It appears to be fairly simple to stimulate the hypoglossal nerve antidromically and to excite it to a great deal of activity.

Hydén: You mean, once again, another type of neuron. We have taken the hypoglossal cells but we have not stimulated them. I will discuss the controls now, because that, of course, is very important.

The controls consisted of rats of the same litter kept on the same diet as that of the learning animals. Of these, one group was taken for functional controls using vestibular rotatory stimulation back and forth through 120° horizontally and through 30° vertically. The animals were stimulated for two periods of 25 minutes each day for four days.

In both the learning and the functional control rats, an increase of 70 μμg of RNA per Deiters' nerve cell was observed and found significant. From a biochemical point of view, therefore, the effect of the stimulation in both instances was the same, as judged by the quantitative change of RNA per cell.

So, taking the increase in both cases, we obtained an increase in RNA per cell, which was significant, but in the one case the animals were active; in the other case the animals were passive, since they could not move very much in the capsule. That is the type of controls we used, and, of course, the type of control is crucial in this experiment.

The other type of control, an additional one, was our analysis of the hypoglossal cells.

John: Do you have a control consisting of data on the animals which have had the pretraining period and know how to climb the wire, but only do so once or twice in the hour, at the beginning of the four-day period, as contrasted with data obtained after the four-day period when the frequency of wire climbing is ten times higher?

Hydén: No, we have not tried to do that.

Finally, we had this increase of RNA which I will show in both cases. In one case, the animals were active and learning; in the other, they were the controls.

Table 8 shows an increase of the adenine and a decrease of the uracil values of the nuclear RNA as compared to the control values; number of

TABLE 8

COMPOSITION OF THE NUCLEAR RNA OF DEITERS' NERVE CELLS FROM CONTROL
RATS AND DURING LEARNING

(Amount of RNA per Nucleus: 30 $\mu\mu$g)

	Controls (mean)	Learning		P
		Mean	V	
Adenine	21.4	24.1 ± 0.39	4.3	0.001
Guanine	26.2	26.7 ± 0.87	8.6	
Cytosine	31.9	31.0 ± 0.95	8.1	
Uracil	20.5	18.2 ± 1.11	16.2	0.05
Number:				
of nuclei	285	243		
of analyses	10	8		
of animals	7	7		

nuclei, 285 and 243 respectively, and number of animals, seven in both cases. These were controls of the same litter, sitting in the cages without vestibular stimulation.

No changes in the base ratio composition of cytoplasmic RNA could be observed, however (as shown in Table 9). Neither could any changes in the RNA base composition be shown in the nuclear RNA of the functional controls (Table 10).

It seems that the neuron and its glia both contribute and collaborate in synthesizing specific RNA polymers well suited to be the substrate of information storage and to produce specific proteins. In such a case the latter can be expected to act as the immediate substrate for recall of information.

In view of the demonstrated metabolic relationship between neurons and glia, the electrophoretic analyses were extended to include the base ratio composition of the *glial RNA* during the same type of learning experiments in rats, using the Deiters' nucleus (27).

Table 11 shows a significant increase in the adenine/uracil ratio of the

TABLE 9

COMPOSITION OF THE CYTOPLASMIC RNA OF DEITERS' NERVE CELLS FROM CONTROL
RATS AND DURING LEARNING

	Controls		Learning	
	Mean	V	Mean	V
Adenine	20.5 ± 0.54	5.5	20.9 ± 0.19	2.6
Guanine	33.7 ± 0.33	2.2	34.0 ± 0.32	2.6
Cytosine	27.4 ± 0.34	3.0	26.8 ± 0.21	2.2
Uracil	18.4 ± 0.26	3.1	18.3 ± 0.13	2.1
Number:				
of analyses	50		90	
of animals	5		8	

TABLE 10

COMPOSITION OF THE NUCLEAR RNA OF DEITERS' NERVE CELLS FROM RATS SUBJECTED
TO VESTIBULAR STIMULATION FOR 25 MIN./DAY AND FOR FOUR DAYS

	Controls (mean)	Vestibular stimulation	
		Mean	V
Adenine	21.4	21.3 ±0.69	6.5
Guanine	26.2	25.7 ±0.46	3.6
Cytosine	31.9	31.3 ±0.88	5.6
Uracil	20.5	21.7 ±0.45	4.2
Number:			
of nuclei	285	173	
of analyses	10	6	
of animals	7	5	

glial RNA in the learning rats compared with control rats. The latter belonged to the same litter and were kept in single cages on a low caloric diet with free access to water. Besides the adenine increase, a decrease of the cytosine value was observed. Table 12 demonstrates that no significant changes occurred in the glial RNA of functional control rats. The same part of the CNS was stimulated as in the case of the learning rats with the difference that the animals were passive during the experiment.

Thompson: In all of your experiments you have examined the brains of these animals immediately after learning or stimulation, is that right? The question naturally arises, how permanent is this change in nuclear RNA? Would you find it two weeks after the completion of the learning experiments?

Hydén: We are pursuing that. We began assaying four days after stopping the experiment, and found the values were back to the control levels. Now we are down to eight hours after the experiment, and find them still at control levels. But we have not finished this research.

I would like to comment a little on these experiments on learning. In

TABLE 11

COMPOSITION OF THE RNA FROM GLIA SURROUNDING DEITERS' NERVE CELLS FROM
CONTROL RATS AND DURING LEARNING

	Controls		Learning		P
	Mean	V	Mean	V	
Adenine	25.3 ±0.16	1.5	28.3 ±0.45	3.9	0.001
Guanine	29.0 ±0.24	1.9	28.8 ±0.31	2.4	
Cytosine	26.5 ±0.43	3.7	24.3 ±0.36	3.7	0.01
Uracil	19.2 ±0.27	3.1	18.6 ±0.21	2.8	
Number:					
of animals	5		6		
of analyses	33		42		

previous papers (21, 22, 23) I have discussed a conceptual model for intra-neuronal storage of information, assuming cytoplasmic RNA with specific base composition to serve this purpose. The changes could arise through ion flux associated with electrical patterns of sensory and motor activities, and could persist for a long time.

The RNA changes (26) reported above were the first results of experiments initiated by the working hypothesis. They show clearly that both the neuron and its glia collaborate in synthesizing specific RNA fractions during the learning of a complicated motor (and sensory) pattern. That RNA of the brain is involved in learning is also supported by results from experiments on planaria. If the cytological findings, reported by Morrell to occur in "mirror foci" in experimental epilepsy (34) prove to reflect RNA changes in nerve cells, they should also provide good evidence.

TABLE 12

Composition of RNA from Glia Surrounding Deiters' Nerve Cells from Control Rats and During Vestibular Stimulation

	Controls		Vestibular stimulation	
	Mean	V	Mean	V
Adenine	25.3 ±0.16	1.5	25.1 ±0.37	2.9
Guanine	29.0 ±0.24	1.9	28.6 ±0.50	3.5
Cytosine	26.5 ±0.43	3.7	27.4 ±0.22	1.6
Uracil	19.2 ±0.27	3.1	18.9 ±0.20	2.1
Number:				
of animals	5		4	
of analyses	33		22	

In general terms, the neurons of learning rats had a different composition, in terms of RNA base composition, from that of the two types of control rats. Therefore, the base ratios of the nuclear RNA synthesized during the acute learning situation must have been highly specific in order to be discernible in the micro-electrophoretic analysis of 30 times 20 μμg of RNA.

What fraction of RNA may constitute this RNA? Only a few comments can be made on this point at the present time. Synthesis of D-RNA showing complementarity to DNA base composition can be excluded. So can nucleolar RNA, since it has been shown that its base ratios closely agree with those of cytoplasmic RNA.

At the present time it seems, however, that the nuclear RNA produced in learning could, by analogy, be chromosomal RNA and also encompass messenger RNA. Edström & Beermann (11) have recently found that chromosomal RNA produced by the Balbiani rings in *Chironomus* differed in base ratios when different chromosomes were analyzed, and also when different puffs of the same chromosome (IV) were analyzed. The puffs are the result of single gene activities. Their RNA showed no complementarity to D-RNA.

In one respect, however, all these chromosomal RNA species showed one characteristic: they had a high adenine/uracil ratio.

Thus, an overall production of neuronal RNA and a production of nuclear RNA with an increased adenine/uracil ratio could be linked with learning of a complicated motor skill in rats in the neurons which belonged to the first link in the neuronal chain activated in the process. According to our view, the functional control experiments exclude the possibility that the results obtained were due to increased neuronal function *per se*.

I would therefore assume, by analogy, that the specific nuclear RNA synthesized in the neurons of learning rats is chromosomal RNA. During the acute learning situation a part of the genome has been rendered more active and RNA with highly specific base ratios produced. That gene sites in chromosomes of neurons can be induced by stimulation from the environment to synthesize RNA in an acute learning situation, within the capacity of the species, is no more surprising than that the addition of galactose induces such gene activities in bacteria.

I would like, as a working hypothesis, to propose that during a learning✓ process certain parts of the genome are induced to synthesize RNA with highly specific base ratios.

Learning, memory and recall of stored information is securely anchored in the genome. The correlation in our learning experiments between the synthesis of specific nuclear RNA fractions and the establishment of a complicated motor (and sensory) pattern underlines the genetic factors in the nervous system of which the nuclear RNA changes are most probably a reflection. Learning during the life-cycle by "change by use" is most probably a superposition on genetically stable mechanisms of the central nervous system reflected in innate behavior.

The specific nuclear RNA produced in the rat neurons during learning can be supposed to reach the cytoplasm. No base ratio changes were, however, registered in the cytoplasmic RNA of 700 µµg. Neither is that to be expected. This does not exclude the possibility that the specific nuclear RNA, after having reached the cytoplasm, will affect or instruct the ribosomal RNA to synthesize specific proteins which can serve as the immediate substrate of memory in the recall mechanism.

The glial RNA changes observed in our rat learning experiments were also characterized by a significantly increased adenine/uracil ratio. The decrease in the cytosine values is another factual observation. It does not seem surprising that the glial RNA reacts conjointly with the neuronal RNA during a physiological process since it is part of the same functional unit. It shows that the glia share the capacity with the neuron to house part of the chemical substrate for storing information.

In the neuron, the nuclear RNA changes were clear and significant, but there were no cytoplasmic RNA changes. In the glia, the bulk of the RNA showed changed base ratio composition in the learning rats. The explanation may be that these changes are easier to observe in the bulk of the glial RNA constituting only one tenth of that of the neuronal RNA.

The glia consist of a multitude of delicately folded membranes. The surface is large, and such a structure could constitute a mechanism well suited for rapid processes. The question may be posed: do the glia and glial RNA constitute the substrate of a *short-term* process, and the neuron and its mass of RNA constitute the substrate of the *long-term*, life-lasting memory?

These are speculations, but I would like to suggest them for what they are worth.

John: The data which you presented are fascinating in the possibilities which they raise. It is because of the fundamental importance of these data that we must examine as carefully as possible the question of whether these changes really result from learning. The changes are clear.

Can we be sure the observed changes are due to learning, and not to accommodation to stressful aspects of the situation? The control group situation was sufficiently different from that of the experimental one, so that one cannot adequately rule out the influence of general factors unrelated to learning *per se.*

The question of when the learning takes place in this situation seems important to consider further. There is a period in which the animal is acquiring a skill, followed by a period in which the skill apparently is exercised more frequently through time. One wonders whether the changes are due to acquisition or to increased performance.

Hydén: I believe Figure 10 is pertinent to some of your questions.

It is very interesting to hear what you say about these two periods and to consider whether there is anything which would change the interpretation of these data.

McConnell: You regard the first period of four days the "not-learning" phase, the second period of four days the "learning" phase of your experiment. And you have assumed the animals did not learn during the first four days because they received no reward or reinforcement. But since the animals do sometimes eat during the first four days, we should remember that sometimes one can show quite clearly that animals will learn just from smelling food, or from the sight of food. So, just the amount of food may not be the important variable to look at in those four days.

Another point I would like to make is that electrophysiological data indicate one gets all the electrophysiological changes before the animal shows behavioral changes. I am sure this may be a crucial thing as far as the RNA changes are concerned.

Hydén: Yes, that is a very good point that you have brought out.

This is a motor skill, and we should not forget that the animals are growing, for they are young animals. How important a factor is that during, let us say, ten days?

Deutsch: Let me ask you about the food deprivation schedule they were on before they were put in the situation, and in the intervening period between your test and your retest. How much were you giving them per day? How much were they allowed to eat?

Hydén: Dr. Larson, the rat psychologist of our University, suggested a certain diet for them. They were put on the diet four days or five days before zero time. Just before the experiment began they were kept on a very low caloric diet. So they did not lose in weight but they stayed approximately the same weight. If we stopped the experiment and let them go back and sit in their cages for a later retesting, they were kept on the same low diet.

We hope, under such conditions, that we can keep our judgment from being influenced by a factor due to the animals growing a little older in the ten days. What would you say about that?

Deutsch: I would be very surprised that ten days should make any difference once they have been taught a motor skill. The only way I could explain the decrement would be by assuming there were motivational factors involved in producing both an apparent learning and an apparent forgetting. That is, much of the learning in each individual instance may be due to the fact the animals were becoming progressively hungrier. Without at least the data showing the weight gain of the animals and the amount they were given each day, it is difficult to exclude the possibility that so-called learning was in fact simply an increase in hunger motivation. Similarly, one would want to see the diet and the weights of the control animals to make sure that any of the differences are not really differences in the amount of food consumed, for instance.

Hydén: But there was very little difference in food consumed. It was only when the rats managed to go up and get a small piece, and down again, that there was a difference.

Deutsch: That is what made me think it was probably some kind of motivational variable producing changes in performance, and not learning.

Sinsheimer: Is it not conceivable that these changes are a consequence of the improved nutrition? Would it not be proper to run a control where the rats are given food without having to learn how to reach it?

Hydén: When we improved the nutritional condition of an animal we did not observe any such changes. I would say, based in the experience we have, that a change in the opposite direction is rather more conceivable.

Deutsch: I think probably quite a few people who work with rats find it surprising that there should have been such a large amount of forgetting, though I have not taught them this particular trick.

Hydén: As regards forgetting, I would like to point out that the biochemical data I have shown has been for the period up to the eight days, and not between the eighth and the eighteenth day. We have not made analyses during the period in which they forget. I have no data to compare with the earlier periods.

It is very pertinent for future work, I think, to be able to follow this down, as suggested by some of you. At what point in time can we first detect significant nuclear or glial changes, and when do they disappear? This involves a technical question.

For example, with the microelectrophoretic method we take 600, 400 μμg, and subject this to hydrolysis. It is perfectly possible to compute the amount of RNA which can be present in such an electrophoretic pattern, but there still may be molecules with another base composition which we cannot detect. We need, in that case, a very careful behavioral test in order to be able to pin down some change in behavior and some change in chemical composition. I think that poses some hard technical questions.

Calvin: My concern has to do with the possibility of there actually being some kind of a sharp break in the presumed learning situation, between the occasion when they do succeed in getting the food, and all the prior trials when they do not succeed in getting the food. It seems to me that is a rather sharp distinction. For the first four days they are trying but there is no reward, and when they attain the reward, somewhere around the fourth day, things are changed then for the next four days. Their receiving the reward makes a rather sharp distinction between the first four days and the second four days.

I know full well how difficult those analyses are—I do not suggest you do them every day—but perhaps you could make an analysis just before that changeover, and then use it as control. One could at least see what happens at that point in comparison to the eighth day.

Mommaerts: I would like to ask how you imagine at this early stage the manner in which the retained information is read back eventually. Do you visualize that there is some macromolecular sequence retained in the cells which is read out directly, more or less as is the case for the hereditary factors? Or do you visualize that the retained code instructs the cells to take part in some circuit network, and just what is remembered depends on the arrangements in these circuits?

Hydén: That is clearly on the speculative level, but I would like to offer the proposal that there is a continuity in each of the millions of nerve cells, and that the substrate for this is the RNA in the ribosomal RNA of neurons, which differs in certain respects from the ribosomal RNA of other, somatic, cells. I suggest that the process initiated by a stimulus from the environment will stimulate the nuclear products, which will then directly affect the cytoplasmic RNA, modified by the glia, for example, rather than by an experience. This is clearly speculative.

There is tendency to speculate when there are no data, but when one has some data, one is less apt to speculate!

Reynolds: It seems to me it is a rather complex task that the rat was being asked to do. It involves several things other than normal learning. One of them is the stimulation of the vestibular system, which is certainly occurring during the period when it does not manage to climb the wire if, in fact, it is trying to balance. Another is some kind of learning and the third is, perhaps, just pure muscular strength. In other words, I gather it is a difficult task for the rat to grip the wire in its paws. Furthermore, I gathered from the data that there was no distinction, biochemically, between the measurements made on the animals that were the functional controls, as far as the RNA is concerned, and the animals that went through the performance.

I wonder if it would be possible to do an experiment to determine if there is any decrease in learning time on the performance experiment of animals that had already had their nuclear RNA increased by passive stimulation of the vestibular system. And another on whether or not there would be a comparable increase in RNA in an animal that was exposed to the same kind of balancing task, but without the necessity for so much grip. I do not know whether this is possible to produce. In other words, try to design a situation in which the animal is not required to grasp, and still is exposed to an equal amount of balancing.

Hydén: I see the principle you are trying to reach. What we have felt to be important is to try to clarify the effect that simple muscular exercise may have in the production of these changes. But we have not found any such nuclear RNA changes to result from motor activity. I would certainly be most grateful for any direct, practical suggestions for more controls.

Weiskrantz: I wonder if you have any data on the effect on RNA content of stressing situations, such as delivery of an electric shock?

Hydén: Yes, we have data from some stress experiments. Some years ago Dr. Richter and also some Russians made some experiments on swimming. They made rats swim, as a stress experiment. We used the same experimental stress, and made some quantitative RNA analyses of the spinal cord. If I remember correctly, in spite of an increased uptake of water by the cells, there was not a decreased concentration of RNA but an increased amount per cell. We did not pursue these experiments to see if the increase was significant.

Hild: I would like to draw attention to a nucleolar phenomenon that is not related to nutritional but to tonicity factors affecting the cell.

In the living neuron shown in Figure 11, which was photographed under the phase contrast microscope, a very well defined nucleolus can be recognized. The optical density of the nucleolus is probably due to the relatively high concentration of protein and RNA in this cell organelle. If the content of RNA in the nucleolus contributes to nucleolar density, then we may assume that an experimental change in this density may reflect some changes in either the amount or the physical state in the RNA molecule.

If, under the microscope, the isotonic culture medium is removed and a hypertonic medium is added, one observes a sudden loss in optical density of the nucleolus (Figure 12). This can be so marked that the nucleolus is no longer recognizable.

If the hypertonic medium is replaced with isotonic medium, the original

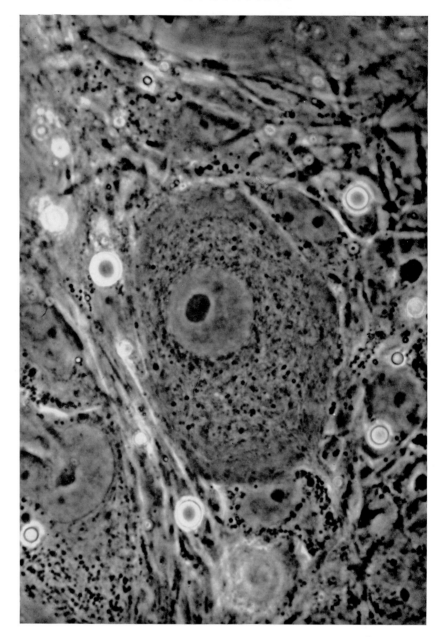

Figure 11. Living neuron in isotonic culture medium photographed under the phase contrast microscope. Note well-defined nucleolus.

density reappears very suddenly (Figure 13). Addition of hypotonic medium causes in some cases a higher nucleolar density than the one seen in isotonic medium (Figure 14).

In addition to the very marked nucleolar changes, one can observe that the nucleus as a whole becomes measurably bigger in hypertonic media. Even though I have no good explanation for these facts, it seems possible

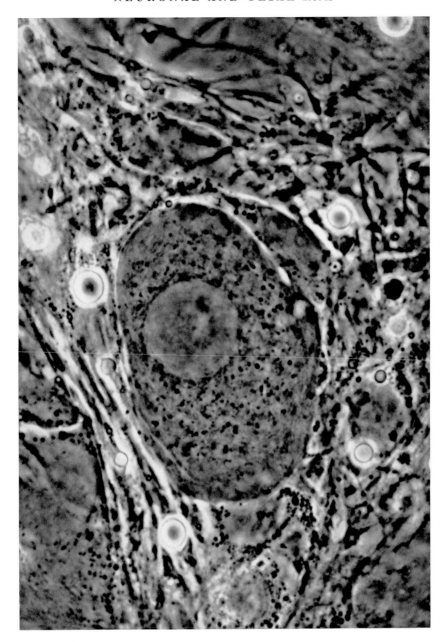

Figure 12. Living neuron in hypertonic medium; nucleous loses optical density.

that these phenomena have something to do with the degree of hydration or swelling or shrinking of nucleolar contents, which could well affect the function of the RNA molecule. Possibly something of this nature should be taken into consideration in Dr. Hydén's experiments.

John: I would like to put on record what I think is an overlooked piece of work on neuron-glia interaction. In 1919, Marui (33) published studies in the *Journal of Comparative Neurology* on the effects of sustained vestibular

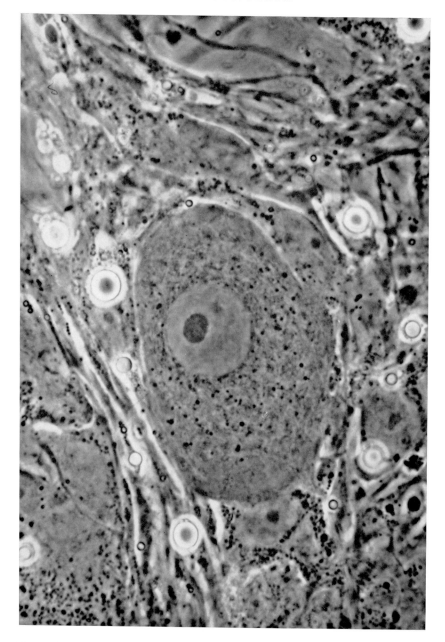

Figure 13. Living neuron after isotonic medium replaces hypertonic medium;
well-defined nucleolus reappears.

stimulation on the Mauthner cell synapse in the teleost. This synapse is
enclosed in a glial reticulum. His histological techniques, I think, were
excellent.

The fish was put into a tank, and a rotatory torque was applied around its
midline—a jet of water high on the back on one side, and low on the belly
on the other side. The fish had to work continuously against these jets in
order to orient itself vertically in the water. As time went on, the position of

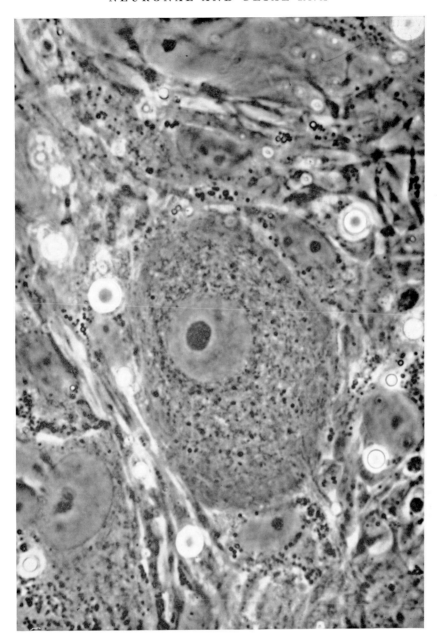

Figure 14. Living neuron in hypotonic medium; nucleolus shows higher density than in isotonic medium.

the fish began to deviate from the vertical. These deviations became larger and larger.

After about 20 hours, the fish very abruptly lost its ability to resist the rotatory torque and started going dorsum over ventrum in the jet. If the jet was now turned off, it was found that the fish had irreversibly lost the ability to orient itself vertically in the tank.

Marui carried out histological examinations of the Mauthner cell synapse at several intervals from the beginning of the application of this vestibular stress through the point where the fish lost the ability to orient itself. Examination of the Mauthner cells showed that there were no visible synaptic changes but that the glial reticulum around the synapse gradually swelled. At the point where the fish lost the ability to orient itself, the glial reticulum burst.

To my knowledge, this early and overlooked demonstration is one of the clearest, showing what seems to be a neural-glial interaction displayed with sustained stimulation.

Magoun: May I try to generalize the nature of the discussion at this point. Dr. Hydén has put his animals through an experience at the end point of which he has examined the biochemistry of their neurons, and has found a modification from what he described as his controls. He characterized this as a learning experience on the basis of its going through certain stages toward formation, and on the basis of a subsequent falling off of performance which may be characterized as extinction.

The psychologists here have been exploring the experience to see whether it might properly be called learning in the classical sense, and have been proposing points, either of agreement or criticism, to try to sharpen up this side of the question.

On the other hand, from the biochemical point of view, the question has been raised as to what the sequential stages are in the establishment of the ultimate change that Dr. Hydén has detected in the analysis taken at a single point in time. What desirable subanalysis, either on the way up to that or on the way back from it afterward would be helpful?

The further question is Dr. Calvin's. Would it be helpful, in this analysis, to be able to determine a sharp end-point which can be called "achievement of learning", and find whether it is in relation to that precise and limited period that the change occurs from the biochemical state before learning as compared with after learning. That is, is this change a precipitous one and related to that specific end-point, or is it a gradual thing as a consequence of the development of the experience over a considerable period of time?

I only offer these remarks because I sense in them some of the generalizations that have come out of the discussion.

REFERENCES

1. BIRKS, R., KATZ, B., and MILEDI, R., Physiological and structural changes at the amphibian myoneural junction, in the course of nerve degeneration. *J. Physiol.*, 1960, **150**: 145-168.
2. BRATTGÅRD, S.-O., and HYDÉN, H., Mass, lipids, pentose nucleoproteins and proteins determined in nerve cells by X-ray microradiography. *Acta Radiol.*, 1952, Supp. **94**: 1-48.
3. ———, The composition of the nerve cell studied with new methods. *Int. Rev. Cytol.*, 1954, 3: 455-476.

4. CUMMINS, J., and HYDÉN, H., Adenosine triphosphate levels and adenosine triphosphatases in neurons, glia and neuronal membranes of the vestibular nucleus. *Biochim. Biophys. Acta*, 1962, **60**: 271-283.

5. DE RÉNYI, G. S., The structure of cells in tissues as revealed by microdissection. II. The physical properties of the living axis cylinder in the myelinated nerve fiber of the frog. *J. Comp. Neurol.*, 1929, **47**: 405-425.

6. ——, The structure of cells in tissues as revealed by microdissection. V. The physical properties of nerve cells of the frog (Rana pipiens). *J. Comp. Neurol.*, 1931, **53**: 497-509.

7. ——, Architecture of the nerve cell as revealed by microdissection. In: *Special Cytology*, Vol. III (E. V. Cowdry, Ed.). Hoeber, New York, 1932: 1369-1402.

8. EDSTRÖM, J.-E., Ribonucleic acid mass and concentration in individual nerve cells. A new method for quantitative determinations. *Biochim. Biophys. Acta*, 1953, **12**: 361-386.

9. ——, Determination of organic compounds below the microgram range. Ribonucleic acid and its constituents. *Microchem. J.*, 1958, **2**: 71-82.

10. ——, Composition of ribonucleic acid from various parts of spider oocytes. *J. Biophys. Biochem. Cytol.*, 1960, **8**: 47-51.

11. EDSTRÖM, J.-E., and BEERMANN, W., The base composition of nucleic acids in chromosomes, puffs, nucleoli, and cytoplasm of *Chironomus* salivary gland cells. *J. Cell Biol.*, 1962, **14**: 371-379.

12. EDSTRÖM, J.-E., EICHNER, D., and EDSTRÖM, A., The ribonucleic acid of axons and myelin sheaths from Mauthner neurons. *Biochim. Biophys. Acta*, 1962, **61**: 178-184.

13. EDSTRÖM, J.-E., EICHNER, D., and SCHOR, N., Quantitative ribonucleic acid measurements in functional studies of nucleus supraopticus. In: *Regional Neurochemistry* (S. S. Kety and J. Elkes, Eds.). Pergamon, Oxford, 1961: 274-278.

14. EDSTRÖM, J.-E., GRAMPP, W., and SCHOR, N., The intracellular distribution and heterogeneity of ribonucleic acid in starfish oocytes. *J. Biophys. Biochem. Cytol.*, 1961, **11**: 549-557.

15. EGYHÁZI, E., and HYDÉN, H., Experimentally induced changes in the base composition of the ribonucleic acids of isolated nerve cells and their oligodendroglial cells. *J. Biophys. Biochem. Cytol.*, 1961, **10**: 403-410.

16. FLUUR, E., and MENDEL, L., Habituation, efference and vestibular interplay. I. Monaural caloric habituation. *Acta Oto-Laryng.*, 1962, **55**: 65-80.

17. GEIGER, A., Chemical changes accompanying activity in the brain. In: *Metabolism of the Nervous System* (D. Richter, Ed.). Pergamon, London, 1957: 245-256.

18. HAMBERGER, A., and HYDÉN, H., Inverse enzymatic changes in neurons and glia during increased function and hypoxia. *J. Cell Biol.*, 1963, **16**: 521-525.

19. HILD, W., Das Neuron. In: *Handbuch der mikroskopischen Anatomie des Menschen*. Vol. IV/4 (W. von Möllendorff and W. Bargmann, Eds.). Springer-Verlag, Berlin, 1959: 1-184.

20. HYDÉN, H., Protein metabolism in the nerve cell during growth and function. *Acta Physiol. Scand.*, 1943, **6**, Suppl. 17: 1-136.

21. ——, Biochemical changes in glial cells and nerve cells at varying activity.

In: *Biochemistry of the Central Nervous System,* Vol. III (O. Hoffmann-Ostenhof and F. Brücke, Eds.). Pergamon, London, 1959: 64-89.

22. HYDÉN, H., The neuron. In: *The Cell,* Vol. IV (J. Brachet and A. E. Mirsky, Eds.). Academic Press, New York, 1960: 215-323.

23. ———, A molecular basis of neuron-glia interaction. In: *Macromolecular Specificity and Biological Memory* (F. O. Schmitt, Ed.). MIT Press, Cambridge, 1962: 55-69.

24. ———, The neuron and its glia—a biochemical and functional unit. *Endeavour,* 1962, **21**: 144-155.

25. HYDÉN, H., and EGYHÁZI, E., Changes in the base composition of nuclear ribonucleic acid of neurons during a short period of enhanced protein production. *J. Cell Biol.,* 1962, **15**: 37-44.

26. ———, Nuclear RNA changes of nerve cells during a learning experiment in rats. *Proc. Nat. Acad. Sci. USA,* 1962, **48**: 1366-1373.

27. ———, Glial RNA changes during a learning experiment in rats. *Proc. Nat. Acad. Sci. USA,* 1963, **49**: 618-624.

28. HYDÉN, H., and LANGE, P., Differences in the metabolism of oligondendroglia and nerve cells in the vestibular area. In: *Regional Neurochemistry* (S. S. Kety and J. Elkes, Eds.). Pergamon, Oxford, 1961: 190-199.

29. ———, A kinetic study of the neuron-glia relationship. *J. Cell Biol.,* 1962, **13**: 233-237.

30. HYDÉN, H., and LARSSON, S., The application of a scanning and computing cell analyser to neurocytological problems. *J. Neurochem.,* 1956, **1**: 134-144.

31. ———, A new scanning micro-analyser for data collection and evaluation from X-ray microradiograms. In: *X-Ray Microscopy and X-Ray Micro-analysis* (A. Engström, V. E. Cosslett and H. H. Pattee, Eds.). Elsevier, Amsterdam, 1960: 51-55.

32. HYDÉN, H., and PIGON, A., A cytophysiological study of the functional relationship between oligodendroglial cells and nerve cells of Deiters' nucleus. *J. Neurochem.,* 1960, **6**: 57-72.

33. MARUI, K., The effect of over-activity on the morphological structure of the synapse. *J. Comp. Neurol.,* 1919, **30**: 253-282.

34. MORRELL, F., Lasting changes in synaptic organization produced by continuous neuronal bombardment. In: *Brain Mechanisms and Learning* (J. F. Delafresnaye et al., Eds.). Blackwell, Oxford, 1961: 375-392.

35. NOACH, E. L., BUNK, J. J., and WIJLING, A., Influence of electroshock and phenobarbital on nucleic acid content of rat brain cortex. *Acta Physiol. Pharmacol. Neerl.,* 1962, **11**: 54-69.

36. RICH, A., On the problems of evolution and biochemical information transfer. In: *Horizons in Biochemistry* (M. Kasha and B. Pullman, Eds.). Academic Press, New York, 1962: 103-126.

37. SANTEN, R. J., and AGRANOFF, B. W., Studies on the estimation of deoxyribonucleic acid and ribonucleic acid in rat brain. *Biochem. Biophys. Acta,* 1963, **72**: 251-262.

38. UTINA, T. A., NECHAJEVA, N. V., and BRODSKII, V. I. DNA in ganglionic cells of a frog retina in darkness and on the illumination with constant and flickering light. *Biofizika,* 1960, **5**: 749-750 (in Russian).

THE STRUCTURAL BASIS FOR NEURAL ACTION[*]

SANFORD L. PALAY
Harvard Medical School
Boston

INTRODUCTION

Ever since the discovery of nerve cells in the early 1830's, histologists have sought methods that would selectively display the different cellular components of the nervous system. The entire progress of neuroanatomy in the nineteenth century may be characterized as a series of conceptual leaps springing from more and more refined techniques for isolating nerve cells and their parts from one another and from the matrix in which they are embedded. The early histologists attempted by tearing and crushing either fresh or fixed specimens to dissect out the essential components of the nervous system. To such rather crude methods, pursued with enviable patience by investigators like Purkinje, Remak, Bidder, Gerlach, Deiters, and many others, we owe fundamental information about the organization of the nervous system, as for example the discovery of the perikaryon, the axis cylinder, the sheaths of the nerve fiber and the satellite cells, the concept of continuity between perikaryon and axis cylinder, and finally the distinction between dendrites and axons.

As Gerlach and his contemporaries appreciated, investigations carried on by these methods rapidly approached the limit of fruitfulness. They were succeeded but not entirely displaced by a group of techniques which performed for the investigator a kind of dissection *in situ*, for example, the Golgi method and methylene blue stain for nerve cells and all their processes, the Nissl stain for perikarya, the neurofibrillary stains for axons, the Weigert method for myelinated nerve fibers, the various glial stains and, more recently, the Rasmussen technique for neural terminals and the Nauta method for degenerating preterminal fibers. All of these stains in the hands of skilled investigators are exquisitely selective, leaving clear and pale or utterly transparent almost everything that is not of immediate interest to the observer. It must be emphasized that, like the older techniques, these methods, too, are isolation techniques. The Golgi method, for instance, shows only about one cell in seventy in the cortex, and the Nissl method

[*] The investigations on which this report is based were supported in part by Public Health Service Research Grant No. B-3659 from the National Institute of Neurological Diseases and Blindness.

69

shows only perikarya and large dendrites. As immensely fruitful as they have been and will continue to be, they have forced us to develop our conception of the nervous system by fitting together a composite picture, a mosaic of overlapping and interdigitating pieces of information resulting from diverse and sometimes mutually exclusive methods. Now, this is a perfectly good way to obtain knowledge about a complex system, even though our piecing together of the picture may not always be completely successful, as, for example, when it gives rise by default to the idea of an extensive intercellular space.

The information derived from these classical procedures can be summarized in a single fundamental generalization describing the organization of the nervous system. This formulation, known as the neuron doctrine, proclaims that the nervous system is composed of independent morphological units: the neurons, each consisting of a nucleated cell body, the perikaryon with its processes, the axons and the dendrites, and their arborizations. In other words, it is simply a statement of the cell theory especially applied to the nervous system. But the great significance of this doctrine lies not so much in its overt assertion as in its implications. It proposes first of all that the nervous system is entirely cellular, an implication first appreciated fully by Nissl (24); second, that its cells are distinctive as to type and functional characteristics; and third, that the cells are related to one another by contact or apposition, not continuity, without significant quantities of intervening extracellular substance.

It is clear that the neuron doctrine is an incomplete description of the nervous system, for it ignores the non-neural elements which are also an important part of the tissue—the Schwann cells in the peripheral nerves, the neuroglial cells in the central nervous system, the ependyma, the sheaths of the axons, and even the blood vessels. In this respect it is faulty and susceptible of amendment. Exactly how the doctrine should be altered to include these elements remains for the moment uncertain until more information on the precise relation between them and the neurons becomes available.

Since we know that, unlike the cells of other tissues, the neurons are not only interrelated morphologically but also interact in a coherent and systematic fashion, it is of considerable importance to define as precisely as possible the intricate pattern of their morphological interrelations. The pattern we now possess has been built up over the past century and a half by fitting together the observations garnered by means of the isolation procedures mentioned above. But until recently we have not been able to obtain directly, in the same preparation, a picture of the tissue with all of its components intact, in place, in immediate proximity to their neighbors. This is the picture with which electron microscopy presents us, together with the serious problem of disentangling the whole bewildering fabric without sacrificing the advantage of visualizing all morphological interrelations at once. At first this advantage was not recognized as such. The investigator was confronted with a surfeit of detail which seemed to restrict the usefulness of electron microscopy for exploring the complex structure of the central nervous system. Actually, this embarrassment was merely the result of inadequate preservation of the tissue (30). When every cell is intact and in its proper place it does become possible to analyze in electron microscopic preparations the detailed intercellular relations which are the essence of the morphology of the nervous system and the substrate of its organized function.

The Fine Structure of the Perikaryon

In preparations examined by optical microscopy the typical neuron appears as a multipolar cell body containing a large vesicular nucleus with a conspicuous nucleolus and an extensive cytoplasm containing the prominent basophilic masses known as Nissl bodies, an elaborate Golgi apparatus, neurofibrillae, and numerous small mitochondria. Because the nucleus of neurons has received little attention from electron microscopists, I shall confine my remarks at this time to the cytoplasm.

The composition of the cytoplasm is clearly shown in Figures 15A and 15B, which are two neighboring panels from an electron micrograph of a Purkinje cell in the cerebellar cortex of a rat. This cell, one of the first neurons to be clearly described and one of the first animal cells to be recognized (32), will serve as an illustration of the typical neuron. The cytoplasm is crowded with granular, membranous, and filamentous organelles oriented in a roughly circular fashion around the nucleus. The high density of the cytoplasm in electron micrographs contrasts with the conventional image of optical microscopy in which, notwithstanding the considerable difference in thickness of sections, selective stains leave much of the cytoplasm invisible.

The neuronal mitochondria are generally small, varying from 1.0 to 0.1 μ in diameter, with a predominance of slender forms close to the lower limit of the range. Their fine structure is similar to that of mitochondria in all other cells, i.e., each is limited by a smooth outer unit membrane which encloses a second unit membrane that is thrown up into folds or cristae across the inner mitochondrial compartment (27, 34). There are, however, two peculiarities of neuronal mitochondria that are worth noting: first, the cristae frequently run longitudinally instead of crosswise, and second, the dense granules that usually appear in the inner mitochondrial chamber in most cells are either totally absent or, at least, infrequent in neurons. In all the figures used to illustrate this paper no intramitochondrial granules appear; a similar collection of granule-free mitochondria from normal liver or pancreas or kidney would be impossible because almost any section of a mitochondrion from one of these tissues would contain from one to seven granules. The significance of these peculiarities of neuronal mitochondria is unknown.

A second membranous structure that is ubiquitous in all cells but es-

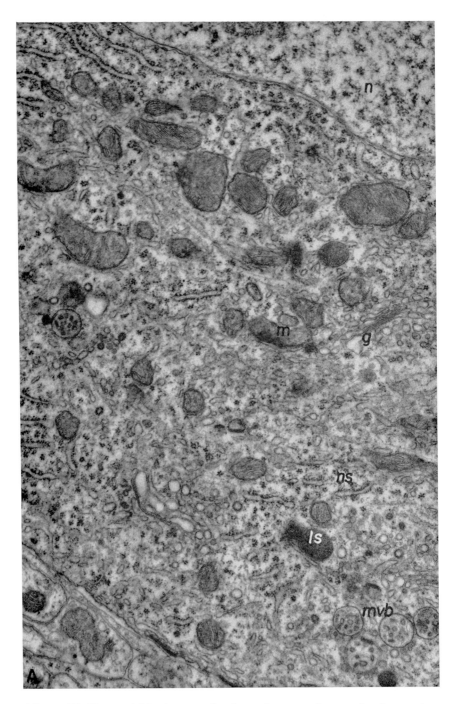

Figure 15. Two neighboring panels of an electron micrograph of a section through a Purkinje cell in the cerebellar cortex of a rat. A portion of the nucleus (*n*) bounded by its membranous envelope is visible at the top of both panels. Masses of Nissl substance (*ns*) lie not only beside the nucleus, where they form the so-called nuclear cap, but also more peripherally. Like the ergastoplasm of gland cells, the Nissl substance is a composite structure consisting of endoplasmic reticulum disposed as stacks of branching and anastomosing cisternae, clustered ribosomes, and the cytoplasmic matrix in which they are suspended (see Figure 16). A widely dispersed Golgi apparatus (*g*) appears (in A and B) as scattered groups of closely apposed cisternae and vesicles through-

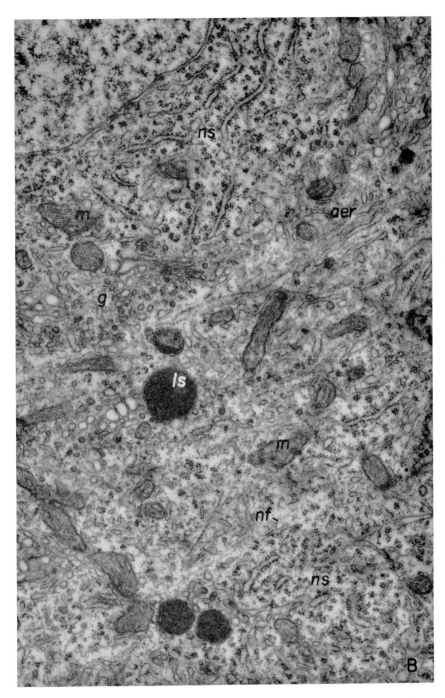

out the cytoplasm but forming an arc roughly parallel to the nuclear envelope. In addition, other tubules and cisternae of agranular endoplasmic reticulum (*aer*) showing no preferred orientation may be seen in between the more highly ordered forms. On close inspection, junctions between these various forms of the endoplasmic reticulum can be found. Fine neurofilaments (*nf*) and canaliculi are also present. The mitochondria (*m*) are generally slender and small and show the longitudinally oriented cristae characteristic of neurons. A cluster of multivesicular bodies (*mvb*) appears in the right lower corner of A and three dense bodies (*ls*), probably lysosomes, appear in B. (Electron micrograph by S. L. Palay.)   × 23,000 pecially elaborate in neurons is the endoplasmic reticulum, which appears in all of its several manifestations in Figure 15. In the neuron the most prominent form (Figure 16) is an ordered array of more or less parallel cisternae, the outer surfaces of which are studded with groups of fine, dense granules disposed in loops, rows, and spirals (31). Granules also occur as rosettes suspended in the cytoplasmic matrix between cisternae. This composition and this arrangement of structures are essentially the same as those of the ergastoplasm, the basophilic material in the cytoplasm of gland cells. In the neuron this material corresponds in distribution, shape, and composition to the Nissl bodies of optical microscopy (31). As is well known, cytochemical studies have shown that in gland cells the fine dense granules, the ribosomes, of the ergastoplasm consist of ribonucleoprotein and are responsible for both the basophilia and the protein synthesizing capacity of the cytoplasm (28, 38). In all probability, they possess the same properties in the Nissl bodies of nerve cells.

It is, however, noteworthy that in the ergastoplasm of gland cells, such as pancreatic acinar cells, the ribosomes are almost uniformly distributed over the surfaces of the cisternae with relatively few lying in the intervening matrix. This homogeneous distribution contrasts with the aggregatory pattern typical of the ribosomes in the Nissl bodies of neurons. Indeed, the clustered pattern of ribosomes was first noticed in neurons (31) and later seen in numerous other cell types. It has recently received prominent attention from biophysicists who, naming the groups "polysomes", have attributed special significance to them in protein synthesis (45).

Another highly organized form of the endoplasmic reticulum is the Golgi apparatus, which consists of closely apposed, flattened cisternae arranged in stacks and surrounded by swarms of small vesicles, as shown in Figure 15. The ends of the cisternae are frequently dilated and may be connected to branching tubules that extend into the surrounding cytoplasm. Ribonucleoprotein granules, or ribosomes, are not associated with the membranes of the Golgi apparatus. On cursory view, the components of the Golgi apparatus appear as isolated clusters and aggregations distributed throughout the cytoplasm. Careful scrutiny of low power electron micrographs reveals that these apparently isolated arrays really form parts of an extensive coarse network surrounding the nucleus and lying approximately midway between it and the surface membrane of the perikaryon. In other words, this network may be said to correspond in three dimensions to the "internal reticular apparatus" of Golgi. The correspondence has recently been made even more conclusive by the histochemical demonstration of an enzyme, thiamine pyrophosphatase, restricted to the Golgi apparatus. In sections prepared for the optical microscope the distribution of the reaction product reproduces the classical figure of the Golgi apparatus. In electron micrographs of the same preparations the reaction product appears in those cisternae of the agranular endoplasmic reticulum that are arranged in close-packed arrays as described above (1, 25, 26).

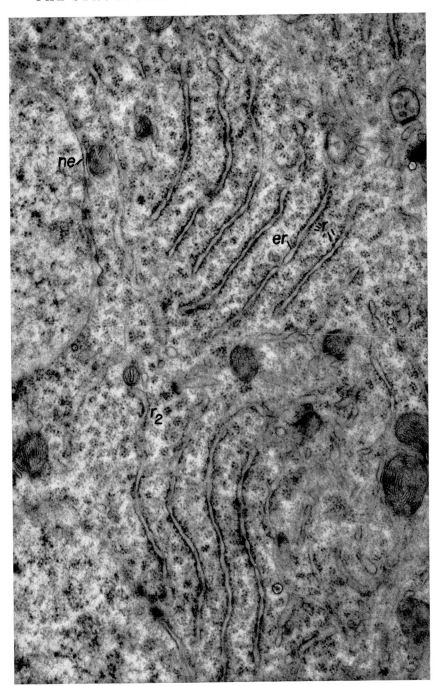

Figure 16. Nissl substance in the perinuclear cytoplasm of a Purkinje cell. The double membrane of the nuclear envelope (*ne*) forms an undulating profile at the left edge of the picture. The granular endoplasmic reticulum (*er*) is arranged as imbricated cisternae studded with ribosomes (*r*). Between the cisternae the free ribosomes are usually clumped as at r_2. Notice that the attached ribosomes are not uniformly distributed over the outer surfaces of the cisternae. (Electron micrograph by S. L. Palay.)   × 23,000

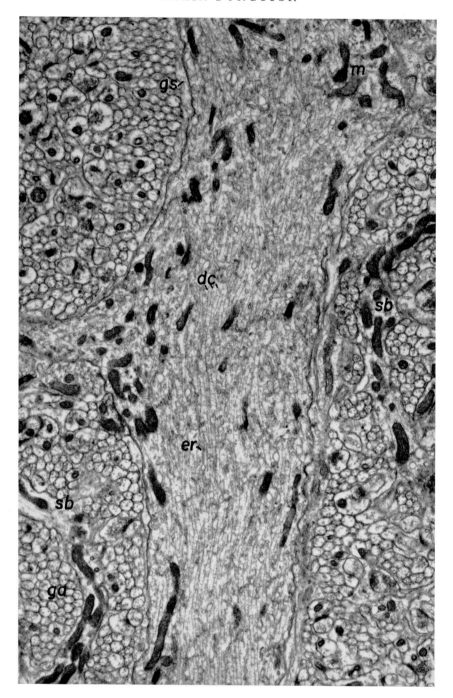

Figure 17. Longitudinal section of a Purkinje cell dendrite coursing through the neuropil of the molecular layer of the cerebellar cortex. The dendrite is filled with fine, long and straight canaliculi (dc), evenly spaced, and largely parallel to one another and to the long axis of the dendrite. Long, slender mitochondria (m), also longitudinally oriented, are disposed in the peripheral regions of the cytoplasm. Long, varicose tubules of endoplasmic reticulum (er) meander through the dendrite generally in a longitudinal direction but

Between the interlocking territories occupied by the Nissl bodies and the Golgi apparatus are also less conspicuous units of the pervasive agranular endoplasmic reticulum (Figure 15). These consist of interconnected tubules and cisternae devoid of ribosomes over most of their surface. Anastomoses between the several forms of the endoplasmic reticulum can be found at numerous points throughout the cytoplasm (Figure 16).

The cytoplasm also contains various other formed elements, including multivesicular bodies (Figure 16), lysosomes, and pigment granules. Fine filaments and tubules appear throughout the spaces not occupied by the more conspicuous organelles. The amount of cytoplasm occupied by these filaments and tubules varies considerably from place to place in the nervous system and may possibly reflect the physiological state of the nerve cell.

Thus, in contrast with the conventional light microscopic image, electron micrographs reveal that the nerve cell body is crowded with organelles, some of which provide the machinery for respiration and protein synthesis, whereas the function of many of the others remains unknown. As will be noted again below, neither the population density nor the variety of structure in neuronal perikarya is unusual among cells. Study of the fine structure of the perikaryon does not reveal any specifically neural characteristics that can be correlated with the special role of neurons in the economy of the organism. Whatever neurons do must, therefore, be done with the same basic machinery as other cells use, a conclusion that can hardly be considered extraordinary.

The Fine Structure of Dendrites and Axons

For more than a century the processes of neurons have been recognized as being of two types—axons and dendrites. Dendrites are merely extensions of the perikaryon, contain Nissl bodies, and are never ensheathed by myelin. Axons, on the contrary, never contain Nissl bodies, but they may or may not be myelinated. Both processes contain neurofibrillae, although dendrites are generally less argyrophilic than axons. These distinctions, visible in the light microscope, have corresponding manifestations in electron micrographs.

As may be seen in Figure 17, a large dendrite contains numerous elongated mitochondria, usually arranged in the peripheral protoplasm. The endoplasmic reticulum, consisting of anastomosing slender tubules and shallow cisternae, extends along the length of the dendrite tending to ag-

---

sometimes also obliquely or transversely. The dendrite is closely ensheathed in the cytoplasmic processes of neuroglial cells (gs). Nearly all of the small circular profiles among which the dendrite is immersed represent transverse sections of "parallel fibers", the axons of granule cells (ga). Spiny branchlets (sb), the terminal branches of the Purkinje cell dendrites, are visible on either side of the main dendrite. Numerous synapses between dendritic thorns and granule cell axons are evident. (Electron micrograph by S. L. Palay.) × 16,000 gregate with clustered ribosomes at sites of branching, a favored position for small Nissl bodies. Most of the dendrite is occupied by long, straight, and parallel canaliculi about 200 Å in diameter. In transverse sections (Figure 18) the canaliculi appear as small, thick-walled circles with a clear center. The wall is approximately 60 Å thick. The dendrites also contain a few very fine filaments. As the dendrites branch and as the diameter becomes smaller and smaller, the number of mitochondria per unit length does not decrease correspondingly; consequently, the mitochondria appear to increase in number in the smaller dendrites. This is not true of the canaliculi, filaments, and the endoplasmic reticulum, which appear to be partitioned among the numerous branches of the dendrites so that close to the terminals the dendrite seems to contain only mitochondria and a few tortuous tubules.

In contrast to the large dendrites, large axons are characteristically filled with long, fine filaments about 100 Å in diameter, usually arranged, like the canaliculi of the dendrites, parallel to the long axis of the process. At high magnifications (Figure 19), it is clear that these fine filaments are also tubular in structure with a dense wall about 30 Å thick and a clear center. In longitudinal section each filament appears as two fine parallel lines, whereas in cross section it appears as a thick-walled circle (Figure 19). These filaments have been given the name "neurofilaments". It is possible that the neurofilaments represent helically organized protein threads. Similar filaments have been extracted from the axoplasm of the giant squid and have been shown to consist of a single protein (37). Recent work by Gray and his collaborators (17) indicates very strongly that the filaments are responsible for the argyrophilia of the axons and correspond to the neurofibrillae of silver stain preparations. Axons also contain longitudinally oriented tubules of the endoplasmic reticulum and distinctive mitochondria (which are often long and extremely slender), as well as canaliculi similar to those in dendrites.

The distinction between axons and dendrites can generally be made in electron micrographs without difficulty so long as the investigator restricts his attention to the large processes. Smaller processes are much more difficult to identify, especially the small unmyelinated axons. The reason for this is that neurofilaments become less and less prominent as the axons become smaller. Very thin unmyelinated axons contain only a few canalicular structures and widely spaced slender mitochondria. A thorough knowledge of the regional architectonics of the central nervous system as revealed by optical microscopy must serve as a guide in difficult places. Such a difficult place is the neuropil, where dendritic and axonal terminals come into contact (see Figures 21 and 22). Here dendrites and axons form an almost impenetrable thicket, the members of which can be recognized only by careful correlation of their internal structure with their topographical distribution and course as known from light microscopy.

In the central nervous system the axons terminate in various bulbous

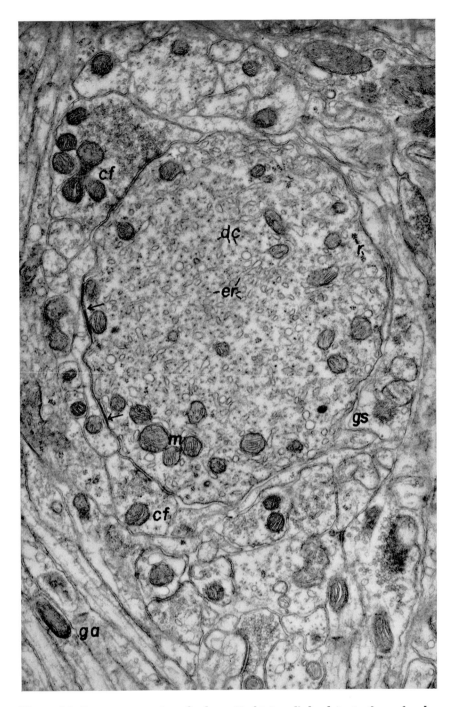

Figure 18. Transverse section of a large Purkinje cell dendrite in the molecular layer. Dendritic canaliculi (*dc*), tubules of endoplasmic reticulum (*er*), and mitochondria (*m*) all appear in nearly circular profile. A few clusters of ribosomes (*r*) can be seen near the dendritic surface membrane. Notice that the dendrite is ensheathed by neuroglial processes (*gs*) except at two places, where a climbing fiber (*cf*) makes synaptic contact with its surface. Two subsurface cisternae (*arrows*) are shown beneath the surface membrane of the dendrite. Granule cell axons (*ga*) in longitudinal section appear in the left lower corner of the figure. (Electron micrograph by S. L. Palay.)　　× 22,000

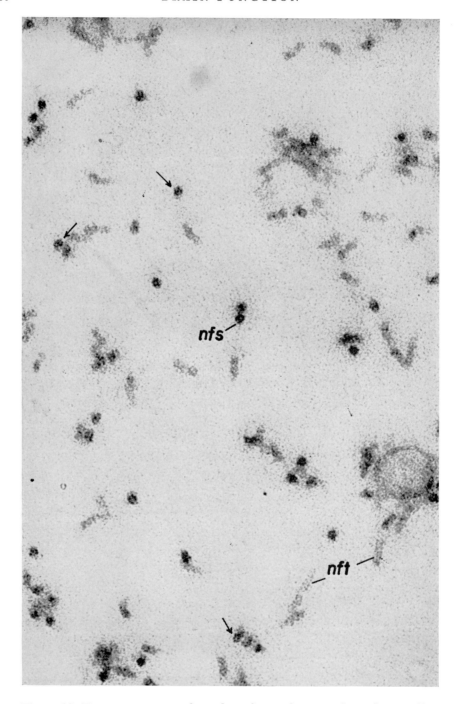

Figure 19. Transverse section of axoplasm from a large myelinated nerve fiber in the white matter of the spinal cord of the rat. Neurofilaments in longitudinal section (*nft*) have a double contour indicating a tubular structure, which is confirmed by the transverse sections (*nfs*), where they appear as circular profiles with dense outlines and clear centers. A few of the transverse sections (*arrows*) show a punctate density in the center, which may represent a subsidiary filament. (Electron micrograph by S. L. Palay.) × 159,000

structures applied to the surfaces of dendrites or the perikarya of other neurons. The surface of the neuron is separated by a narrow cleft about 200 Å wide from the presynaptic terminals. The apposed surface membranes display dense and thickened patches which are characteristic of all inter-neuronal synapses. Gray (15) has described two types of synapse in which the dense patches are either on the postsynaptic side or symmetrically arranged on both sides of the synaptic cleft. Within the terminals lie numerous mitochondria and clusters of small vesicles 150 to 600 Å in diameter, the so-called synaptic vesicles. The vesicles tend to accumulate against the presynaptic surfaces of the terminals. This typical structure of the synapse, as shown by electron microscopy, signifies the resolution of the classic controversy between the reticularists and the neuronists concerning the morphological relations between neurons. Protoplasmic continuity between synaptic elements is clearly excluded by the electron microscopic findings. It must be pointed out, however, that this classic structure of the synapse fits only those synapses known or presumed to be concerned in chemical transmission of the nervous impulse. There are several examples now in which the pre- and postsynaptic membranes appear to be fused, with the resultant obliteration of the synaptic cleft (cf. 35). In each of these instances the morphological data can be correlated with physiological evidence that electrical transmission of the nerve impulse occurs at these sites (12).

THE FINE STRUCTURE OF THE NEUROPIL

We have now seen examples of all parts of the neuron. It would seem, then, a relatively easy task to examine different regions of the nervous system, identify all the cellular elements, and derive structural principles describing the various possible arrangements and correlating them with known or hypothetical functional characteristics. To do this we must analyze not only the obvious collections of neurons, such as the nuclei of the medulla oblongata, the thalamus, etc., but also the vast regions of gray matter in between the perikarya, such as the neuropil of the cerebral cortex.

Because of the regularity of its architecture, the cerebellar cortex is a good place to begin such an analysis. Furthermore, as most of its cellular and fiber components are already recognized in optical microscopy (20), it is not too difficult to identify them in electron micrographs and to visualize their interrelations on a much more detailed level than was possible with optical microscopy. I have selected three synaptic zones of the cerebellar cortex as illustrations: (a) the synapses between the mossy fibers and the granule cell dendrites in the glomeruli, (b) the synapses between the granule cell axons and the Purkinje cell dendrites in the molecular layer, and (c) the synapses between the Purkinje cell axons and the basket cell axons in the granule cell layer.

A) THE GLOMERULUS. One of the principal pathways of afferent impulses to the cerebellar cortex, the mossy fiber enters the granule cell layer and divides a number of times; each branch terminates as a tuft, articulating with the dendrites of granule cells in a complicated synaptic formation known as the glomerulus. In optical microscopy the organization of this synapse has been the subject of prolonged controversy (20) because the relationships of the two synapsing components cannot be clearly visualized in silver preparations. In electron micrographs (Figure 20) it can be seen that the mossy fiber terminal occupies the center of the glomerulus and that the dendritic terminals of the granule cell nestle in coves and bays on the surface of the axon. Each axon terminal is, therefore, intimately related to numerous, perhaps dozens, of dendritic twigs (16, 29).

The tufted end of the mossy fiber contains a central core of neurofilaments, surrounded by a collection of elongated, slender mitochondria, which are in turn surrounded by hordes of vesicles filling out every branch and filament of the tuft. The dendrites are separated from the axon by a synaptic cleft continuous with the intercellular spaces between all of the cellular processes in the central nervous system. At certain spots the apposed surface membranes of both axon and dendrite are apparently denser and thicker. This effect is produced by an aggregation of very fine filaments inserted into the cytoplasmic surfaces of these patches. At these sites the synaptic vesicles tend to cluster against the surface of the axon and the synaptic cleft is slightly widened. The significance of these specialized regions in the surface of the synaptic junction is still mysterious, but the resemblance between them and the desmosomes (maculae adhaerentes, 9) of ordinary epithelial cells is striking enough to make one suspect that these, too, are zones of adhesion between cells. It may be pointed out that similar attachments exist between *dendritic* loops in the glomerulus (Figure 20). As vesicles and clustered mitochondria are absent, there is no reason to postulate that these interdendritic contacts represent a kind of physiological synapse. Although neuroglial cells do not occur within the glomerulus, occasional astrocytic processes can be identified among the dendrites at the periphery of the formation. A few glomeruli appear to be partially encircled by the processes of astrocytes.

B) THE SYNAPSE BETWEEN PURKINJE CELL DENDRITES AND GRANULE CELL AXONS. The axons of the granule cells ascend through the Purkinje cell layer into the molecular layer, where they divide into a T with two branches which course in a plane parallel to the surface of the cerebellar folia and perpendicular to the plane of the Purkinje cell dendritic tree. They constitute the "parallel fibers" of the molecular layer and are the principal, but by no means the only, afferent pathway to the Purkinje cells. In Figure 21, A and B, which shows neighboring fields from an electron micrograph of a section roughly parallel with their course, they can be seen in longitudinal section. These axons are very slender and contain only a few neurofilaments, canaliculi, and occasional thin mitochondria. They are characterized by fusiform dilatations and stubby excrescences at those points where they come close to

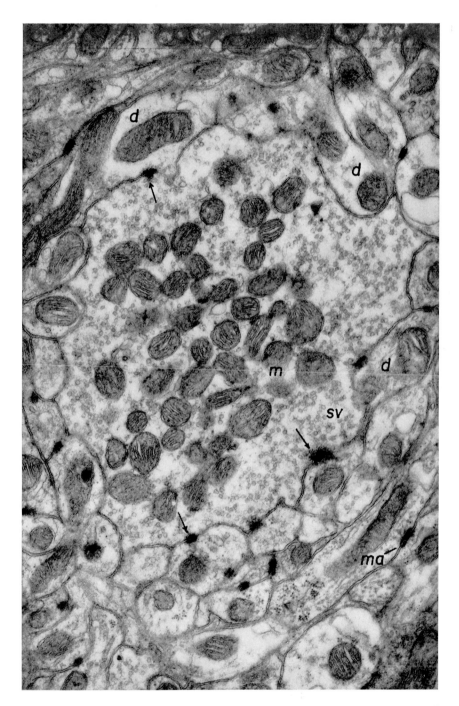

Figure 20. A glomerulus in the granule cell layer of the cerebellar cortex of the rat. The terminal axoplasm of a mossy fiber lying in the center of the field is occupied by numerous mitochondrial profiles (*m*) and throngs of synaptic vesicles (*sv*). The delicate tubules lying among the mitochondria belong to the endoplasmic reticulum. Dendritic tips (*d*) indent the surface of the axon and their attachments to the axon are marked by symmetrical dense plaques (*arrows*). Similar plaques occur between some of the dendritic tips forming the usual maculae adhaerentes (*ma*) of epithelia. (Electron micrograph by S. L. Palay.)   × 25,000

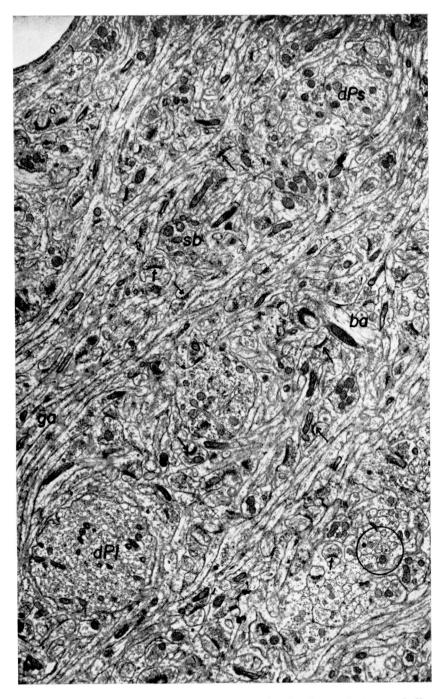

Figure 21. Two neighboring fields in the molecular layer of the cerebellar cortex of the rat. Larger dendrites (*dPl*) of Purkinje cells appear in transverse section, and some of the smaller dendrites (*dPs*) appear in longitudinal section. Spiny branchlets (*sb*) and thorns (*t*) can be seen in either orientation. "Parallel fibers", or granule cell axons (*ga*) course diagonally across the field and constitute the majority of the long profiles. The clusters of round profiles,

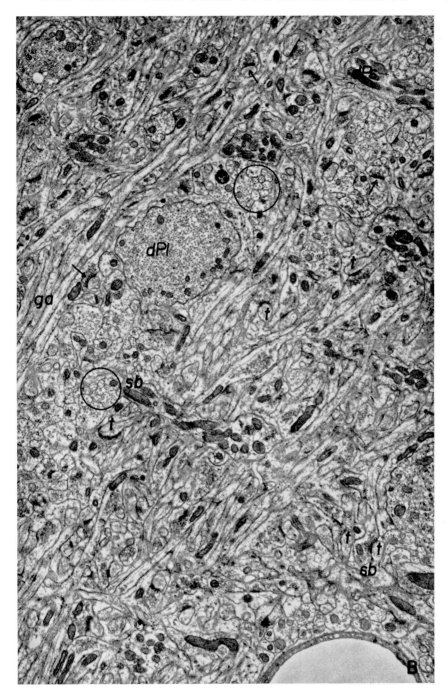

such as those enclosed in circles, are bundles of the primary stems of granule cell axons ascending into the higher reaches of the molecular layer. Synaptic contacts (*arrows*) between granule cell axons and the thorns of the Purkinje cell dendrites occur everywhere in both panels. A basket cell axon (*ba*) is identifiable in A, and parts of two capillaries appear in the left upper corner of A and the right lower corner of B. (Electron micrograph by S. L. Palay.)

× 8,000

the spiny branchlets of the Purkinje cell dendrites. At these sites the granule cell axon comes into synaptic contact with the spines, or thorns, on the surface of the Purkinje cell dendrite.

The details of this synapse can be seen in Figure 22, which shows a transverse section of a spiny branchlet from which two thorns extend, making contact with granule cell axons that are coursing by. The thorns have bulbous tips which fit into shallow depressions in the dilated portion or varicosity of the axon. The characteristic vesicles in the axon and the desmosome-like modification of the apposed surface membranes identify this contact as a synapse. In favorable planes of section (Figure 22) axonal mitochondria may also be seen in the varicosities. No special organelles, such as the spine apparatus found in the cerebral cortex (15), occur in the thorns of the Purkinje cell dendrites. This synaptic contact is often asymmetrical in that only the dendritic surface of the synapse may have dark patches. On the other side of the synapse, regularly patterned, dense, filamentous material frequently occurs among the synaptic vesicles that lie close to the contact surface.

It is clear that the granule cell axon carries a chain of *terminaisons en passant*. These structures enable the granule cell to make many functional contacts not only with many branches of one Purkinje cell, but also with several Purkinje cells in series. The divergence of incoming impulses to the molecular layer is complemented by the enormous convergence of impulses upon each Purkinje cell, for hundreds of thousands of granule cell axons pass through the dendritic field of any one Purkinje cell and make contact with it at myriad points (10).

c) THE AXO-AXONAL SYNAPSE BETWEEN BASKET CELL AND PURKINJE CELL. The Purkinje cell also receives information from a small neuron oriented horizontally in the depths of the molecular layer and known as the "basket cell" because its axonal collaterals envelop the perikaryon of the Purkinje cell. Many of these fibers give off *terminaisons en passant* to the surface of the Purkinje cell perikaryon (Figure 22) and continue into a brush-like formation around its axon. The endings upon the surface of the perikaryon form typical synaptic junctions. The endings fit closely into interruptions in the neuroglial sheath covering the rest of the perikaryon and they contain the usual vesicles and mitochondria. The presynaptic surface is modified by dense aggregations of fine filamentous material, but the postsynaptic surface appears not significantly different from the rest of the neuronal plasmalemma. Subsurface cisternae (36), which are conspicuous in the Purkinje cell because of their association with large mitochondria (18), are not consistently related to overlying synapses.

The axon of the Purkinje cell is the only path for efferent impulses from the cerebellar cortex. It leaves the perikaryon at its base and plunges across the granule cell layer in a nearly straight line, acquiring its myelin sheath at a distance of several micra from its origin. In this initial segment it has

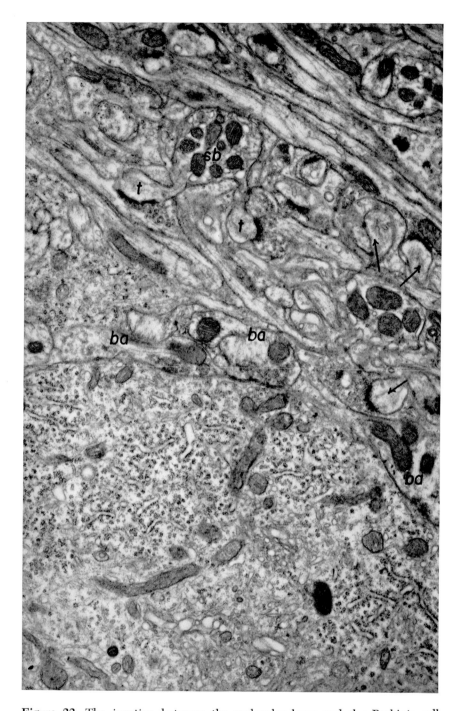

Figure 22. The junction between the molecular layer and the Purkinje cell layer. The lower third of the picture is occupied by a Purkinje cell containing a large Nissl body, Golgi apparatus, and mitochondria. Three terminals of basket cell fibers (*ba*) form synapses on the surface of this cell. In the molecular layer a small spiny branchlet (*sb*) of the Purkinje cell dendrite gives off two thorns (*t*) which make synaptic contact with granule cell axons coursing by. Other examples of this type of contact are indicated by arrows. (Electron micrograph by S. L. Palay.) × 15,000

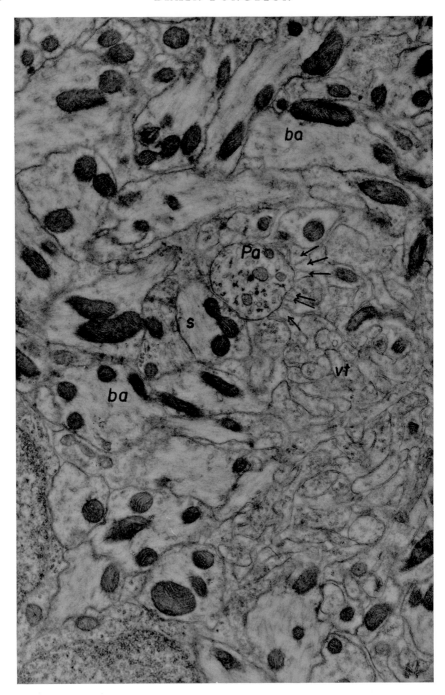

Figure 23. Tranverse section through the Purkinje cell axon (*Pa*) and the basket surrounding it. The axon contains several profiles of mitochondria, bundles of dense walled canaliculi, thin filaments, and tubules of endoplasmic reticulum, all in transverse section. Parts of two granule cells are visible in the left lower corner of the picture. Almost all of the remainder of the figure consists of the basket cell axons (*ba*) which form a whorl-like pattern around the Purkinje cell axon. One of these fibers (*s*) comes into synaptic contact with

a characteristic internal structure more like that of a large dendrite than like that of an axon (Figure 23). It contains clustered, dense-walled canaliculi, several mitochondria of various sizes, tubules of the endoplasmic reticulum, and fine filaments. Fine filaments are arrayed longitudinally just beneath the surface membrane and at low magnifications they give to the axolemma the spurious appearance of being doubled and thickened. The neuroglial sheath surrounding the perikaryon extends down along the axon as extremely fine, longitudinally-oriented ribs, or ruffles. Again, as on the perikaryon, the endings of the basket fibers come into contact with the Purkinje cell axon only through interruptions in this neuroglial sheath.

The basket cell fibers continue down the axon almost to the beginning of the myelin sheath and form a broad vortex-like arrangement surrounding the axon. These formations are readily recognized in stained preparations for the optical microscope because they form a cell-free zone beneath each Purkinje cell. They are just as readily identified in electron micrographs because of the characteristic swirling arrangement of the basket cell fibers centered upon the distinctive Purkinje cell axon (Figure 23). The basket cell fibers, which at this level are rather large and contain numerous mitochondria and neurofilaments, break up into slender, branching terminals containing many vesicles and only a few mitochondria. This great concentration of axons has only a few contacts with the Purkinje cell axon passing through them. This is a highly unusual type of synapse and can be compared to only one other known example, the axon cap of the Mauthner cell in the goldfish (35). It seems reasonable to expect that the electrical characteristics of this synapse resemble those of the Mauthner cell axon (13, 14).

SUMMARY

It is important to recognize that the structural units of the neurons are not different from those of other cells. All cells contain mitochondria, ergastoplasm, vesicles, filaments and nuclei, the commonplace armamentarium of metabolism and specialized function. These are not specific for the nervous system, although they may have certain idiosyncracies in neurons. What is specific for the nervous system is its organization—the way in which its constituent cells are put together and interact.

In this paper I have progressed by steps from the single nerve cell as the focal element in the nervous system to the intricate organization of

the Purkinje cell axon. The remaining surface of the Purkinje cell axon is ensheathed in thin neuroglial processes (*arrows*). Some of the basket cell axons branch profusely, giving rise to the small round terminals (*vt*) that are filled with vesicles but do not come into synaptic contact with the Purkinje cell axon. This is a new type of interneuronal junction which is much more complicated than one would expect from the usual term "axo-axonal synapse". (Electron micrograph by S. L. Palay.)   × 15,000 higher centers. The neuron doctrine has been confirmed. We have seen that the nervous system is cellular almost to the exclusion of any other component. It is an epithelium in structure. It can hardly come as a surprise, therefore, that intercellular components are extremely restricted in amount, limited in fact to the minute crevices between cells as in all other epithelia. This does not mean that in certain sites intercellular material may not be pooled (35), where it has relevance to specialized and peculiar functional features. In general, however, it seems to be confined to the narrow clefts between cell membranes.

But perhaps more significantly for the future, we have seen that electron microscopy can be used advantageously to analyze the intimate relations between cells to an extent that had never been possible before with previous methods. This advance is due to the fact that in properly prepared specimens with every cell intact and in place, electron microscopy reveals all of the cellular components at once and in great detail. Already the progress made suggests that it is not only possible but worthwhile to carry out an electron microscopic analysis of all parts of the central nervous system, beginning with the regions well known from classical neuroanatomy and moving to the more complicated regions that are incompletely understood at present. During the course of this effort many difficult problems will be cleared up—for example, the problem of the construction of the cerebellar glomerulus—and, of course, many more problems will be uncovered. In this way, it will be possible to translate the science of neuroanatomy from the level of light microscopy to the new domain of detail afforded by the electron microscope. The result should be a vastly improved understanding of the intimate intercellular relationships which are the essence of the morphology of the nervous system and the substrate of its coherent function.

Bickford: I want to ask Dr. Palay if electron microscopy has produced evidence of functional changes at synapses comparable to what has been observed in the myoneural junction. Are there any changes that can be seen in relation to activity? This would be relevant to problems in learning.

Palay: So far as I know, no one has shown any change in the neuromuscular junction or elsewhere by the electron microscope. Many people have tried and the changes which have been seen have been in rats, in extreme experiments which are very hard to interpret. In the neuromuscular junction, no change has been seen following continuous stimulation. This has had no effect so far. It is a lot to expect. There are probably several hundred million vesicles in the neuromuscular junction. If the ideas about the transmitter being in the vesicle are assumed to be correct, then there are probably something like 300 ejected for each impulse transmitted. At the same time, new ones are being made. I think it would be hard to define an experiment that would show there was no change, and it is extremely difficult to see a change of this magnitude.

Feindel: Would Dr. Palay give his opinion as to the possible function of these vesicles in the synaptic region?

Palay: We have information from the physiologists concerning quantal release or unitary release of transmitter substances at the junction that has been most seriously and reliably studied, the neuromuscular junction. I do not really doubt that in this instance acetylcholine is released in a quantal fashion from the ending, and that the number of quanta released at any given time determines whether an impulse is transmitted. In the neuromuscular junction, the only instance in which this has been worked out, the physiological evidence is that the transmitter is in packets. When we look in the electron microscope, we find packets of what might be considered the proper dimensions. It is, of course, reasonable to assume that the packets we see have something to do with the packets that physiology requires. But that is the only basis so far for making this identification.

It is an extremely attractive hypothesis and one I personally think is reasonable. It is also very difficult to obtain evidence that can help make it more than a hypothesis. These vesicles are in all of the endings that have ever been described, even in endings which are sensory in nature, and also in the electrical synapses where there is no transmitter. So, having the vesicle there does not mean there is a transmitter, but it is a plausible idea.

Mommaerts: Is it not possible, in principle, to count in a given area the number of vesicles, and to determine how much acetylcholine there is, and so find the number of acetylcholine molecules per vesicle? If this would correspond roughly to the number of molecules figured to be present in one "quantum", the hypothesis of quantal release would be strongly supported, whereas, if there were a discrepancy of a millionfold or so, the whole idea would be ruled out. Can this be done?

Palay: Counting the vesicles could be done at least to an approximate order of magnitude. But can you be sure that acetylcholine is only in the ending?

French: Dr. Palay, do any of these vesicles contain anything besides acetylcholine? What about adrenergic endings?

Palay: There is an entire family of synaptic vesicles and they do not all contain acetylcholine. The vesicles I described and illustrated appear to be empty and are approximately 200 Å in diameter. There are also larger vesicles which may be of the order of 1000 Å, or a tenth of a micron. They very frequently, or in certain sites, contain a large droplet, and these are typical for the regions known as neurosecretory. In other words, they contain droplets which presumably have in them antidiuretic hormone, vasopressin, oxytocin, etc. They, of course, are in regions where the endings are on blood vessels, and the hormone is discharged into the blood vessel.

In addition, we find vesicles of intermediate size which have extremely dense centers. They are most common in the autonomic nervous system, both parasympathetic and sympathetic. So it is hard to know for sure whether they are adrenergic or cholinergic.

There is also another group, about 400 Å in diameter, which has in it just a tiny dot, and this may be one of the transmitters, or it could be a residue when one of the transmitters has been discharged. So, it is entirely possible that we have a cluster of chemicals inside these structures that could be quite specific, but we do not have chemical or pharmacological correlations yet.

In known adrenergic centers, where there is a sympathetic nerve known to release norepinephrine, and where radioactive labeling shows that the ending does contain norepinephrine, the endings have vesicles in them which are of the order of 400 or 500 Å, and have an extremely dense center.

Luco: In prolonged stimulation, do they disappear or decrease? This question has been discussed very often. Birks, Huxley & Katz (3) failed to obtain reduction of terminal vesicles after synaptic stimulation in the frog's neuromuscular preparation.

Palay: Many people have tried to test this in the neuromuscular junction. According to work reported by De Robertis (8), in certain instances there is a decrease. The practical difficulty is one familiar to physiologists, namely that one cannot continue the stimulation long enough because the pre-terminal part of the ending fatigues and cuts off. One cannot exhaust the ending.

Luco: After degeneration of the motor nerve, when the glia cells cover the end-plate membrane, it is possible to observe the miniature end-plate potential. So, it is of interest to ask if in these glial cells some kind of synaptic vesicles can be seen.

Palay: Birks, Katz & Miledi (4) found in the Schwann cells, which replace the ending, large numbers of vesicles, but vesicles are not specific by their form and we do not know what would be inside them. These authors did suggest, however, that the miniature potentials were due to the release of acetylcholine from the Schwann cell now replacing the nerve fiber.

Nirenberg: Is my understanding correct that norepinephrine is found in the axon? And has anyone looked in the dendrite or the region that the axon would innervate?

Palay: This has been done in the axon and also in the nerve cells. It is all work on the peripheral nervous system. In fact, if you ask some of the stricter physiologists, they will say they know nothing about any transmitter in the central nervous system.

Nirenberg: Has anybody looked for activation of glycogen phosphorylase during stimulation?

Palay: I am not aware of any such study.

Bickford: Along the same lines, could you use tagging with ferritin? How applicable is this tagging technique? Could acetylcholine be tagged?

Palay: I would not want to say it could not be tagged. It might be difficult because acetylcholine is a very small water-soluble molecule, and it is bound. You can extract acetylcholine from particular fractions of homogenates. Apparently it is attached to membranes or to protein, or something which is less soluble, so it can be separated by differential centrifugation. What we want to know in these preparations is whether the acetylcholine is inside attached to the membrane, or is it in something else that came along with the vesicles in the centrifuge fraction.

Mommaerts: Taking my cue from Dr. Nirenberg's question on phosphorylase, I would like to say that there is a very wide gap between the excitatory events on the scale of milliseconds, and the memories that last over the years.

The starting point will be the work in Sutherland's laboratory at Western Reserve, on the question of how glycogen phosphorylase in liver is activated (39). This may sound very remote, but I will show that it is not. Phosphorylase is activated under the influence of epinephrine, which Sutherland found to act upon a particulate component of the cell, which it causes to form a substance that, in turn, stimulates an enzyme which activates phosphorylase. The substance in question he identified as cyclic adenylic acid, which is formed from ATP by splitting off a pyrophosphate and combining the remaining phosphate with the No. 3 hydroxyl on the ribose in addition to the No. 5 to which it was already bound.

Now it turns out that this cyclic adenylic acid may be of much wider significance than merely for the regulation of phosphorylase activity. For one thing, there appear the first indications of a role in active transport phenomena, while we ourselves have been concerned with its possible role in the regulation of muscle contraction, so far with uncertain results. These possibilities upon further investigation might prove to be very relevant to our problem. For the moment, I will base my remarks mainly on the demonstration that in certain systems epinephrine and serotonin can enhance the cyclic adenylate levels.

Thus, we might recognize the possibility that neurohumoral transmitter or inhibitor substances might regulate the level of cyclic nucleotides in brain cells. If, in turn, it could be demonstrated that cyclic nucleotides can affect the incorporation of nucleotides into nucleic acids, there would be a possibility of relating the excitation of cells to some feature of nucleotide sequence coding.

All of this is total fantasy at the moment, but it is a possible thought to explore in the region that lies between the single millisecond impulses and the long-range storage phenomena.

Pappas: Since this is a conference on RNA and Brain Function, I would like to present some of the results of electron microscopic studies carried on by Dr. Virginia Tennyson at Columbia University on the development of Nissl granules in immature nerve cells.

The medullary cells of the neural tube of the rabbit embryo rapidly differentiate (from the 10th to about the 19th day) into the large neuroblasts of the ventral horn area and develop prominent Nissl granules in their cell bodies (40, 41). In Figure 24, a portion of the medullary cell taken from

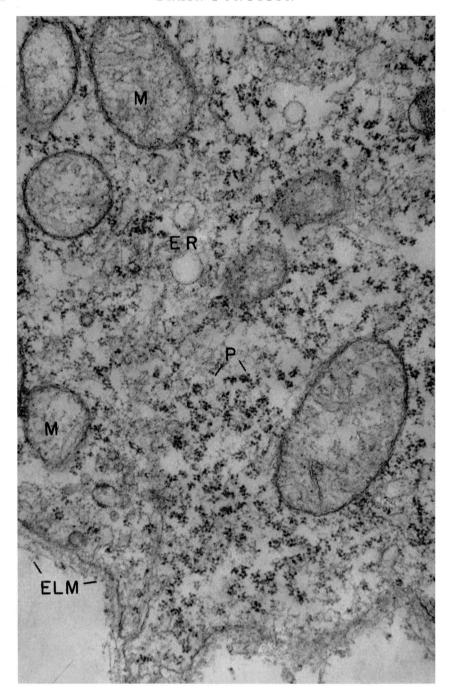

Figure 24. Electron micrograph of a portion of a medullary cell taken from the ventral lateral area of the neural tube of an 11-day old rabbit embryo. Clusters of RNP granules (*P*) are distributed randomly in the cytoplasm. Very few membranous elements of the endoplasmic reticulum (*ER*) are present. The mitochondria (*M*) have few cristae. The external limiting membrane (*ELM*) appears fibrillar. (Taken by V. M. Tennyson.) × 36,700

the ventral lateral region of the neural tube of an 11-day old rabbit embryo is shown. These medullary cells contain clusters of ribonucleoprotein (RNP) granules distributed randomly in the cytoplasm. Very few membranous elements of the endoplasmic reticulum are present. It is difficult to demonstrate cytoplasmic basophilia in these embryonic cells. However, this may be attributed to the leaching out of these unattached RNP granules during the preparation for light microscopic examination, particularly if the procedure is a long one requiring many changes of solvents. The mitochondria are typical of those found in undifferentiated cells as they have few cristae, a light matrix, and are globular in shape (42).

In the ventral horn region of the 12-day old rabbit embryo, definite neuroblasts can be recognized by newly formed processes. A portion of such a cell is illustrated in Figure 25, which shows an axon hillock. The axon contains thin filaments and an elongated mitochondrion. Clusters of RNP granules are randomly dispersed in the perikaryon. A few more membranous elements of the endoplasmic reticulum may be found in the cell body than are seen in the younger medullary cells shown in the previous figure.

In fourteen days, the neuroblasts of the ventral horn region have become multipolar. Cisternae of the endoplasmic reticulum appear flattened and more abundant in the cell body of the neuroblast (Figure 26). Clusters of RNP granules are more concentrated in the perikaryon than during earlier stages of development. The cytoplasm, when examined with the light microscope following cresyl violet staining, has a diffuse but definite basophilia.

The cell bodies of the ventral horn cells increase greatly in size in the next few days. At about the 19th day in the rabbit embryo, Nissl granules in the perikaryon can be demonstrated with the light microscope. A portion of such a cell is shown in the electron micrograph of Figure 27. Clusters of RNP granules are heavily concentrated in the cytoplasm. The flattened cisternae of the endoplasmic reticulum (ER) with attached RNP granules are also found throughout this area. When such an area is examined in the light microscope it appears as a dense Nissl granule.

In adult neurons, there are even greater accumulations of flattened cisternae of the endoplasmic reticulum with dispersed and attached RNP granules. The membranes of the endoplasmic reticulum may be oriented parallel to each other in the conspicuous Nissl bodies of large motor neurons (31). Electron microscopic examination of these sections of well-prepared tissue reveals all the membrane-bounded elements present. In contrast to this, and as Dr. Palay pointed out, metallic techniques for light microscopy bring out only one cell in seventy in nerve tissue. Such isolation of elements in the nervous system has contributed greatly to our present knowledge of the cytoarchitecture of the brain. But the difficulty in electron microscopy is that all the elements are seen in slices 1/20th to 1/40th of a micron thick—and all membranes appear similar. Recently, however,

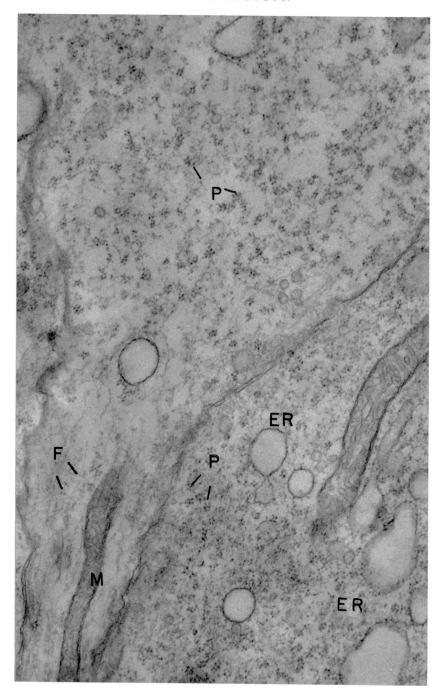

Figure 25. Electron micrograph of a portion of two neuroblasts in the ventral horn region of the 12-day old rabbit embryo. An axon hillock, containing thin filaments (*F*) and an elongated mitochondrion (*M*), is present. Clusters of RNP granules (*P*) are randomly dispersed in the perikarya, as well as a few membranous elements of the endoplasmic reticulum (*ER*). (Taken by V. M. Tennyson.)   × 36,500

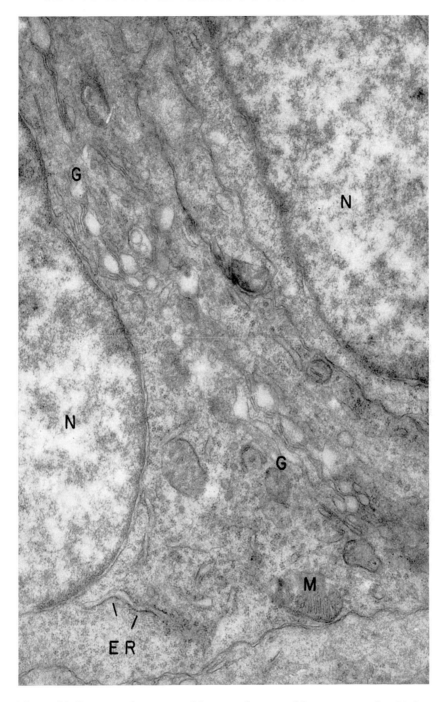

Figure 26. Portions of two neuroblasts in the ventral horn region of a 14-day old rabbit embryo. Cisternae of the endoplasmic reticulum (*ER*) appear flattened and more abundant than in earlier stages shown in Figures 24 and 25. Clusters of RNP granules are dispersed throughout the perikaryon. A prominent Golgi complex (*G*) is present in the cell body. Portions of two nuclei (*N*) can be seen in the micrograph. (Taken by V. M. Tennyson.)

× 21,000

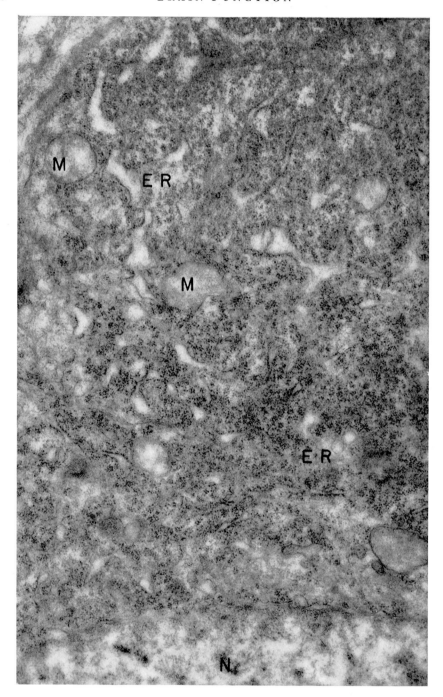

Figure 27. A portion of a ventral horn cell in a 19-day old rabbit embryo. Clusters of RNP granules are heavily concentrated in the cytoplasm. Also, flattened cisternae of the endoplasmic reticulum (*ER*) with attached granules are found throughout the area. This region of the cell body is a section through a Nissl granule. A portion of the nucleus (*N*) is seen at the bottom. *M:* Mitochondria. (Taken by V. M. Tennyson.)   × 22,000

techniques for chemical differentiation of some enzymatic activities have been developed by combining the methods of electron microscopy and cytochemistry (2, 25). These procedures use lead and other heavy metals in localizing the final product. Such methods employing heavy metals which appear opaque in the electron microscope will become more useful in differentiating various elements. Rifkind et al. (33) have developed electron microscopic methods for localizing antigen with the use of ferritin-conjugated antibody. They have conjugated ferritin to antibodies of γ-globulin and have subsequently demonstrated ferritin in the cisternae of the endoplasmic reticulum of guinea pig plasma cells—i.e., in the actual site of γ-globulin production.

More recently, Beiser, Tanenbaum and others (7) at Columbia University have reported work on purine-specific antibodies which react with deoxyribonucleic acid (DNA). Also at Columbia University, Hsu has been able to conjugate such antibodies with ferritin (cf. 33). We are now working on direct techniques to demonstrate nuclear DNA by electron microscopy. The ferritin antibody complex does not penetrate through cell membranes and therefore only exposed or cut nuclei are examined in the electron microscope. We have met with somewhat limited success in studying the sites of ferritin deposition in rat spermatocytes. In a few instances, ferritin can be demonstrated on the DNA threads radiating from the chromosome cores (23). However, one of the problems of these ferritin complexes is the non-specific adhesiveness of this compound to the fixed nucleoplasm. The results are encouraging to date but much remains to be done. This type of approach, i.e., the use of heavy metals in conjunction with antibodies of known specificity to identify molecules *in situ,* undoubtedly will illuminate the localization of many physiological processes occurring in the CNS.

The antibodies with purine specificity have been prepared by immunizing rabbits with purinoyl-protein conjugates. According to Butler and co-workers (7), these antibodies react with heat-denatured DNA as judged by complement fixation, and the reaction can be inhibited by various purines and purine derivatives. For cytological localization, the tissues are initially fixed in either formalin or glutaraldehyde. The former does denature DNA and the latter, a dialdehyde, probably does.

Nirenberg: Would these antibodies recognize RNA?

Pappas: These antibodies show no affinity for RNA. In cytological examination, the ferritin-conjugated antibodies are not found on or near the ribosomes in the cytoplasm.

Luco: I would like to ask Dr. Palay about the recognition of the presence or absence of dendrites. The preparation we are using in our research is the ganglion of the cockroach, whose structure has been studied by J. D. Vial and O. Marin* in Chile.

---

* Unpublished.

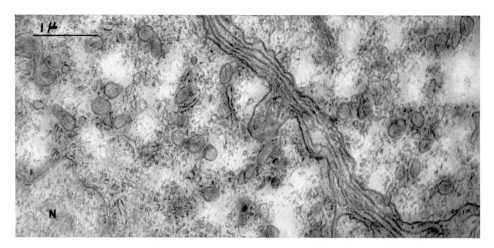

Figure 28. Several membrane profiles, presumably of glial nature, are interposed between adjacent neurons. Inside the neuron body is the nucleus (N); Golgi zone and
mitochondria are seen. The cell membrane of the lower cell shows a deep invagination.
(J. D. Vial & O. Marín, unpublished.)

All electron micrographs are made from osmium-fixed material, embedded in methacrylate and contrasted with lead acetate. There are two
cells in Figure 28, and the nucleus of one of them can be seen. In between
the cells is a number of membrane profiles suggesting cytoplasmic pro-
longations of neuroglial elements.

In Figure 29 one sees the edge of a giant axon. The entire axon measures
no less than 20 μ. No synaptic contacts are seen along the edge of this axon.

Figure 30 shows an axon that has some kind of invagination, full of
synaptic vesicles. Probably this is an axo-axonal synapse. One of the possibilities that interests us is that of having a preparation with no dendrites,
and with only axo-axonal synapses. There is either some kind of invagination
at the end of the terminal of the axon or a dilatation of the terminals, not
at the end itself but near the end of the axon which has synaptic connections with some other axon.

Figure 31 corresponds to a place where fine fibers are seen, but no synapsis is present. Figure 32 shows the neuropil, similar to one of the pictures
Dr. Palay presented on the cerebellum (Figure 17); some elements are full
of vesicles and other elements have no vesicles at all. No typical dendrites
are seen. Figure 33 is a higher magnification of Figure 32.

In the preparation we are using, we are interested to know whether there
are dendritic synapses or only axo-axonal ones, as described previously by
Hess (19), who found all the synaptic junctions to be axo-axonal.

If I understood Dr. Palay correctly, he said that probably the main distinction between axon terminal and dendrite would be the presence of the
Nissl body in the dendrite, and the absence of this element in the axon. But
we have just seen that during the development and during the degeneration
of the axon there is a Nissl body present also in the axon. It is still an axon
and it has the Nissl body, but at an undeveloped stage or in an abnormal

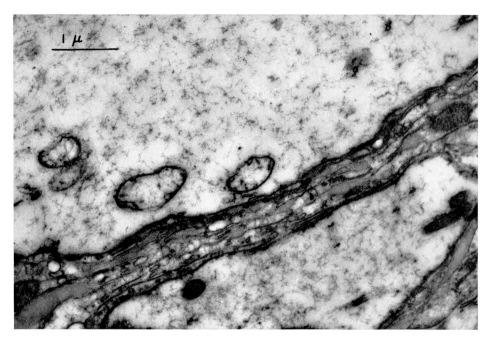

Figure 29. Two axons separated by folds of glial protoplasm. The larger axon measured at least 20 μ in diameter. No synaptic contacts are seen. (Vial & Marín, unpublished.)

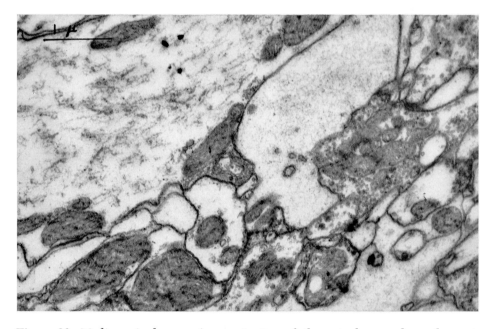

Figure 30. Medium sized axon. An evagination of the cytoplasm and membrane is filled with vesicles. At the lower right appear other profiles of neuronal expansions also full of vesicles. (Vial & Marín, unpublished.)

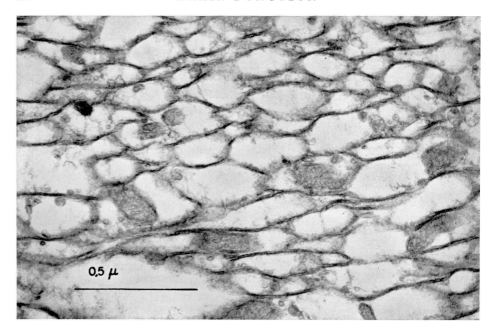

Figure 31. An area of the neuropil adjacent to the one shown in Figure 30. A large number of very small axons are cut in various planes. No synaptic connections are seen. (Vial & Marín, unpublished.)

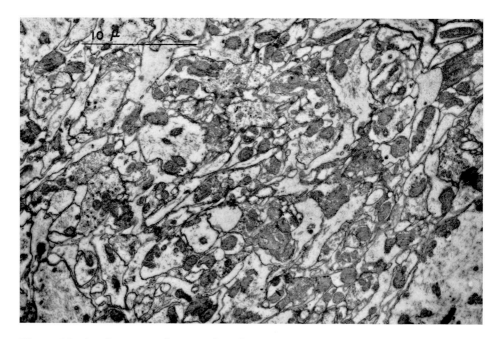

Figure 32. Another area of neuropil with numerous synaptic structures. Small axons are found in discrete areas of the neuropil. (Vial & Marín, unpublished.)

condition. In other words, it is possible to have an axon with Nissl bodies.

Palay: The distinction between dendrites and axons is not a simple one. If we make any generalization, we immediately think of certain exceptions to it. Probably the most consistent definition is the one which Bodian (6) has brought out in the past few months: that the dendrites really are just the receptive region of the nerve cell, and the axon is the effector—that is, the one which carries the impulse to another cell.

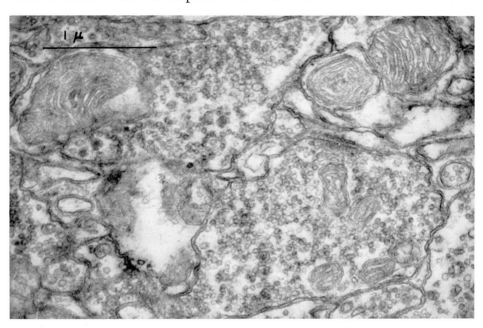

Figure 33. Higher magnification of Figure 32, showing synaptic structures. (Vial & Marín, unpublished.)

The difference between the axons and the dendrites is rather clear in the central nervous system; it is not clear for the dorsal root ganglion. The reason for this is that the dorsal root ganglion is a unipolar cell, without additional processes from the cell body or at least any other processes of any consequence. It has only one major process which then divides; one branch is receptive, the other goes to an effector area. That is the situation in the invertebrates. All of the nerve cells in the invertebrate, or nearly all of them, are unipolar cells, and they make their contacts by means of intertwining axons. I would not expect to find dendrites in the neuropil of the cockroach.

Green: I felt, in connection with Dr. Palay's beautiful presentation, that there are some functional aspects that arise from these very striking connections in the nervous system, particularly with respect to the extremely small space available between neurons.

When recording inside most cells, one sees action potentials and the depolarizing after-potential, thought to be due to a momentary accumulation of potassium outside the neuron. Then there is the after-hyperpolarization, which is thought to be due to the escape of potassium away from the cell so that it is left with a net negative charge. On the rising phase, there is a little notch which indicates the time of firing of the initial segment of the axon. Each of these features seems to me to be of some relevance to the structure seen with the electron microscope.

After seeing the fantastic connections with dendrites in the cerebellum, or in virtually any other group of neurons, one wonders why the trigger region fires first. What concentrates the current flow from the dendrites to trigger the initial segment of the axon?

Next, it may be possible to infer something from these two after-potentials about the behavior of neurons and to see whether, in fact, there is some agreement between morphology and physiological findings. In the squid, Frankenhaeuser & Hodgkin (11) showed the after-potentials could be altered in a predictable way by changing the external potassium of the axon. These changes fitted well with the changes seen when the same axon was fired repetitively, and calculations of potassium extrusion were made relative to the extraneuronal space. In fact, they found that the extraneuronal space was in rather good agreement with the electron microscope findings. That is the situation of a large cylindrical nerve with a sheath around it, with a very small extracellular space and an occasional cleft from it to further spaces within peripheral tissue fluid. This is a situation of very limited space. It only is necessary to stimulate the squid axon at 20 per second to alter the after-potentials in a way predictable from the expected distribution of potassium ions in the three spaces.

I would like to draw a comparison between the action potentials recorded intracellularly from two different types of neuron. One is the hypoglossal neuron, which has many synaptic contacts and branches; one can, therefore, assume rather free extracellular diffusion. The second is the hippocampal motor neuron, which, as demonstrated by Kandel & Spencer (21), has large neuro-neuronal contacts, and shows the depolarizing after-potential. There are extensive areas where one dendrite is apposed to another without actually making synaptic junction, and extensive areas where one soma is apposed to another. This, then, is a situation where two adjacent nerve cells may interact with each other.

I would like to suggest that this situation may play an important role in sensitizing neurons. One neuron may sensitize an adjacent one because of limited space. Conceivably, seizure phenomena may be related to such changes. Whether or not this can have any direct relationship to memory, I do not know, but it strikes me as entirely conceivable that there may be a relation. Perhaps depolarizing a cell leads to changes in axoplasmic viscosity. This might, in turn, establish some different kind of pattern of synaptic contacts on the membrane.

Luco: I want to mention an observation related to what Dr. Green said. He is talking about the possibility of having quite isolated neurons and of some other neurons that are surrounded by the *milieu intérieur.*

We have to think in terms of what we have called the "intimate *milieu intérieur*" (22). That is, according to histological studies, some cells are open to the general *milieu intérieur* and others are quite isolated. If you modify the composition of this intimate *milieu intérieur*, let us say by a prolonged tetanic stimulation, you may obtain a change in the reaction. But if the surrounding *milieu intérieur* is wide open you may have no possibility for this effect. In this case the reaction will not be changed by the past experience of the system.

Green: Yes, I think this is really what I was trying to express. The two situations we were comparing were Ammon's horn and the hypoglossal nucleus. Blackstad & Dahl (5) have recently made measurements in Ammon's horn of how much of the neuron membrane is covered by another neuron. It appears that in this case the soma is almost completely covered and there is a partial covering at the apical dendrite, so that the spaces are small and there are few branches. In the case of the hypoglossal motor neuron, however, we have a neuron which is stellate, with dendrites radiating in all directions and many terminals with many processes between them. Thus, the spaces are branched in just the way that Frankenhaeuser & Hodgkin (11) discussed. These two cases seem to me to form a favorable comparison. It is true that the hippocampus shows post-tetanic potentiation and the hypoglossal nucleus almost none.

Adey: We have measured, with a very sensitive impedance measuring technique, the changes which occur as an evoked impedance transient in the course of the performance of a learned task, and the changes which appear in the impedance transient as this habit is acquired.

I hope to present these data in detail later but mention them here because they show very clearly that it is not until the animal's performance has risen above chance level that these actual conductance changes appear in the brain tissue. If the learned performance is habituated or extinguished, then the conductance changes likewise disappear. With retraining, they will reappear again. I think this is a fairly direct evidence of some ionic shift or change in the distribution of ions in the various tissue compartments, rather than something which could be construed as a change in the afferent aspect of the storage mechanism.

Glaser: Where do you measure the impedance change?

Adey: Within the very restricted volume of hippocampal tissue.

Glaser: You put in two electrodes, close to each other? How far apart?

Adey: It is a coaxial dipole. The effective volume of tissue through which the current is flowing is about three-quarters of a cubic millimeter.

Deutsch: I do not see why this is relevant. I agree that storage takes place somewhere, and you may very well have measurements to show that it does take place before you actually observe overt learning. I would not want to deny this but I do not see why it shows that, if you put various substances in the cat's brain, this necessarily is affecting the process. It seems to me it would leave the interpretation open.

Adey: As to the changes in conductance which we observed, if they are mere chance relationships to the process of acquisition, so then is everything else that one observes with electrophysiological techniques or with any other form of physiological monitoring of the state of the brain. Perhaps you can explain to me why you did not consider that the changes that we observed have any relationship to this acquisition process.

Deutsch: I did not say the changes you observed had no relation to the acquisition process. It is simply that I could not see why your observations enabled us to decide between two rival interpretations.

Thompson: In some lesion experiments of mine, some of which are published (43, 44), bilateral damage involving either the striate cortex or pretectal area (in the case of a visual signal), cingulate cortex, prefrontal cortex, midline thalamic nuclei, hippocampus, septum, lateral hypothalamus, substantia nigra, or the interpeduncular nucleus, grossly interferes with post-operative performance of a conditioned avoidance response. Some of these neural structures undoubtedly are directly concerned with the storage mechanism, while others are more aptly related to emotional, sensory or motor activities. The positive effects obtained from chemical injections, therefore, cannot be indiscriminately attributed to a disturbance of memory until it is known upon what neural sites these chemicals act.

REFERENCES

1. ALLEN, J. M., The properties of Golgi-associated nucleoside diphosphatase and thiamine pyrophosphatase: 1. Cytochemical analysis. *J. Histochem. Cytochem.*, 1963, **11**: 529-541.

2. BARRNETT, R. J., The combination of histochemistry and cytochemistry with electron microscopy for the demonstration of the sites of succinic dehydrogenase activity. In: *Fourth International Conference on Electron Microscopy*, Vol. II (W. Bargmann, D. Peters and C. Wolpers, Eds.). Springer-Verlag, Berlin, 1960: 91-100.

3. BIRKS, R., HUXLEY, H. E., and KATZ, B., The fine structure of the neuromuscular junction of the frog. *J. Physiol.*, 1960, **150**: 134-144.

4. BIRKS, R., KATZ, B., and MILEDI, R., Physiological and structural changes at the amphibian myoneural junction, in the course of nerve degeneration. *J. Physiol.*, 1960, **150**: 145-168.

5. BLACKSTAD, T. W., and DAHL, H. A., Quantitative evaluation of structures in contact with neuronal somata. An electron microscopic study of the fascia dentata of the rat. *Acta Morph. Neerl.-Scand.*, 1962, **4**: 329-343.

6. BODIAN, D., The generalized vertebrate neuron. *Science*, 1962, **137**: 323-326.

7. BUTLER, V. P., BEISER, S. M., ERLANGER, B. F., TANENBAUM, S. W., COHEN, S., and BENDICH, A., Purine-specific antibodies which react with deoxyribonucleic acid (DNA). *Proc. Nat. Acad. Sci. USA*, 1962, **48**: 1597-1602.

8. DE ROBERTIS, E., and VAZ FERREIRA, A., Submicroscopic changes of the nerve endings in the adrenal medulla after stimulation of the splanchnic nerve. *J. Biophys. Biochem. Cytol.*, 1957, 3: 611-614.

9. FARQUHAR, M. G., and PALADE, G. E., Junctional complexes in various epithelia. *J. Cell Biol.*, 1963, **17**: 375-412.

10. Fox, C. A., and BARNARD, J. W., A quantitative study of the Purkinje cell dendritic branchlets and their relationship to afferent fibres. *J. Anat.*, 1957, **91**: 299-313.

11. FRANKENHAEUSER, B., and HODGKIN, A. L., The after-effects of impulses in the giant nerve fibres of *Loligo*. *J. Physiol.*, 1956, **131**: 341-376.

12. FURSHPAN, E. J., "Electrical transmission" at an excitatory synapse in a vertebrate brain. *Science*, 1964, **144**: 878-880.

13. FURSHPAN, E. J., and FURUKAWA, T., Intracellular and extracellular responses of the several regions of the Mauthner cell of the goldfish. *J. Neurophysiol.*, 1962, **25**: 732-771.

14. FURUKAWA, T., and FURSHPAN, E. J., Two inhibitory mechanisms in the Mauthner neurons of goldfish. *J. Neurophysiol.*, 1963, **26**: 140-176.

15. GRAY, E. G., Axo-somatic and axo-dendritic synapses of the cerebral cortex: an electron microscope study. *J. Anat.*, 1959, **93**: 420-433.

16. ——, The granule cells, mossy synapses and Purkinje spine synapses of the cerebellum: light and electron microscope observations. *J. Anat.*, 1961, **95**: 346-356.

17. GRAY, E. G., and GUILLERY, R. W., The basis for silver staining of synapses of the mammalian spinal cord: a light and electron microscope study. *J. Physiol.*, 1961, **157**: 581-588.

18. HERNDON, R. M., The fine structure of the Purkinje cell. *J. Cell Biol.*, 1963, **18**: 167-180.

19. HESS, A., The fine structure of nerve cells and fibers, neuroglia, and sheaths of the ganglion chain in the cockroach (*Periplaneta americana*). *J. Biophys. Biochem. Cytol.*, 1958, **4**: 731-742.

20. JANSEN, J., and BRODAL, A., Das Kleinhirn. In: *Handbuch der mikroskopischen Anatomie des Menschen*, Vol. IV/8 (W. Bargmann, Ed.). Springer-Verlag, Berlin, 1958.

21. KANDEL, E. R., and SPENCER, W. A., Electrophysiology of hippocampal neurons. II. After-potentials and repetitive firing. *J. Neurophysiol.*, 1961, **24**: 243-259.

22. LUCO, J. V., El medio íntimo extracelular. *An. Fac. Med. Montevideo*, 1959, **44**: 351-354.

23. MOSES, M. J., Patterns of organization of the fine structure of chromosomes. In: *Fourth International Conference on Electron Microscopy*, Vol. II (W. Bargmann, D. Peters and C. Wolpers, Eds.). Springer-Verlag, Berlin, 1960: 199-211.

24. NISSL, F., *Die Neuronenlehre und ihre Anhänger*. Gustav Fischer Verlag, Jena, 1903.

25. NOVIKOFF, A. B., and ESSNER, E., Pathological changes in cytoplasmic organelles. *Fed. Proc.*, 1962, **21**: 1130-1142.

26. NOVIKOFF, A. B., ESSNER, E., GOLDFISCHER, S., and HEUS, M., Nucleoside-phosphatase activities of cytomembranes. *Symp. Int. Soc. Cell Biol.*, 1962, **1**: 149-192.

27. PALADE, G. E., An electron microscope study of the mitochondrial structure. *J. Histochem. Cytochem.*, 1953, **1**: 188-211.

28. PALADE, G. E., A small particulate component of the cytoplasm. *J. Biophys. Biochem. Cytol.*, 1955, **1**: 59-68.

29. PALAY, S. L., The electron microscopy of the glomeruli cerebellosi. In: *Cytology of Nervous Tissue*, Proc. Anat. Soc. Great Britain and Ireland. Taylor & Francis, London, 1961: 82-84.

30. PALAY, S. L., McGEE-RUSSELL, S. M., GORDON, S., and GRILLO, M. A., Fixation of neural tissues for electron microscopy by perfusion with solutions of osmium tetroxide: *J. Cell Biol.*, 1962, **12**: 385-410.

31. PALAY, S. L., and PALADE, G. E., The fine structure of neurons. *J. Biophys. Biochem. Cytol.*, 1955, **1**: 69-88.

32. PURKINJE, J. E., Neueste Untersuchungen aus der Nerven- und Hirn-Anatomie. *Ges. Deutsch, Naturforsch. Aerzte Verhandl.*, 1838, **15**: 177-180.

33. RIFKIND, R. A., HSU, K. C., MORGAN, C., SEEGAL, B. C., KNOX, A. W., and ROSE, H. M., Use of ferritin-conjugated antibody to localize antigen by electron microscopy. *Nature*, 1960, **187**: 1094-1095.

34. ROBERTSON, J. D., Cell membranes and the origin of mitochondria. In: *Regional Neurochemistry* (S. S. Kety and J. Elkes, Eds.). Pergamon, Oxford, 1961: 497-534.

35. ROBERTSON, J. D., BODENHEIMER, T. S., and STAGE, D. E., The ultrastructure of Mauthner cell synapses and nodes in goldfish brains. *J. Cell Biol.*, 1963, **19**: 159-199.

36. ROSENBLUTH, J., Subsurface cisterns and their relationship to the neuronal plasma membrane. *J. Cell Biol.*, 1962, **13**: 405-421.

37. SCHMITT, F. O., and DAVISON, P. F., Biologie moléculaire des neurofilaments. In: *Actualités Neurophysiologiques*, 3e sér (A.-M. Monnier, Ed.). Masson, Paris, 1961: 355-369.

38. SIEKEVITZ, P., and PALADE, G. E., A cytochemical study on the pancreas of the guinea pig. V. *In vivo* incorporation of leucine-1-C^{14} into the chymotrypsinogen of various cell fractions. *J. Biophys. Biochem. Cytol.*, 1960, **7**: 619-644.

39. SUTHERLAND, E. W., and RALL, T. W., The relation of adenosine-3′5′-phosphate and phosphorylase to the actions of catecholamines and other hormones. *Pharmacol. Rev.*, 1960, **12**: 265-299.

40. TENNYSON, V. M., Electron microscopic observations of the development of the neuroblast in the rabbit embryo. In: *Electron Microscopy*, Vol. 2 (S. S. Breese, Jr., Ed.). Academic Press, New York, 1962: N-8.

41. ————, Electron microscopic observations of the neural tube of the fetal rabbit. *Anat. Rec.*, 1962, **142**: 285.

42. TENNYSON, V. M., and PAPPAS, G. D., Electronmicroscope studies of the developing telencephalic choroid plexus in normal and hydrocephalic rabbits. In: *Disorders of the Developing Nervous System* (W. S. Fields and M. M. Desmond, Eds.). Thomas, Springfield, 1961: 267-325.

43. THOMPSON, R., Interpeduncular nucleus and avoidance conditioning in the rat. *Science*, 1960, **132**: 1551-1553.

44. ————, Thalamic structures critical for retention of an avoidance conditioned response in rats. *J. Comp. Physiol. Psychol.*, 1963, **56**: 261-267.

45. WARNER, J. R., RICH, A., and HALL, C. E., Electron microscope studies of ribosomal clusters synthesizing hemoglobin. *Science*, 1962, **138**: 1399-1403.

ELECTROPHYSIOLOGICAL PHENOMENA OBSERVED IN SINGLE NEURONS AND NEUROGLIAL CELLS IN CULTURES OF CENTRAL NERVOUS TISSUE*

WALTHER HILD

The University of Texas

Galveston

The results reported here were obtained in collaboration with Dr. Ichiji Tasaki of the Laboratory of Neurobiology of the National Institutes of Health. Without his profound knowledge of electrophysiological techniques as applied to single cells *in vitro* this investigation could not have been performed.

Even though we may reasonably assume that the neuronal population of the central nervous system plays a major role in what we summarily call brain function, it seems equally important to investigate the glial population from all possible angles. Since so little is known about glial function in general and even less about the specific role of glia in conjunction with neurons, every bit of information that we gain may be of importance to our understanding of the intricate mechanisms involved in the general term "brain function". In this connection it is worthwhile to remember that glial cells outnumber the neuronal population by a factor estimated between 10 and 15. This, however, does not say anything about the actual cytoplasmic masses involved; the volumes of the two cell species are very difficult to estimate. We must assume the existence of a very intricate interplay between neurons and glia, but the nature of this interplay is what has to be defined. We cannot continue to be satisfied with the often repeated notion of glial cells as the "supporting elements" for neurons without a thorough explanation of the term "supporting". Does it mean giving simply mechanical support, does it include nutritive functions, does it mean that glia interact with neurons in other ways, or does it also include the possibility that glia may have functions which we are tempted to attribute to neurons only?

One way to elucidate some of these problems is the analytical approach. If it were possible to investigate neuronal and glial properties quite separately, and if one could determine specific characteristics of single, isolated cells, one might be in a better position to theorize about the influences that

* This investigation was supported by Research Grant USPHS NB-03114.

one cell type may exert upon the other. Tissue culture preparations provide the material for this type of investigation. Such preparations, when they are suitably flattened, contain essentially isolated neurons which have lost their synaptic connections that existed *in vivo*. It is therefore possible to investigate actually on the cellular level and to find out what a neuron or various parts of a neuron may be capable of accomplishing if there is no influence exerted upon it by other neurons, as in the *in vivo* condition.* The same is true for glial cells. The great advantage of this approach is that, if we investigate electrophysiological properties of these cells, we can operate at all times under visual control since we actually see the cell and many of its details, and we can place microelectrodes with great accuracy on various parts of a neuron—perikaryon, axon, dendrites—and record from these parts or stimulate the cell at various sites. All speculation on where the electrode is located is eliminated by this technique. The same technical possibilities exist for glial elements and any other cell types present in cultures of central nervous tissue, e.g., connective tissue cells derived from blood vessel walls or meninges.

The technique of maintaining central nervous tissue *in vitro* has advanced to such a degree that this material can be kept alive and functioning for several weeks or months. Details of the methods differ somewhat in various laboratories, and every investigator has certain preferences as to the composition of nutrient media, the type of culture vessels, or the manner of preparing and cleaning glassware. The results are astonishingly similar. The main fact that one has to recognize is that under certain conditions (namely when the explant is sufficiently spread) an explanted piece of central nervous tissue is almost reduced to its component parts. This means that an explant of cerebral or cerebellar cortex or any nuclear region does not behave any more in the same way as it behaved in the intact organism. This is due to the lack *in vitro* of an ordering principle or a superior coordinating force. Intercellular connections are greatly reduced, synapses that existed *in vivo* are broken up or degenerate as a result of rather extensive cell damage during explantation, and cells do separate more and more from each other as a result of migratory activities exhibited by connective tissue and glial cells. The desirable result of these and several other changes occurring in the explants is the flattening of the tissue fragment to such a degree that transillumination and recognition of details in the microscope become possible. In other words, the originally cubic explant must be transformed into a rather flat membrane-like specimen because thicker layers are quite useless for the observation of details with phase contrast optics. If the membrane-

---

* *Dr. Hild's note:* At the time of proof reading in August 1964, all my statements concerning loss of synaptic connections *in vitro* have to be regarded *cum grano salis,* since we have been able to demonstrate, with the electron microscope, the existence of synaptic connections in our cultures (2). The electrophysiological results reported here, however, remain correct and do not lose any of their significance except for the possibility that what we considered as spontaneous firing in some neurons may have been due to excitation by another (presynaptic) neuron.

like condition is not reached, and if the explant remains rather thick, the intercellular relations may be entirely different, and synapses may be maintained. Such preparations are not suitable for experiments on the cellular level, and it is quite impossible to position electrodes within them with any degree of accuracy.

In Figure 34 a microscopic field from a culture of cat cerebellum is shown. Among glial cells one observes a relatively large neuron which is still recognizable as a Purkinje cell. Several ramifications of the dendritic stem can be seen at one side and the axonal origin at the other. Finer dendritic branches are not clearly discernible in the meshwork of glial cells and processes. The cell shows other peculiarities: Nissl substance in the form of cloudy patches, mitochondria, and larger phase-dense cytoplasmic inclusions. A sex chromatin nucleolar satellite reveals that this cell is derived from a female animal.

Figure 35 shows a field traversed by axonal processes which have acquired a myelin covering during their life *in vitro*. The formation of myelin sheaths *in vitro* indicates that there is no total reduction to the cellular level but that there still exists a degree of collaboration and interaction between cells, since myelin deposition presupposes an interplay between

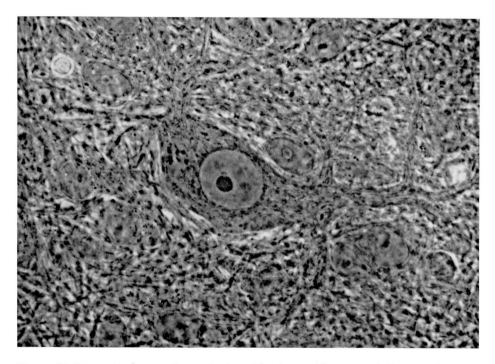

Figure 34. Living Purkinje cell in a 21-day old culture of kitten cerebellum. Rod-shaped and filamentous mitochondria are recognizable in the perikaryon and the dendritic ramifications. A heterochromatic nucleolar satellite indicates that this cell is derived from a female animal. Nissl substance is represented by cloudy patches at the periphery of the cytoplasm. Phase contrast. (From Hild, 6.)   × 1425

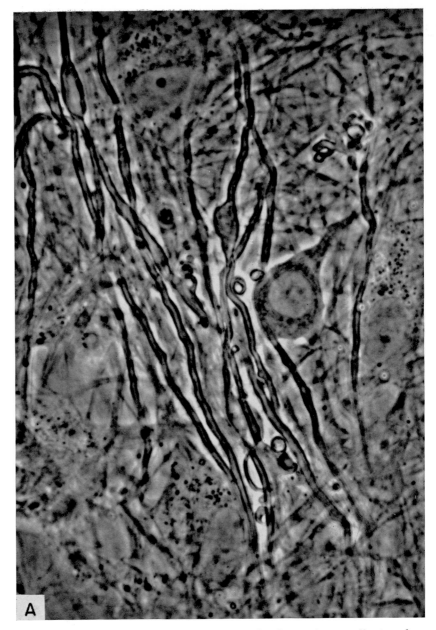

Figure 35A. Myelinated axons in a 17-day old culture of rat midbrain; phase contrast. The same field is shown in Figure 35B (polarized light).   × 1500

axoplasm and surrounding glial cells. The true myelin nature of these sheaths is evidenced by their birefringence and typical staining properties.

Figure 36 presents a microscopic field which gives an impression of the degree to which the separation of cells can proceed without loss of interaction. There are three neuronal cell bodies visible in which one can distinguish various processes. In one cell the origin of the axon can be seen,

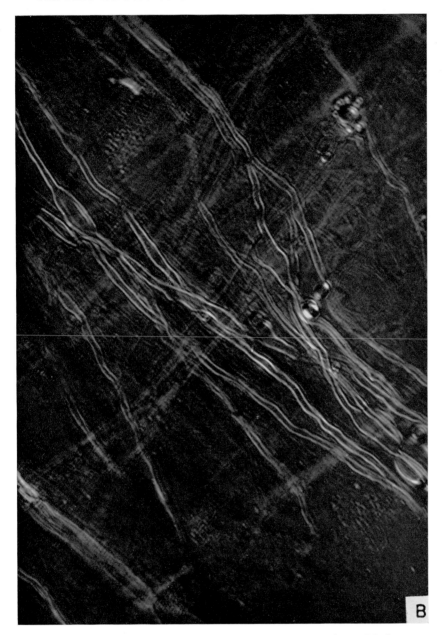

Figure 35B. Same field as in Figure 35A, shown in polarized light.

and this axon is covered by a myelin sheath beginning a short distance away from the perikaryon. The background is made up of glial cells. In many places, cells and their extensions are in contact with each other but there are also many areas completely free of cellular substance. In the electron microscope these areas would appear as large empty spaces between the cells. It is this type of explant that is most useful for our present purposes because everything is clearly visible, and there can be no doubt con-

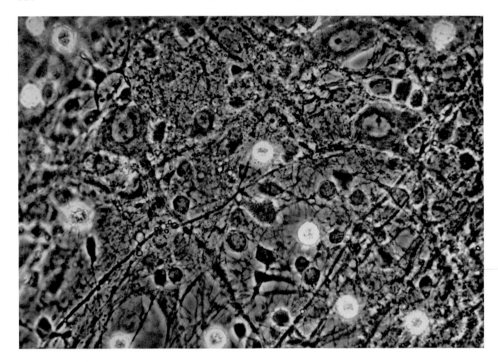

Figure 36. Living neurons and glial cells in thinly spread portion of a 15-day old culture of rat cerebellum.   × 600

cerning the exact location of a microelectrode placed in or on one of these cells.

The next figure (No. 37) gives some idea about the mechanical and electrical set-up used in our investigation. The culture is mounted in a chamber on the microscope stage in such a way that the electrodes can be inserted through the open sides of the chamber. The electrodes are moved by means of micromanipulators and are positioned under visual control. Microelec-

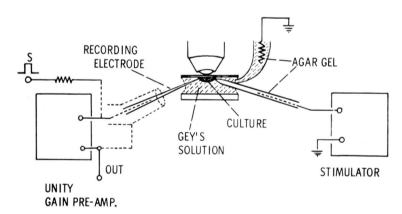

Figure 37. Simplified diagram illustrating the experimental arrangements. (From Hild & Tasaki, 8.)

trodes used for recording intracellular potentials had a tip diameter of less than 1 micron; they had a resistance of about 4 to 10 megohms. As far as the connections of the electrodes and the stimulating and recording equipment are concerned, I refer to our previous description (8).

Upon penetration of a neuronal cell body by a recording microelectrode (Figure 38), resting potentials of about 50 mV were usually observed. Immediately after successful penetration and stimulation through the recording microelectrode, action potentials could be evoked (Figure 39). Their amplitude was mostly between 50 and 70 mV and their duration was 1.5 to 3 msec. at 36° C. At 26° C. the duration was somewhat longer; however, because of the wide variability among various neuronal types, it was difficult to make exact comparisons of the results obtained at different temperatures. Initially the action potentials followed the all-or-none principle. However, after deterioration of the impaled neuron or after faulty penetration, variable responses with no clear-cut threshold were observed. After injury to the cell membrane by the electrode, the morphological characteristics of neurons changed progressively; in all such cases a simultaneous fall in the resting potential was observed. After withdrawal of the electrodes from the cells, there occurred demixing of cytoplasmic constituents and a granular disorganization of the whole cell (Figure 40). In this condition neither resting nor action potentials could be recorded from such cells.

Figure 38. Microscopic field showing neurons in a 25-day old culture of cat cerebellum. One neuron is impaled by a hyperfine recording electrode. This picture illustrates the electrode arrangement for records such as shown in Figure 39. (From Hild & Tasaki, 8.)

A   B   C

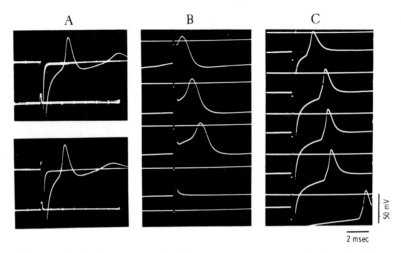

2 msec

Figure 39. Action potentials of neuron somata recorded with intracellular microelectrodes, as shown in Figure 38. Stimuli were 0.05-
0.1 msec. in duration, repeated 7-8 shocks per second, and delivered
through recording microelectrode. Records were taken from cultures
of cat cerebellum: 20-day old (A), 12-day old (B), and 14-day old
(C). Threshold intensity for outward current pulses was approximately 7×10^{-8} amp. in this case. Records A and B were obtained
at 26° C. and records C at 36° C. (From Hild & Tasaki, 8.)

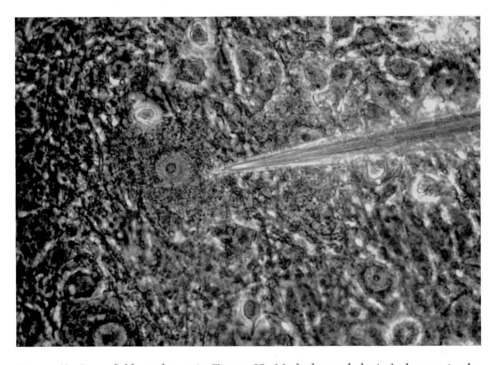

Figure 40. Same field as shown in Figure 38. Marked morphological changes in the
two neurons indicate cell death after cells had been impaled and electrode was withdrawn. The same changes could be observed when a dendritic stem or an axon was
torn. Sometimes this occurred inadvertently in cells lying in the vicinity of neurons
which were under investigation. (From Hild & Tasaki, 8.)

We attempted on several occasions to introduce microelectrodes into large dendrites. They are far more sensitive to injury caused by penetration. However, on two occasions we could record action potentials of 30-40 mV in amplitude from the main stem of dendrites, approximately 50 μ away from the cell soma.

If one approaches a neuron with a microelectrode and brings the tip of the electrode close to the cell membrane without penetrating it, one can see in many cases small action potentials at irregular intervals in the absence of artificial stimulation. The amplitude of such spontaneously fired potentials, recorded extracellularly, was usually less than 0.5 mV. Their frequency varied from about 15 per second to one per several seconds. Three examples of spontaneously fired action potentials of neuron somata are shown in Figure 41. The most common configuration of these potentials was, as in

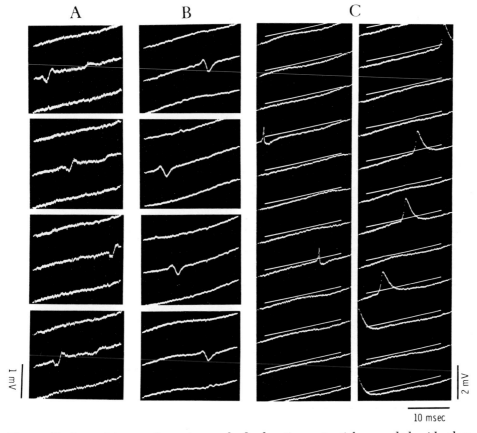

Figure 41. Several types of spontaneously fired action potentials recorded with glass microelectrode making contact with surface of neuron somata. Upward deflections represent positivity of recording electrode. Records were taken from neurons in cultures of rat cerebellum: 13-day old (A), 10-day old (B), and 15-day old (C). Sudden change in configuration of recorded action potentials in record C was induced by pushing recording electrode harder against neuron surface. Oscilloscope sweep was the same for all records; deflection sensitivity for B was the same as that for C. (From Hild & Tasaki, 8.)

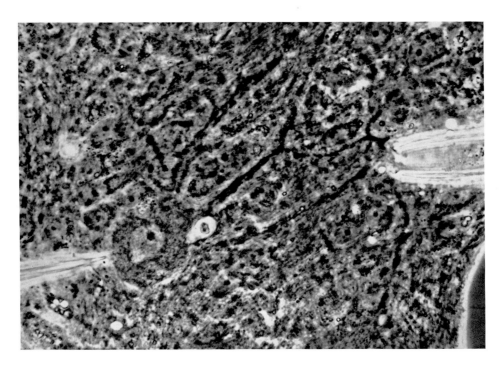

Figure 42. Neuron with three branching dendrites in a 22-day old culture of rat cerebellum. The origin of the axon is not clearly visible in this microphotograph because it was out of the plane of focus at the lower left circumference of the cell body. Hyperfine recording electrode is close to cell membrane. Larger stimulating electrode is located close to dendritic branch. This picture illustrates the electrode arrangement for records such as shown in Figure 43. (From Hild & Tasaki, 8.)

record B in the figure, of the positive-negative type. The last column in Figure 41 shows an example of injury discharge caused by extensive pressure applied to the cell membrane by the recording electrode. The absence of a negative phase in such an injury discharge is an indication of the loss of a physiological response at the site of recording.

Figure 42 represents a neuron in a cerebellar culture. A recording electrode is positioned close to the cell body and a larger stimulating electrode lies close to one of the dendrites of the same cell. With such an experimental arrangement attempts were made to stimulate one of the dendrites when

》》》→

Figure 44. Neuron showing axon (Ax) and dendritic main stem in a 12-day old culture of cat cerebellum. Hyperfine recording electrode is pushed against dendrite. Stimulating electrode is located close to cell soma. This picture illustrates electrode arrangement for records such as shown in Figure 45. By moving stimulating electrode to dendrite, one would have the arrangement shown in the diagram in Figure 46, left side. (From Hild & Tasaki, 8.)

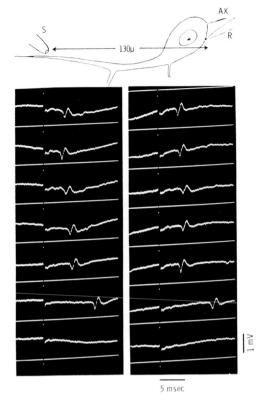

Figure 43. Extracellularly recorded action potentials of a neuron soma evoked by stimulation of a dendrite in a 14-day old culture of rat cerebellum. Arrangement of stimulating and recording electrodes (both extracellular) is shown in diagram above; only clearly discernible dendrites are shown. S: Stimulating electrode; R: recording electrode; AX: axon. Stimulating pulses were 0.1 msec. in duration, and intensity at threshold was in the order of 25 μamp. (From Hild & Tasaki, 8.)

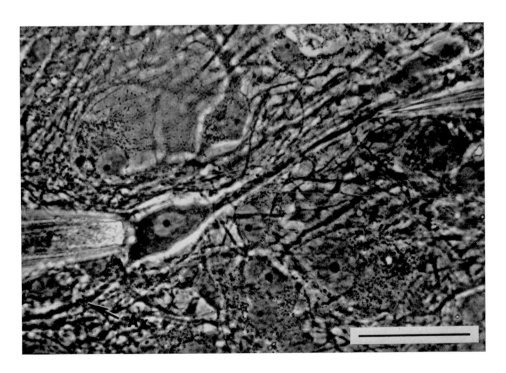

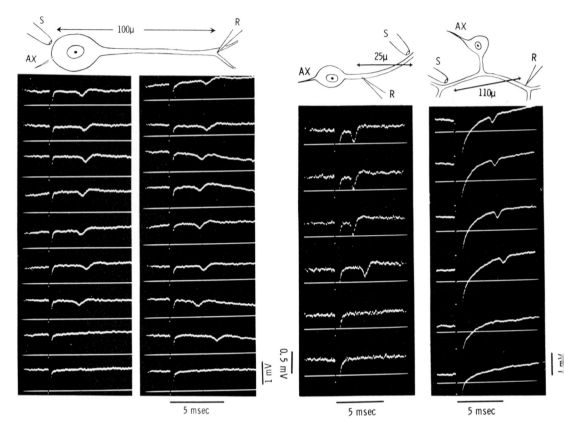

Figure 45. Action potentials recorded at the surface of a dendrite on stimulation of the neuron soma. Stimulation shocks were 0.05 msec. in duration, approximately 20 μamp. at threshold, and repeated at a rate of 7/sec. Arrangement of electrodes (S: stimulating; R: recording; both extracellular) and major, clearly discernible portion of dendrite are shown. Ten-day old culture of cat cerebellum. (From Hild & Tasaki, 8.)

Figure 46. Action potentials evoked by stimulation of dendrites and recorded from the surface of dendrites. Arrangement of stimulating (S) and recording (R) electrodes is shown in diagram. Short, downward deflections of current trace show intensities of stimulating current pulses, 0.1 msec. in duration. (From Hild & Tasaki, 8.)

the recording microelectrode was picking up spontaneous action potentials from the surface of the soma. It was found by this technique that, whenever there were spontaneously fired action potentials in a neuron soma, stimulation of the dendrite could induce similar responses in the same soma (Figure 43). Evoked action potentials could also be recorded from neuron somata which were not firing spontaneously. Stimulating current pulses applied to the dendrite were cathodal and were repeated at a frequency of 5 to 20 times per second. Whenever a neuron had a long, clearly discernible dendrite it was possible to move the stimulating electrode along the dendrite. The latency increased with the length of the intervening portion of the dendrite.

In Figure 44 another experimental arrangement of the electrodes in relation to a cerebellar neuron is shown. Here the recording electrode is brought
close to a dendrite, whereas the larger stimulating electrode lies in the vicinity of the cell soma. In a number of neurons it was possible to record spontaneously fired action potentials with a glass pipette microelectrode pushing
gently against the surface of a dendrite. In order to pick up extracellular
responses from the dendrite, it was necessary to dimple slightly the surface
of the dendrite. In dendrites showing a spontaneous discharge of impulses,
it was simple to demonstrate that stimulation of the neuron soma could
elicit dendritic responses of the same configuration (Figure 45). Dendritic
responses to stimuli applied to the soma were always all-or-none. When a
long portion of a dendrite was discernible it was possible to record dendritic
responses evoked by stimulation of the same dendrite. An example of this
type of experiment is furnished in Figure 46, left. In neurons with long
bifurcating dendrites (Figure 47), we were able to stimulate one branch of
a dendrite and record from the other branch of the same dendritic stem.
Figure 46, right, shows an example of observations made with this type of

Figure 47. Neuron showing branching dendrite and origin of axon in a 19-day old
culture of cat cerebellum. The cell body seems somewhat distorted because it lies outside of the focal plane of the dendrites, on which the camera was focused. A hyperfine recording electrode is applied to a Y-shaped branching of the dendrite. The larger
stimulating electrode is located close to other branches of the dendrite. This picture
illustrates the electrode arrangement for records such as shown in Figure 46, right
side. The bar represents 50 μ. (From Hild & Tasaki, 8.)

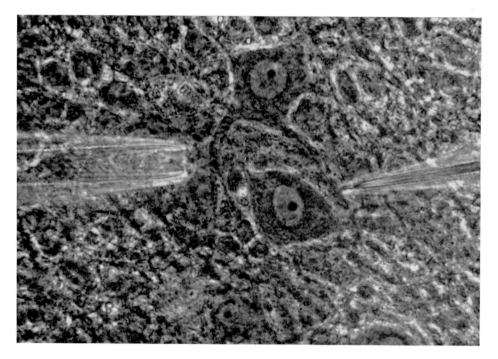

Figure 48. Two neurons in a 25-day old culture of rat cerebellum. One cell displays three clearly visible dendrites and an axon. Hyperfine recording electrode and larger stimulating electrode are placed close to two different dendrites. (From Hild & Tasaki, 8.)

electrode arrangement. In neurons with two or more dendrites arising from the soma (Figure 48), we had no difficulty in demonstrating propagation of impulses initiated by stimulation of a dendrite to a different dendrite via the neuron soma.

Next to neurons there is a very numerous population of glial cells in the central nervous tissue. What we know about neuroglia is astonishingly little as far as their normal significance is concerned, even though the pathologists have gathered a considerable body of information on glia under abnormal conditions. Neuroglia are easily maintained *in vitro* and represent a favorable subject for experiments with microelectrodes.

We do not pretend to be able to distinguish *in vitro* the various glial cell types which we conventionally group together under the headings of astrocytes and oligodendrocytes. There are many transitional forms to be seen in cultures as well as in histological preparations. Therefore, we like to deal with "glial cells" only, especially because the measurable electrical activities that can be recorded with great regularity are the same in all forms.

In Figure 49 a microscopic field with neuroglial cells is represented. One cell is impaled by a recording microelectrode. A larger stimulating electrode is located in the close vicinity of the impaled cell. The introduction of

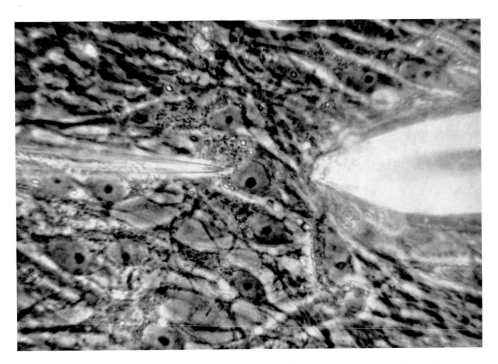

Figure 49. Photomicrograph showing living glial cells and the position of the electrodes during the recording time. The field is close to the center of the culture, where the cells have retained their original net-like connections to some extent. A recording electrode is introduced into one glial cell, whereas a larger stimulating electrode is located near the cell. At times the stimulating electrode was used as an injection pipette by means of which a limited amount of isotonic KCl could be placed in the immediate vicinity of the cell. (From Hild, Chang & Tasaki, 7.)

a microelectrode into a glial cell presents no difficulties at all and is very easy in comparison with the impalement of a neuron. Upon penetration into a glial cell by a recording microelectrode, D.C. potential shifts of 50-70 mV were obtained (Figure 50). The resting potential of glia was reduced when the potassium concentration in the medium was increased. This experiment was performed in a number of cases by using a relatively large micropipette for the injection of isotonic KCl solution directly in the vicinity of an impaled glial cell under observation (Figure 50). By electrical stimulation the resting potential of a glial cell could be reversibly lowered. The extent of lowering depended, within a certain limit, upon the intensity of the stimulus. The time required for the restoration of the resting potential was three to five seconds. When two or more shocks were given at short intervals they gave rise to a summated potential change. Cathodal stimuli were more effective than anodal ones, although both cathodal and anodal stimuli could produce a response.

Although the resting potential of glia could be maintained in some cases over a period of several minutes, it was generally impossible to maintain it for longer than 40 to 60 seconds. Since it is well known that the surface membrane of glial cells *in vitro* is not stationary and that the cell may migrate or sometimes show pulsating movements, it is not surprising that the recording microelectrode did not stay in the cytoplasm indefinitely, and that the resting potential of the impaled cell fell to a low value within about one minute after penetration. When the recording microelectrode no longer picked up the full-size resting potential, no D.C. potential shift could be observed after stimulation. This is proof that stimulation brings about a

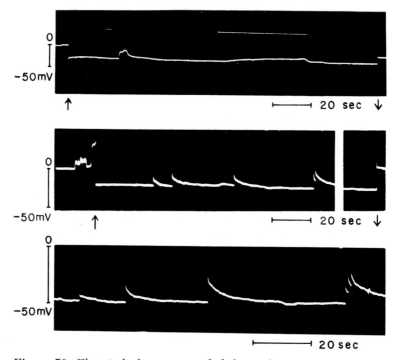

Figure 50. Electrical changes recorded from glia *in vitro* on a continuously moving film. Zero (0) is the potential level of the recording electrode when it is in the external fluid medium. The moment of impalement of the cell by the recording electrode is indicated by an upward arrow, that of its removal from the cell by a downward arrow. *Top:* shift of resting D.C. level caused by the introduction of KCl solution into the immediate vicinity of the cell; horizontal bars represent the KCl inflow, the first one was rather fast and the second quite slow. *Middle:* responses of glial cells to electrical stimuli; the shock intensities across the stimulating electrode with a resistance of 2 megohm were (from left to right): −50 V (showing almost no response), −80 V, −100 V, +100 V, and + and −100 V at one-second intervals. *Bottom:* similar responses to the shocks of: +40 V, −40 V, −50 V, and three −40 V at one-second intervals. Note the difference in response magnitude to the cathodal and anodal shocks of the same intensity and the summated responses to the rapidly repeated stimuli. (From Hild, Chang & Tasaki, 7.)

fall in the resting potential and that we are not dealing with an artifact in the recording system caused by the flow of a strong current.

The electrical response that can be elicited from glial cells by stimulation is characteristic for glia only. Other cell types which are present in our cultures, such as macrophages or fibroblastic cells or white blood cells, were also examined. None of these cell types had a resting potential comparable to that of glia. Observable resting potentials in the mesodermal cells investigated were between 5 and 15 mV, and electrical stimuli, even if they were rather strong (up to 50 μamp. through a 10 μ stimulating electrode), never did produce any shift in the low D.C. potentials of those cells. Negative results were also obtained with cells of various cell strains *in vitro*.

That glial cells *in vivo* have a similar property has been shown by Tasaki & Chang (11). Therefore, we can exclude the possibility that our findings are specific for this cell type in culture only.

Another characteristic reaction of glia to electrical stimulation should be

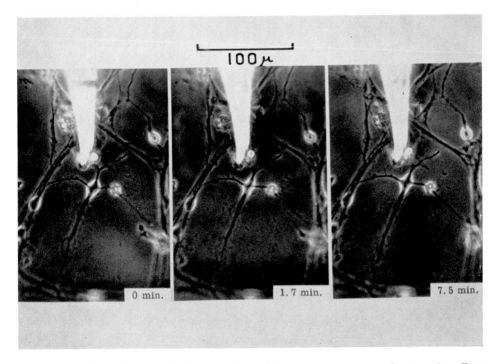

Figure 51. Three selected film frames of a motion picture sequence showing the effect of electrical stimulation on an isolated glial cell. Eight-day old culture of kitten cerebellum; phase contrast. A stimulating electrode with a tip diameter of about 12 μ is located at a distance of about 24 μ from the cell body. Immediately before stimulation the cell body shows normal size and configuration; 1.7 minutes after stimulation the cell body is markedly contracted and the processes slightly thickened due to shifting of cytoplasm from the cell body into them; 7.5 minutes after stimulation the cell body has expanded again and regained its original configuration. The total duration of this contractile response was 7.5 minutes, which represents one of the shortest times observed. The average was about 11 minutes. (From Chang & Hild, 3.)

mentioned here. This phenomenon has been reported in 1959 in collaboration with Chang (3). It consists of a slow contraction upon stimulation. The contraction phase lasted about 1 to 2 minutes and the relaxation phase was 7 to 13 minutes (Figure 51). The low membrane resistance of the glial cells may be regarded as one factor which favors graded responses. The membrane resistance of glia could be measured with relative ease because it was fairly simple to introduce two microelectrodes into one cell from opposite sides. Figure 52 shows the electrode arrangement for such an experiment. Passage of a pulse of constant current through one of the intracellular microelectrodes is expected to bring about across the plasma membrane a potential variation which is a measure of the membrane resistance. Such potential variations can be measured directly by the use of a second intracellular microelectrode. An example of the records obtained in this way is shown in Figure 53. In six measurements in which the fall in the resting potential upon the second penetration was less than 10 mV, the membrane resistance of a glial cell of about 15 μ diameter was found to be from 0.5 to 1.4 megohm. There was no detectable difference in the membrane resistance between cells from cat brain and those from rat brain. The resistance of the glial cell membrane was calculated to be 3 to 10 ohm per cm^2. This figure is only 1/100 to 1/500 of the generally accepted value of the membrane resistance of various neurons.

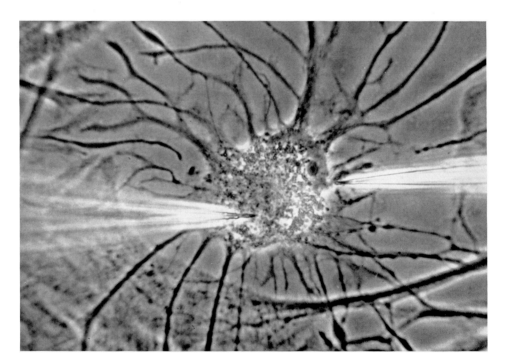

Figure 52. A flatly spread-out glial cell somewhat isolated in the outer zone of the outgrowth from a 35-day old culture. The picture illustrates the electrode arrangement for recording events as shown in Figure 53. (From Hild, Chang & Tasaki, 7.)

It does not appear proper at this time to draw any conclusions as to the possible significance of our findings. Many more data are needed to establish a basis for the formation of functional hypotheses. But we are confident that with this approach, namely the analysis of single cell potentialities, we may obtain information that will complement knowledge gained with quite different methods, information that may lead to a better understanding of mechanisms involved in brain function.

Green: I would like to raise one point. You can show that the dendritic membrane is excitable in tissue culture, but it does not seem to me to follow that it is excitable in the brain, because in the latter case we have a neuron with quite different surface contacts. I think Grundfest & Purpura (5) introduced the term "electrically inexcitable" for dendrites, having in mind the subsynaptic membrane, and the eel electroplaque as a model. I wonder if it is generally agreed that these membranes are electrically

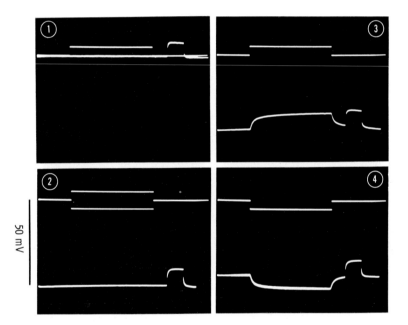

Figure 53. Variations in the membrane potential of a glial cell produced by the passage of constant current pulses. Both current and potential electrodes were intracellular. Record 1 was taken when both microelectrodes were immediately outside the cell membrane. In record 2 the potential electrode was introduced into the cell; there was a shift of 52 mV in the recorded potential; two records with different current polarities were superposed. In record 3 the current electrode was also introduced into the cell. In record 4 the polarity of the current was reversed. Applied current shown by upper oscillograph beam was 7×10^{-9} amp. in intensity and 5 msec. in duration. Rectangular deflection of 1 msec. duration of potential trace is measure of resistance of potential electrode (about 7 megohm). (From Hild & Tasaki, 8.)

inexcitable or, if it is not, that they are electrically unexcited under normal conditions, which is somewhat different.

I would suggest it may well be in the case of the very slow propagation rates which you have demonstrated with Tasaki (8) that, once there is an enclosure of glial and synaptic processes, the space-constant of the membrane might be so altered that no propagation would occur at all. I would like to hear other views, also, on this point.

Hild: I have pointed out that the situation *in vitro* is very different from that *in vivo*. In the flat portions of the explant there are no synaptic connections maintained. However, since the dendrites contain the same neuroplasm and cell membrane as the perikaryon, it is not clear why these two portions of the same cell should behave differently. In the *in vivo* situation, it is estimated that 35 per cent of the perikaryal and dendritic membranes is covered by synaptic endings. It is possible that this may account for quite dissimilar membrane properties from those *in vitro*.

Luco: In the system you used, there must have been denervation, because several days had passed before you tested. It is well known that denervation produces an important modification of the membrane excitability to chemical stimuli. So excitability, not present normally, could reappear under these conditions. Therefore, in your case the prolonged and complete denervation may also result in a change of electrical excitability.

Magoun: I think Dr. Luco is making reference to the sensitization of denervation, as pointing to a contrast between the tissue in the culture and that within the intact system.

Luco: Are all dendrites electrically inexcitable or do we have to consider the possibility that there are two kinds of dendrites? As far as I remember, in the hippocampus it has been shown that the classical histological dendrite can be stimulated electrically.

Green: I think you can say they are excitable.

Hild: I cannot quite follow your discussion. You refer to a dendrite in the hippocampus from which recordings are made. How can you be sure that the electrode records from a dendrite?

Green: There is practically no alternative because you can mark the position of your recording electrode and show that it is exactly in the unbranched area of the stria radiatum. There you have only the choice of the finely myelinated fibers, which can be detected separately (particularly deeper in the molecular or the large apical dendrites); there are no cell bodies. The layer is over one millimeter thick, so it is not difficult to be sure that you are recording in the appropriate region.

Adey: It would be interesting to know if Dr. Hild saw the other side of the picture in the form of graded, slow electrotonic activity in the vicinity of, or actually recorded within, the dendritic structures.

Hild: No; we never saw anything of that nature. All responses from undamaged dendrites followed the all-or-none principle. To record extracellularly from a dendrite is quite easy, as can be seen in the illustrations; to record from the inside of a dendrite is quite difficult because of the high vulnerability of the dendrites that we encountered in our efforts to impale them. Only on three occasions did we obtain clean intradendritic responses, but unfortunately we do not have the records on film.

Luco: How do you test for the all-or-none feature if you have not enough time? You need to increase the intensity of the stimulus to be sure that the response is all-or-none. You may have just a graduated response.

Hild: An all-or-none response is verified quite simply. One first places the stimulating electrode in the desired position. Then one approaches the dendrite with the recording electrode while stimulating currents are applied. As soon as a response is picked up, that is, when the recording electrode is very close to or touching the dendritic membrane, one increases or decreases the intensity of the stimulating current in order to establish threshold. If one decreases below threshold, the response is no longer noted. If one increases the intensity of the stimulating current above threshold, that does not change anything in the response.

Adey: This preparation would seem an ideal one to test another enigma for those of us who work with whole brain. What about volume conductor effects? How far away does the electrode have to be?

Hild: The recording electrode has to be very close to the cell membrane, certainly not more than 1 μ away, possibly closer than that. The stimulating electrode should not be further from the cell than about 5 to 8 μ.

Brazier: But the field of your stimulus is rather difficult to define. It is a stigmatic electrode with a reference. Where is the anode?

Hild: The reference electrode is in the culture fluid that fills the chamber in which the culture is suspended. It consists of a large Ag-AgCl electrode enclosed in a glass tubing having a tip diameter of 3-4 mm.

John: You mentioned the possibility that these glial zones functionally represented the extracellular space that we have been measuring. This might be an ideal preparation in which to put in radioactively labeled form those substances usually considered to be extracellular, and then do high resolution radio-autography, with suitable emulsion overlaying. With the available resolution, it would seem that one could answer once and for all this disturbing question of where is the extracellular space.

Hild: I doubt that our material is very suitable for this purpose. The original close packing of cells as it exists *in vivo* is lost, and there are intercellular spaces of tremendous dimensions.

Green: May I make one more comment in that connection? In making studies on the hypoglossal nucleus recently, we were using a bridge circuit which allowed us to measure membrane capacity and membrane resistance.

In exploring through this hypoglossal nucleus, we frequently encountered resting potentials which were not accompanied by spikes. Since we were in the hypoglossal nucleus, we could drive most neurons antidromically.

On encountering resting potentials without spikes, we tested with current pulses to see if the cells were excitable, and what exactly was going to happen. We found three types of phenomena. One was that when we applied a depolarizing current pulse, we obtained an ordinary action potential; in other words, it was a silent cell that we had penetrated. The second one was very possibly a glial cell: it turned out to have a low membrane resistance, as you have described, and a very long time-constant, compared with those you have shown; the membrane resistance was higher than you described, of the order of 100,000 to 500,000 ohms, but the time-constant was of the order of 20 to 30 msec., which is tremendously long compared to a neuron or to your values. Third, it seems that, occasionally, when poking an electrode down in this way, a large negative potential that looks initially like a resting potential is seen; it may be as large as 80 mV but, in fact, it turns out to be due to a blocking of the pipette. It is not due to grid current, however. The recording resistance is increased.

Hild: In our experiments we have never seen a negative potential when the electrode tip was blocked. A very sure sign of blocking, for instance by a collagen sheet, was that the resistance of the electrode rose suddenly and very significantly. Under these circumstances it was impossible to introduce the electrode into a cell without seriously damaging it. Potential shifts which could have possibly been mistaken for resting potentials were never observed under these conditions.

Green: I suppose the effect is due to a charge, and the charge is leaking slowly away through the input impedance of the probe. However, we could never make the cells, of whatever the type they were, fire with current pulses of the magnitude we felt we could deliver, which was not very high.

Hild: You mean you did not employ a current pulse that was considerably higher than that needed to stimulate a neuron? The pulse has to be rather large in order to evoke this response.

Green: Our current was considerably higher than that needed to stimulate a neuron but not necessarily high enough for glia, to judge by the stimuli which Tasaki (8) gave. We gave a maximum of about 7×10^{-9} amp., which is not very large. It is plenty for the hypoglossal motor neuron, however.

Nirenberg: Can you dissociate single cells one from another and grow them in suspension, rather than on a flat surface?

Hild: I have not tried this method, and I think it is not very promising with central nervous tissue. Neurons and glial cells with all their processes are so much intertwined that mechanical separation is impossible. Equally unsuccessful is the enzymatic method. Nakai (9) reported in 1956 on survival of embryonic spinal ganglion cells which were isolated by teasing and proteinase treatment. These cells survived for 10-14 days. This, however, does not mean that they were healthy individuals. Neurons *in vitro* apparently do need a critical concentration of glial cells around them for their well-being. This assumption stems from the observation that in our cultures we invariably see neuronal degeneration in areas of extreme flattening. In multilayered areas neurons and glia may be maintained for several months, whereas in monolayers the cells retain a healthy appearance for only two to three weeks. In spite of numerous attempts, nobody thus far has succeeded in propagating a cell line from glial explants.

Adey: In connection with the interrelation between the neuron and the glial surround, do you have any thoughts about the relationship of the glial distribution near the axon hillock, as this may determine either some metabolic symbiosis or, in the physiological sense, may contribute to the excitability changes during the impulse initiation?

I seem to recall having seen electron micrographs—I think maybe some of Dr. Green's—in which the hippocampus, in the vicinity of the axon hillock, had a very dense accumulation of glial cells. Was that correct?

Green: I do not know quite what you are referring to. The nonmyelinated segment has glial processes on it.

Adey: Is there anything characteristic about the distribution of glia in that region?

Green: I would not have thought so.

Sinsheimer: I gather, from what you said, Dr. Hild, that if you made a hole in a neuron, that pretty well finished it. Is this true out on the axon, too?

Hild: We are dealing here with a strange phenomenon. In preparing our explants we injure probably all neurons contained within a tissue fragment of about one millimeter in diameter, yet a great number of them do survive, establish themselves *in vitro* and regenerate their processes. In this condition neurons seem to be very vulnerable. If one injures them at this stage they die within a few minutes.

Sinsheimer: Are there no cases where you get processes growing out of nerve tissue culture?

Hild: Yes, there is tremendous regenerative activity in certain types of cultures. I have measured axonal processes of more than 20 mm in length originating from a fragment that was no larger than about 1 mm at the time of explantation.

Bickford: I wonder if these findings might explain something that has puzzled us for a number of years about stimulation in man, in areas that, by all calculations we could make, were in white matter. Are there enough glial cells there so that possibly some of the sustained afterdischarges which we have recorded in white matter could arise in the glial cells? Do you feel this is possible?

Hild: I do not know. Possibly the time-course of the response could have given you some clue.

Bickford: This is a rhythmic discharge; it is not just a single response. May I ask Dr. Adey what he might think about it?

Adey: This is very thin ice for me. Is it not unlikely that the glial cells establish an organization which will permit anything in the nature of either a local or propagated phenomenon that we would interpret as electrical afterdischarge? My personal views are that the glial function is merely to modulate the activity of the neurons, and not to initiate a conductive process such as Galambos proposed (4). Can you imagine in cerebral white matter the sort of organization that could be achieved between glial cells and axons? This is a different situation entirely from the one where glial cells surround and envelop neuronal cells in a nucleus or in the cortex. In subcortical white matter, we are considering a trunk fiber-conducting system which is interrelated with glia, but in which there are few, if any, neurons.

Bickford: Have you had occasion to be puzzled by discharges from an electrode which you thought should be in white matter?

Adey: I am afraid our own studies relating to the impedance changes in epileptic discharges have been strictly in gray matter.

Magoun: May I ask Dr. Bickford if he ever had an opportunity to stimulate or record from an astrocytoma or any other kind of glioma during clinical neurosurgery in man? From this current presentation, it may be desirable to pay more attention in the future to the opportunities for the study of glial function in clinical electroencephalography.

Mishkin: Is there any period during the life of this culture, say before the migration of the cells took place, when it might be possible to study synaptic characteristics of transmission, or is that completely impossible?

Hild: That is entirely possible. Shortly after explantation, and also later in thicker layers, synaptic connections should be maintained—at least to a certain degree. However, such synapses, if they exist, thus far could not be observed in the living condition. They cannot be approached with microelectrodes under visual control and therefore are only of secondary importance to us at this moment, since we are trying to operate with the exclusion of all guesswork as to the position of the electrodes. However, we are hopeful that in the near future we may be able to visualize living synapses in retinal cultures. The preliminary observations are promising.

Feindel: I wonder if Dr. Hild could tell us about the possibility of studying the effects of repetitive stimulation on these nerve cells. Does he think they are in good enough shape for him to see any changes going on in the character of the cell, as one continues to stimulate and presumably, say, exhaust it? Has that been done at all?

Hild: No, we have not tried to exhaust neurons by repetitive stimulation. There is no reason why this could not be done as long as the electrodes remain extracellular. Anyway, during our investigation we did not recognize any exhaustion phenomena. I do not recall the longest period during which we stimulated and recorded from one particular neuron, but certainly repetitive stimulation for about five minutes did not produce any exhaustion.

Morrell: I believe Dr. P. D. Wall has reported contacts made between neurons and muscle cells which appear to be differential.

Hild: I know of these experiments. I have tried myself, and I have closely followed the experiments of others, to establish neuromuscular connections *in vitro.* The results were quite negative. While it is true that nerve fibers growing out from an explant will reach a conjoint muscle culture and even grow in between the muscle fibers, there has never been observed a functional connection because no true junctions are established.

John: I wonder if you might have a suggestion for us. We were very interested in the possibility of obtaining neural culture in which we could explore some of our conditioning ideas.

It seemed to us that working with vertebrates was perhaps less advantageous than using an animal like the planarian which has a tremendous capacity for regeneration. One of our students, Barry Hoffer, started doing tissue culture work with *Planaria* and encountered a difficulty which was also reported by Buchsbaum in a recent paper (1).

The old German biologists reported that if they cut a planarian in fifths or sixths, it would regenerate. Buchsbaum would cut up the planarian, take a very small piece, put it into a culture dish, and it would start to grow. Then, he said, it started to make a sheet, and would go along quite well. Suddenly it would fold back on itself and draw into a globule, and one could see under the microscope that the cells which seemed to be of a certain type dedifferentiated and redifferentiated. On some occasions a planarian grew out of this very small explant.

One can get what seems to be thriving sheets of tissue, only it is exceedingly difficult to keep these static. One can identify a number of different kinds of cells in the culture; put down a cylinder on what looks like a homogeneous group, float it up with trypsin, and make up a clone which starts out being essentially one kind of cell.

As this is cultured over a couple of days, it changes and is again many different kinds of cells. It has a tremendous capacity for differentiation, which I think may be quantitatively different from what seems to be the case in the higher species. Unfortunately, we cannot keep it stable.

Hild: To keep a continuous culture absolutely "stable" is almost impossible. All cells will finally undergo a certain degree of change. However, there are cell types in which these changes are minimal and there are others in which changes are very considerable. The last group comprises, for instance, most of the cell strains. One example is the HeLa strain of which Rose (10) has recently published a ten-year survey. Owing largely to unknown factors, even cloned strains do develop cells of very different shapes and sizes, and more than that, their chromosomal patterns change very considerably, too. On the other side of the scale are such very slowly changing cells as neurons and glia. Neurons do not multiply at all. Their changes are limited to certain transformations of their outer form due to withdrawal or degeneration of some of their extensions and the development of others. Glial cells are capable of mitotic division *in vitro,* but not to such an extent as to overcome or even compensate for the loss of cells that occurs in these cultures. Cultures of nervous tissue, therefore, are not proliferating systems but can be maintained only for several months. Nobody as yet has succeeded in making subcultures or passages of nervous tissue. I do not know what I should recommend as far as your problem is concerned.

REFERENCES

1. ANSEVIN, K. D., and BUCHSBAUM, R., Observations on planarian cells cultivated in solid and liquid media. *J. Exp. Zool.*, 1961, **146**: 153-161.
2. CALLAS, G., and HILD, W., Electron microscopic observations of synaptic endings in cultures of mammalian central nervous tissue. *Zschr. Zellforsch. mikr. Anat.*, 1964, **63**: 686-691.
3. CHANG, J. J., and HILD, W., Contractile responses to electrical stimulation of glial cells from the mammalian central nervous system cultivated *in vitro*. *J. Cell. Comp. Physiol.*, 1959, **53**: 139-144.
4. GALAMBOS, R., A glia-neural theory of brain function. *Proc. Nat. Acad. Sci. USA*, 1961, **47**: 129-136.
5. GRUNDFEST, H., and PURPURA, D. P., Inexcitability of cortical dendrites to electric stimuli. *Nature*, 1956, **178**: 416-417.
6. HILD, W., Das Neuron. In: *Handbuch der mikroskopischen Anatomie des Menschen*, Vol. IV/4 (W. von Möllendorff and W. Bargmann, Eds.). Springer-Verlag, Berlin, 1959: 1-184.
7. HILD, W., CHANG, J. J., and TASAKI, I., Electrical responses of astrocytic glia from the mammalian central nervous system cultivated *in vitro*. *Experientia*, 1958, **14**: 220-221.
8. HILD, W., and TASAKI, I., Morphological and physiological properties of neurons and glial cells in tissue culture. *J. Neurophysiol.*, 1962, **25**: 277-304.
9. NAKAI, J., Dissociated dorsal root ganglia in tissue culture. *Am. J. Anat.*, 1956, **99**: 81-129.
10. ROSE, G. G., The morphological diversity of Gey's Strain HeLa after ten years in tissue culture. *Texas Rep. Biol. Med.*, 1962, **20**: 308-337.
11. TASAKI, I., and CHANG, J. J., Electric response of glia cells in cat brain. *Science*, 1958, **128**: 1209-1210.

PLASTICITY OF NEURAL FUNCTION IN LEARNING AND RETENTION*

J. V. LUCO
Laboratorio de Neurofisiología
Universidad Católica de Chile
Santiago

During the last three years our laboratory has been interested in an electrophysiological approach to what may be called the neural basis of plasticity. Now I would like to summarize some of the results obtained, and I would like to discuss the interpretation and the hypothetical basis of our research, since this work is not yet published.

It may be useful to start by discussing the meaning of plasticity. William James said: "Plasticity, in the wide sense of the word, means the possession of a structure weak enough to yield to an influence, but strong enough not to yield all at once . . . the nervous system seems endowed with a very extraordinary degree of plasticity of this sort" (11).

The definition proposed by Konorski (13) is, to us, a confusing one. The distinction made by this author between excitability and plasticity characterizes the former property by acute and reversible changes produced by a stimulus, and the latter by permanent and irreversible changes. But the terms are not antinomies, because, in order to be plastic, the system has to be excitable.

We consider plasticity of the central nervous system as its quality of being versatile. This versatility is an intrinsic potentiality that can be brought into effect by the experience of the individual. It is a property of the very nature of the nervous system, present during all its developmental existence. The effect of this property can be recognized by a change in the behavior of the organism or by a modification of the reactions of some of its systems.

Should a trace be left by a past experience, plasticity would mean the possibilities opened by having such a trace. At present we are able to report only some physiological activity which may be interpreted as a manifestation of such a trace—not the trace itself.

* This investigation has been carried out in collaboration with Dr. Adolfo Davidovich and Dr. Leonidas Aguilar, with support through grants from the John Simon Guggenheim Memorial Foundation of New York and the Gildemeister Foundation of Chile. Our current research is aided by grants from the U. S. Air Force Office of Scientific Research (grant AF-AFOSR 62-387) and the Rockefeller Foundation.

We know several physiological instances where a trace remains after the event is over. These can be divided into two groups; to begin with a definition of the problem, we may consider two possible influences of a neuronal trace: decrease of the potentiality of the system, and its increase (Table 13).

Neuronal traces left by fatigue cannot be considered really plastic phenomena, for they do not increase the possibility of a better adaptation. Post-tetanic potentiation is an example of what we mean by an increase of potentiality. We define plasticity as those properties that leave a trace that in some way means a better adaptation in the future.

TABLE 13

Decreases Potentiality		Refractory Period. Fatigue
	Short-lasting	Facilitation Inhibition
Increases Potentiality	Medium-lasting	Post-tetanic potentiation Post-tetanic effect on spontaneous activity
	Long-lasting	Habituation Conditioning Learning

A critical analysis of theories of learning and conditioning under the name of "trace theory" of memory was advanced by Gomulicki in 1953 (7). In recent years, some of these theoretical considerations have been partially excluded. There are many references (the last one I know of is by Mauro and Rosner, quoted by Lorente de Nó, 14) stating that memory persists after long-lasting total cessation of circulation of impulses in cortical chains of neurons. When I attended the meeting on Brain Mechanisms and Learning in 1959 at Montevideo (4) I was, therefore, surprised to hear the opinion expressed that the accepted theory for an understanding of a long-lasting process was the reverberating circuit, for it was already known that learned behavior persists after suppression of this neuronal activity.

Now, it is not correct to say that this circulation of impulses has nothing to do with the beginning of memory, with the installation of the process of memory, but it is not the process itself.

There are other hypotheses that are becoming outdated. A working hypothesis, to be considered pragmatically acceptable, should last a relatively short period. This is the case of the regrowth theory. At the same conference, Fessard & Szabó (5) stated that the regrowth of new axon terminals to form new synapses was being left out because of lack of experimental evidence.

New interpretations have been suggested in order to answer the two old questions of what is the trace and where is it located. Regarding the first question, the biochemical and the biophysical approaches seem to provide the dominant concept at the present time. Regarding the second question, we have to consider, in addition to the neuron, the glia as a possible locus where the trace can be held.

Turning now to our experiments, we have sought a simple structure which could give *in vitro* electrical activity that might be correlated with the already known processes of plasticity. A paper by Pumphrey & Rawdon-Smith (16) suggested to us the isolated ganglion of the cockroach as a suitable preparation.

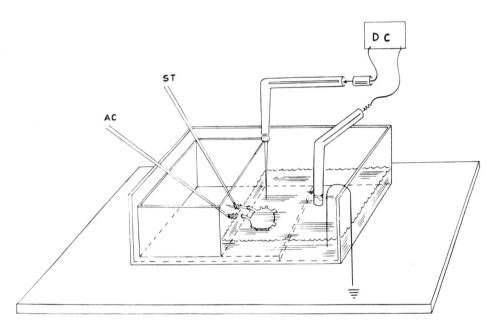

Figure 54. Diagram of experimental arrangement for recording the activity of a ganglion *in vitro*. AC: extracellular electrodes recording from fibers; DC: intracellular electrodes recording from the ganglion; ST: stimulating electrodes in the connective tissue. (J. V. Luco & L. Aguilar, unpublished.)

The sixth abdominal and the metathoracic ganglion of the *Blatta orientalis* were used. Figure 54 illustrates *in vitro* experiments we have done. Several afferent fibers were stimulated, and activity in one efferent fiber was recorded. In some cases a population of efferent fibers was observed. In another group of experiments, intracellular potentials from the ganglion cells were recorded. At the same time, Dr. A. Davidovich, in our laboratory, has studied the process of habituation in the intact cockroach.* The correlation of both types of investigation is part of our plan.

The method used by Davidovich for the intact cockroach is illustrated in Figure 55. The abdomen of the cockroach is fixed with glue. All the legs

---

* Unpublished data.

are free. The electrodes are just under the sclera, to get some muscle reaction or leg reaction. In some experiments, the cercal nerve was isolated
for the placing of a stimulating electrode. In others, lights, air puffs, or
sound from a loudspeaker were used for stimulation.

Returning to the studies of the ganglion *in vitro,* we studied carefully
each of the different responses observed. Some of these responses are well
known, of course (see Roeder, 17), but we systematized their study. Figure
56 illustrates what we call the *servile response.*

The servile response, as the word suggests, is the one in which the ganglion behaves as would be expected until it becomes fatigued. I am not as
sure now as I was some years ago that I know what fatigue is.

If a ganglion is stimulated at a rate of one per second or five per second,
it gives a constant response. But in this preparation, as is clear from Figures
31, 32, 33, the neuropil is a complicated system, full of axo-axonal synapses.
If the stimulation is prolonged, fatigue results, of course. This is shown in
Figure 56 in another way: it is interesting to note the lengthening of the
latency until the spike finally disappears.

Bickford: Would you tell us what you are stimulating and recording?

Luco: We stimulate the nerve tracts that connect one ganglion to the
other. We use the third thoracic ganglion because the third leg of the cockroach serves its most important motor system: the most important behavior

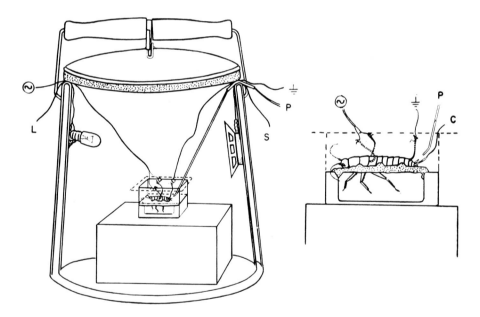

Figure 55. Diagram of experimental arrangement for recording muscle activity
in the intact cockroach. Cockroach fixed in place as shown at right. L: Light
stimulation; S: sound stimulation; P: path of air stimulation; C: electrical stimulation of the cercal nerve. The preparation is isolated in a closed container.
(A. Davidovich, unpublished.)

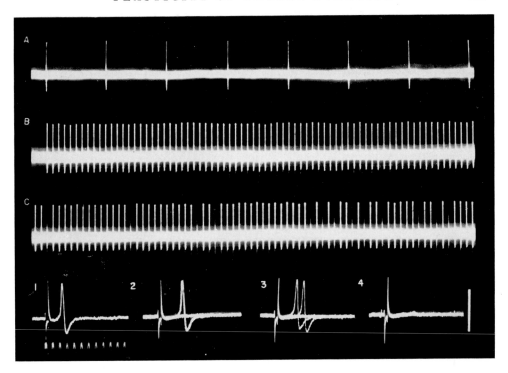

Figure 56. The servile response; cockroach abdominal ganglion *in vitro*. Stimulating electrodes on cercal nerve, recording electrodes on abdominal nerve cord. All recordings from the same preparation. A: Stimulation at 5/sec.; B and C: stimulation at 50/sec. *Below:* 1, 2, 3, and 4 are recordings taken at 0.5, 1, 2.5, and 4 seconds respectively after onset of 50/sec. stimulation. Calibration mark at right: 0.5 mV for all the records. Time-marker: 2 msec. for records 1, 2, 3, and 4. (J. V. Luco & A. Davidovich, unpublished.)

for the cockroach is that for survival, and for survival it must be able to run away. We record from one of the nerves of the third pair of legs. These are mostly mixed nerves. We are recording here from the motor fibers and quite frequently from a single unit.

In the experiment recorded in Figure 57, we stimulated as just described. All of the recent history of the ganglion *in vitro* has to be taken into consideration when analyzing the response. On the first application of the stimulus, one unit gives two responses, as can be seen in Figure 57. With very low frequency of stimulation, say one pulse every two or three seconds, each stimulus evokes a single response and this can be obtained indefinitely. But if the rate is accelerated to five per second, the response follows as far as the second stimulus but fails to be evoked by the third, fourth, and so on (Figure 57). Therefore, we have called this activity the *labile response*. A response may be obtained some time later, as shown at the eleventh stimulus in Figure 57D.

Why does the response disappear? Some years ago one might have said this is fatigue. But were this indeed fatigue, increasing the frequency of stimulation should increase the lack of response. But this is not what happens. With a shift of stimulus frequency from 5/sec. to 50/sec., there is no response to the first stimulus, but after this there is at first a response to each stimulus until, later on, it disappears because of fatigue (Figure 57E). So, there is a condition here, an experimental situation where, in a simple system, something other than fatigue must cause the response to disappear.

Figure 58 illustrates the third category of response, the *intratetanic response*. In some preparations there is no response if the stimulation rate is 1/sec., 5/sec., or 10/sec., but stimulation at 20/sec. evokes a response (Figure 58). The response illustrated started some time after the tetanus was applied. Probably, in order to evoke a response, it is necessary to produce some summation. Figure 58 also shows the response to a stimulation at 50/sec.

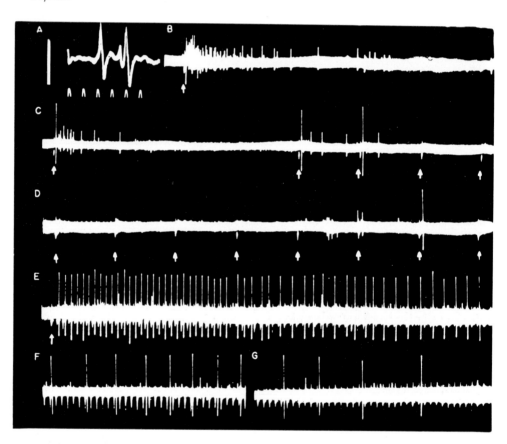

Figure 57. The labile response; preparation as in Figure 55. A: Recording, at a fast sweep-speed, of response to the first single stimulus; time-marker: 2 msec.; B: response to the first of a series of three stimuli at 0.5/sec.; C: first arrow indicates the third stimulus of the series initiated at B, second to fifth arrows mark the first four stimuli of a series at 5/sec. lasting 30 seconds; D: continuation of the series at 5/sec.; E: the arrow marks shift from the 5/sec. to a 50/sec. stimulus rate, which continues throughout this record and records F and G. A lapse of two seconds separates E from F, and F from G. (Luco & Davidovich, unpublished.)

Figure 59 illustrates the fourth and the fifth types of response. In the experiments illustrated, the preparation was stimulated tetanically before recording. The following can be observed with three stimuli at 5/sec.: what we called the intratetanic response, the classical afterdischarge and the delayed response. The fourth type of response, the *afterdischarge*, has not been specifically studied by us. It appears in many of the experiments we have done (see Figures 59, 60 and 70) and it is mentioned here just to complete the systematization.

Figure 60 is another example of the *delayed response*. In this case, the stimulus was given every ten seconds and lasted for one second. The afterdischarge appears only after the stimuli numbered 1, 2, 7, 8, 9 and 10. This type of response can be present in the absence of any classical afterdischarge, and it can be absent when afterdischarge is present. Thus, we can see the two different reactions of this same unit: the afterdischarge and the delayed response. The delayed response can be summated with previous delayed responses.

The sixth type of response is what we have called the *natural response* (15). This is illustrated in Figure 61. A tetanic stimulation at 100/sec., applied to the abdominal cord, produces in one efferent fiber of the metathoracic ganglion of the cockroach a peculiar activity. This starts only after several stimuli have been given. The discharge frequency of this response increases from its beginning until it reaches a maximum and then declines. The time elapsing from the beginning of the tetanic stimulation to the onset of the response has been called the "utilization period". If the tetanic stimulation is shorter than this utilization period, no response is recorded (Figure 61B). Once the response starts, it follows its own evolution regardless of tetanic duration. In other words, it behaves like an all-or-none phenomenon. When the stimulus reaches a certain thresh-

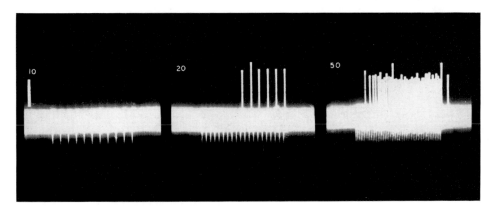

Figure 58. The intratetanic response; cockroach metathoracic ganglion *in vitro*. Stimulating electrodes on abdominal cord, single efferent unit recorded extracellulary. Tetanic stimulation lasting for one second at 10, 20, and 50 stimuli per second. Calibration: 1 mV. (Luco & Davidovich, unpublished.)

Figure 60. Delayed response; preparation as in Figure 58. Twenty tetani of one-second duration were given at 9-second intervals (as shown in abscissa, 1 to 10). Each mark indicates presence of the same unit spike during inter-tetanic periods. Column A: number of order of each tetanus in the series; column B: frequency of tetanic stimulation; column C: number of spikes appearing during application of tetanic stimulation (impossible to count during tetani at 50/sec. because other units interfered). Abscissa: time in seconds. Marks at lower left: afterdischarge. (Luco & Davidovich, unpublished.)

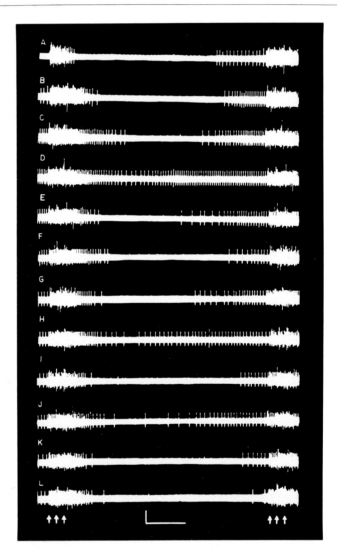

Figure 59. Afterdischarge and delayed responses; preparation as in Figure 58. Record taken after several tetanic stimulations. From A to L, continuous recording. Arrows indicate the application of three stimuli at 5/sec. The second series of three stimuli on each row is shown again at the beginning of the following row. Calibrations: 1 mV and 1 sec. (Luco & Davidovich, unpublished.)

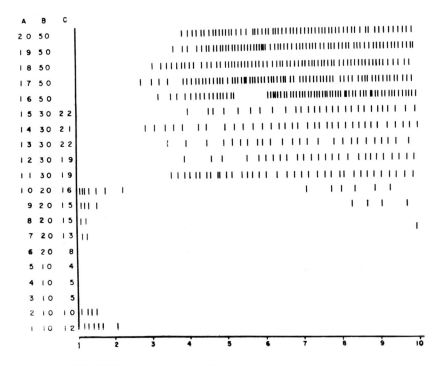

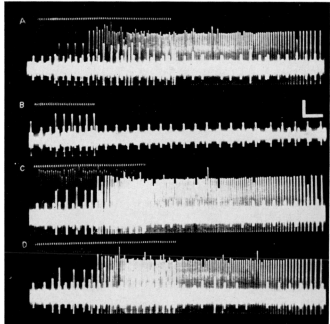

Figure 61. The natural response; preparation as in Figure 58. The dotted line indicates onset and termination of tetanic stimulation at 100/sec. A, C, and D show effect of tetani of longer duration than utilization period; B shows effect of tetanus of shorter duration than utilization period. Series shown in chronological order. Calibrations: 0.5 mV and 0.1 sec. (Modified from Luco, 15.)

old, the complete response is discharged. The threshold in this case includes, as a further parameter, the utilization period. Figure 61 includes the results of tetanic stimulation of three different durations; when these are longer than the utilization period, the response remains unaltered.

Thompson: In these *in vitro* experiments, are the appendages attached to the motor tract you are recording from? Do you have any kind of muscle system attached to your preparation? Is there any movement in the preparation?

Luco: No, the nervous system preparation is completely isolated. The only movement is of Ringer, with oxygen and 5% CO_2, flowing very slowly over the *in vitro* preparation.

I want to insist on this natural response. This may have a hypothetical meaning in relation to the problem we have here. Something is potentially present in the system and can be released by a sequence of stimulation, as shown in Figure 61. Let us analyze the response a little more.

The utilization period is a function of the frequency of stimulation, as demonstrated in Figure 62. The higher the frequency, the shorter the period of stimulation needed.

We have also been able to study, on some occasions, the effects of a very rapid repetitive stimulation, as charted in Figure 63. Here the stimuli were given for 1.5 seconds with 1.5 seconds of interval between bursts; in this case the response declined, and the utilization period was prolonged until no response was obtained. In other words, just to give it a name, we think that this is a "fatigue" of the natural response.

Let us go back to the beginning. What is plasticity here? Why am I describing these experiments that seem so far from the brain and from RNA? Well, first of all, I would not try to localize plasticity. Anatomical localization in neurophysiology is always dangerous. I will just try to analyze these six types of response in regard to the possibility of a versatility, of a change, dependent on the past.

Is the servile response plastic? It is in some ways. In most species it can be modified by past experience, as happens in post-tetanic potentiation. In our preparations it is not plastic because we have not been able to observe post-tetanic potentiation in cockroaches. It was also shown by Fielden (6) that no post-tetanic potentiation appears in crustacea. The author relates this lack of potentiation to the fact that, in crustacea, the synapses are axo-axonal. In the cockroach they are supposed to be of the same type. As Granit has said, post-tetanic potentiation may be considered as the simplest example of memory.

We have observed versatility in the labile response reaction. The cessation of the response to the stimuli at a frequency of 5/sec. was, by definition, not the result of fatigue, because a shift from 5/sec. to 50/sec. in the stimulation frequency caused the response to appear again. Continuation of stimulation at 50/sec. evoked classical fatigue. This observation resembles the process

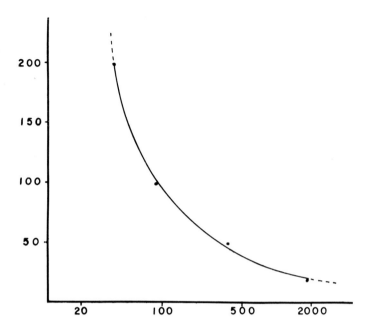

Figure 62. Utilization period as a function of stimulation frequency; preparation as in Figure 58. Abscissa: time in msec.; ordinate: frequency of stimulation. (Luco & Aguilar, unpublished.)

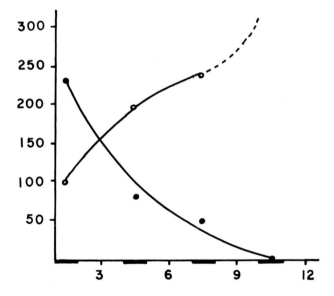

Figure 63. Effect of tetanic stimulation at short intervals; preparation as in Figure 58. Open-circle curve indicates the duration of the utilization period; full circles indicate the number of spikes in each response. Abscissa: time in seconds; bars indicate duration (1.5 sec.) of each tetanus at 100/sec. Ordinate: msec. for opened circles and number of spikes for full circles (Luco & Aguilar, unpublished.)

of dishabituation caused by increasing the frequency of stimulation. Davido-vich has shown habituation in the intact cockroach, and dishabituation by increasing the frequency of stimulation (Figures 64 and 65). It probably is not fatigue because, as already emphasized, if the stimulus is increased in frequency, the reaction reappears. So, in a ganglion *in vitro* we have ob-served a phenomenon similar to the habituation and dishabituation seen in the cockroach *in vivo*.

The intratetanic response is an activity that can be modified by past experience. Repeated bursts of tetanic stimulation may cause the release of activity between bursts that lasts for several minutes. This activity, when it reaches a certain frequency, may interfere with the intratetanic response.

In the case illustrated in Figure 66, there was no spontaneous activity in this unit over a long period. When stimulated at 100/sec., activity appeared. Thus the application of tetanic stimulation changed the whole pattern of the intratetanic response.

The repetition of a tetanic stimulation results in a change of delay of each of the repetitive responses to each tetanus. Each one of the spikes compos-ing the response suffers a different degree of modification in its delay.

When the intervals between bursts of tetanus are about one second long, and when these are given as a long series, a "fatigue" prolongs the delay of all spikes, until responses can no longer be recorded. These repeated tetanic

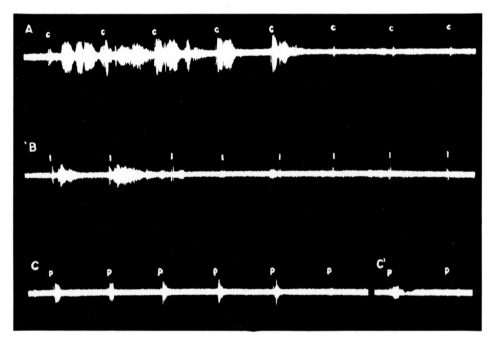

Figure 64. Habituation in the intact cockroach; preparation as in Figure 55. Effect of stimuli repetition. A and B, continuous recording. At A, the cercal nerve was stimu-lated with pairs of electrical shocks (c); at B, light stimulation (l) was applied; at C, a puff of air (p) was used to stimulate. (A. Davidovich, unpublished.)

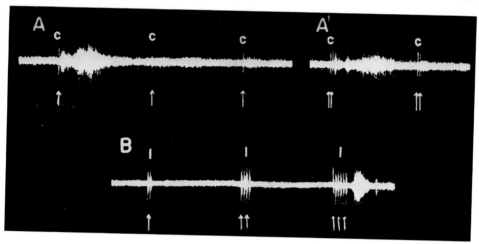

Figure 65. Dishabituation in the intact cockroach; preparation as in Figure 55. At A, a long series of single-shock stimuli were applied at the cercal nerve (c) every ten seconds; at A′, two shocks instead of one were given every ten seconds; at B, the response to light stimulation (l) had disappeared, but three light stimuli produced a reaction. (A. Davidovich, unpublished.)

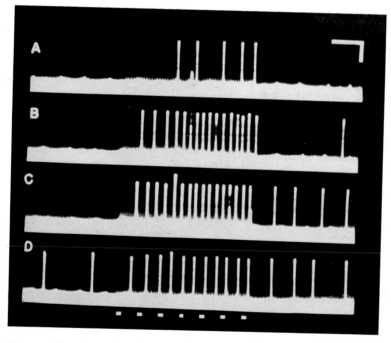

Figure 66. The intratetanic response during spontaneous activity; preparation as in Figure 58. Tetanic stimulations lasting for one second (marked by dotted line) were given at nine-second intervals. At A, stimulating frequency was 50/sec.; at B, C, and D, 100/sec. (Luco & Davidovich, unpublished.)

stimulations may leave an activity of the responding unit lasting for several minutes.

The activity recorded outside the period of stimulation may be considered as an afterdischarge or as a "spontaneous" activity induced by stimulation. In the experiment illustrated in Figure 67, the spontaneous activity started at very low frequency after the 14th tetanus, and then the frequency increased. Just before the 20th tetanus one discharge was present (Figure 67 I, D.) and during this tetanus the pattern of discharges changed from that expected (Figure 67 II). In other words, the reaction changed after several stimulations had been applied. This change can be interpreted as being caused by the spontaneous activity released by previous stimulation.

The first spike observed during the application of the 23rd tetanus (Figure 67 II) is probably a "spontaneous" discharge. The intratetanic response is again an unexpected pattern of discharge.

The extrapolation of this type of reaction offers an interesting speculation. The frequency of the spontaneous activity may probably reach a certain statistical value. In such a case, the pattern of discharges during tetanic stimulations will also be statistically the same. This interpretation implies three different stages: (a) before the spontaneous activity appears, the pattern follows a certain law (Figure 67 II, tetani 1 to 19); (b) a stage in

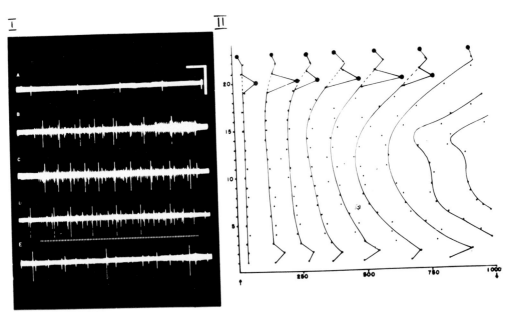

Figure 67. I. The intratetanic response; preparation as in Figure 58. A: Recording without stimulation; 23 tetani at 100/sec. lasting one second each (marked by dotted lines) were then given at 4-second intervals; B shows the first tetanus; C, the 13th tetanus; D, the 20th tetanus of the series; E: activity recorded one minute after the last tetanus. Calibrations: 1 mV and 0.12 sec. II. Abscissa: time in msec.; ordinate: number of order of tetanus. The intratetanic spike of the unit yielding the largest response shown at I was plotted in II. (Luco & Davidovich, unpublished.)

which the pattern of discharge is unpredictable because of the continuously changing frequency of the spontaneous discharges; (c) the discharge may again follow an expected pattern as a consequence of stabilization in the frequency of spontaneous activity.

This phenomenon may seem to offer a neurophysiological mechanism for a short-lasting memory. However, as in the case of the reverberating circuit theory, it implies the necessity for a continuous activity. But, as mentioned above, memory persists after total and long-lasting cessation of nerve impulses.

Furthermore, the past may leave a trace in the autogenic generator that modifies the frequency of spontaneous activity triggered by the stimulation; or the past activity may cause a lowering of the threshold for the release of this activity. Should such be possible, this memory trace outlasts the cessation of electrical activity.

The experiment shown earlier in Figure 59 is another case of plasticity, of versatility. The delayed response is also liable to change because of previous stimulation. The silent period observed between the afterdischarge and the onset of the delayed response implies the need for the building up of some mechanism. The repetition of the stimulation that causes the delayed response results either in an increase of its amplitude ("cumulative summation") or in a tendency to disappear, following a waxing and waning course.

In our scheme, delayed responses are one of the expressions of an autogenic activity triggered by stimulation and having some characteristics similar to the behavior of the whole organism in the process of learning.

Bickford: What happens to the delayed response if you randomize the stimuli, instead of having them predictable? By this means one could determine whether this is a delayed or an anticipatory response.

Luco: We have given the stimuli at constant intervals, not randomized.

John: I think Dr. Bickford's question is directed at whether something comparable to what is called cyclic conditioning is found here. If stimuli are presented at regularly spaced intervals, one can get a response which is based on the time interval. The question is, do you get this delayed response if the intervals between stimuli are irregular?

Luco: I think this is very important, because we are sure that the cockroach reacts to the timing. In some cases we have observed the following: if the stimulus is repeated several times, say every 10 or 20 seconds, and then suddenly is stopped, the response may be present at approximately the expected time of stimulation. This has been observed in the intact cockroach by Davidovich.

In experiments *in vitro* this possibility has also arisen. We did not study this reaction during the delayed response, but we have observed it when studying the natural response.

In Figure 68, two units are seen giving the natural response. The unit with the larger spike was active throughout the entire experiment. Before the preparation was stimulated, no spontaneous natural response was present at all. The stimulus was then applied many times at regular intervals. In Figure 68C, a spontaneous natural response of the same unit appears and the stimulus, applied (regularly every ten seconds) after this activity had started, did not modify the response. After the series of stimulations stopped, some spontaneous natural responses were observed.

Figure 69 illustrates an experiment in which we gave a very short tetanic stimulation, that is to say, shorter than the utilization period; no response was present (Figure 69A). When the stimulation was repeated several times, a natural response appeared, as shown in Figure 69B. It can be conceded that there is summation here, because the stimuli being applied were subthreshold. If a one-second tetanus is applied instead of a half-second one, the same unit gives a response (Figure 69C). In this case, the response is somewhat different from the one in Figure 69B. Usually the natural response is practically the same.

Figure 70 refers to another reaction that can also be considered as a versatile effect. Stimulation at 10/sec. for one second of the afferent fibers of a ganglion *in vitro* gives no discharge through the efferent fibers (Figure 70A). This result was observed several times at nine-second intervals. But if two tetanic stimulations at 100/sec. during one second are intercalated, keeping the intervals of tetani constant, stimulation at 10/sec. does result

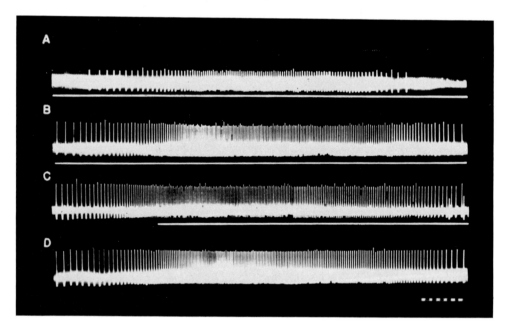

Figure 68. Natural response as a spontaneous activity; preparation as in Figure 58. Tetanic stimulation at 100/sec., marked by continuous line. A and B: continuous recording; several tetani were given between B and C; C: natural response started before the tetanus; D: record taken at a time when no stimulus was applied. Time-marker (dotted line): 0.25 sec. (Luco & Aguilar, unpublished.)

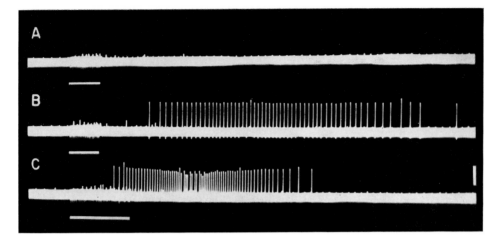

Figure 69. The effect on the natural response of repetition of tetanic stimulations of shorter duration than the utilization period; preparation as in Figure 58. Eight tetani of 0.5-second duration at 100/sec. were given for ten seconds; no response was observed in the first seven tetani, one of which is shown at A; B: the eighth tetanus of the series of the same duration and frequency; C: first tetanus at 100/sec. lasting one second. Calibrations: 1 mV and 0.5 sec. (Luco & Aguilar, unpublished.)

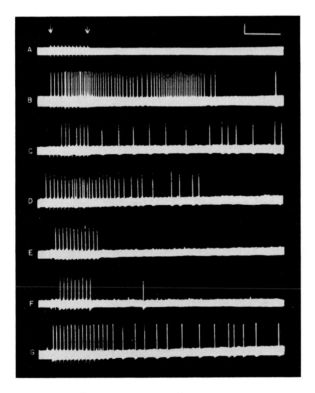

Figure 70. The intratetanic and spontaneous response; preparation as in Figure 58. From A to G, tetanic stimulations at 10/sec. given between the arrows. See text for explanation. Calibrations: 1 mV and 1 sec. (Luco & Davidovich, unpublished.)

in an intratetanic response, and in post-tetanic activity (Figure 70, B to G) that can be interpreted as an afterdischarge or a delayed response. The repetition of the 10/sec. stimulation elicited a variable post-tetanic activity that waxed and waned for four minutes until the unit was lost.

The physiological activities described in this paper, and considered as expressions of plasticity, allow us to suggest a hypothesis as to some of the events that determine a plastic change. In the isolated ganglion of the cockroach, an afferent stimulation causes two groups of reactions. A first group of reactions encompasses the performance of any of the six responses already described. A second group of reactions consists in an alteration in the equilibrium of the system and thus may modify the performance of any of the six responses.

The second group of reactions seems to be related to some trace left by the experience. At least three examples pertaining to this group of reactions can be given: (a) the effect on the process of generation of the endogenous activity, (b) the modification imposed by this stimulation on the reactivity of the system, and (c) the possibility that a pattern of discharge is molded in the organism.

Regarding the first of these examples we have found that when an endogenous activity is present the stimulations alter the pattern of discharge. In the cases where such endogenous activity was not present, the stimulation produced an arousal-like reaction and started this activity. As has been reported above, the quality of the response to a stimulus depends on the intensity of the endogenous activity present at the time of stimulation.

The second example (b) of these reactions, namely the modification of the reactivity of the system, has been inferred from the fact that a subthreshold stimulus, either because the frequency is low or because the duration of application is shorter than the utilization period, becomes threshold after tetanic stimulations. This effect is not a typical post-tetanic potentiation because such a potentiation has never been observed in these experiments. On the other hand, intracellular recordings show a modification in the spontaneous activity of single cells during tetanic stimulation, as I will show later. This suggests a postsynaptic effect of the tetanus rather than a presynaptic effect.

Both the effect on generation of endogenous activity and the modifications of the reactivity of a system are reactions which last for a period of several minutes, and can be considered as factors that may facilitate the initiation of the process of consolidation in the mechanism of retention.

The third example of reactions mentioned (c), i.e., the possibility that a pattern of response may be molded, refers to the pattern of the natural response. The results permit us to suggest that the pattern of natural response discharge is potentially present in the system.

Is the pattern of the natural response a trace belonging to the species or has it been molded by the individual experience? The latter suggestion implies that plasticity would also mean a possibility to mold a pattern of discharge which, once molded, could be released by a stimulus as a learned response.

Bullock: I would like to take the occasion, in the first place, to confirm all this variety of nerve cell behavior. Together with my collaborators, C. H. Baxter and N. Ishiko, I too have seen many of the features described by Dr. Luco.

We have been looking at the cockroach preparation, not *in vitro* but *in vivo*, with the insect opened up. Dr. Ishiko has been recording a little farther out on the peripheral nerves, where there are smaller branches and fewer units. Actually, one can get the same two or three units day after day.

I have not thought of these interesting names and Dr. Luco's scheme of systematization, but it is certainly true that one can see his kind of dependent response, his kind of labile response, autogenic activity, and activity which is only triggered by the stimulus and then will go on repeating itself. I want to emphasize that these things which sound, in a way, so remarkable, are quite confirmable.

Furthermore, they are very similar to what is being seen in several laboratories in the marvelous preparation of *Aplysia*. As Arvanitaki (1, 2) and Tauc (20) in France have shown, and now Segundo in Los Angeles and Strumwasser in Bethesda (18), there are various identifiable units in the visceral ganglion of this marine gastropod. One can penetrate intracellularly into a selected type of unit, and observe responses or autogenic activity which are quite different from those one would find in another cell. For example, there are responses which are characterized by long-lasting bursts which wax and wane in frequency, after an initial triggering stimulus. Others never do this. There are some which show a great deal of inhibitory post-synaptic potentials and some which do not show any. These are reproducible from time to time, providing one keeps track of the time of day. Strumwasser has shown some identifiable units of quite characteristic spontaneous behavior according to the time of day. He has to work late at night to see them; then he gets a form of response from a certain cell which does not occur at any other time of the day. This is true day after day, in preparation after preparation in Bethesda, for animals shipped from Los Angeles and maintained in an aquarium.

The last thing I wish to say may be familiar to all of you; there is an opportunity, in this particular preparation of the isolated ganglion of the cockroach thorax, to observe classical learning, as shown quite recently by Horridge in St. Andrews, Scotland. He has reported this in a preliminary note in *Nature* (10) and the full paper has been published in the *Proceedings of the Royal Society* (10a).

In the beheaded cockroach, Horridge set up a situation where the insect is suspended from its back, with legs dangling, and a dish of water or a metallic contact arranged under one leg, so that when the leg sags and makes the contact, it closes a circuit and receives a shock. After several repeated shocks, the leg remains withdrawn.

Luco: I am happy you mention this, because three years ago Davidovich observed the same thing in our laboratory using a different technique.*

Bullock: The shock does not immediately cause the leg to withdraw. This is not like a "hot stove" response. At first the leg gives a jerk which may not remove it from the water, so that it keeps on receiving shocks for a number of seconds. Every shock the leg is giving to itself on failing to withdraw can be easily recorded. If the number of shocks it is receiving is plotted, the record is very sporadic but it will gradually taper off and, in about thirty minutes, the leg has learned quite well how to avoid the shock.

There is need for a control because the leg receives many shocks and possibly some kind of tone could be being set up in the levator muscles. It is easy to control for this by delivering the same shocks, controlled by cockroach A, to cockroach B whose legs are also dangling but, of course, are sagging and rising at independent times. Though it receives the same number of shocks in the same length of time, roach B does not learn when roach A is holding its leg up and therefore preventing shocks to either preparation. If the leads are switched, so that roach B is controlling the stimulator, it seemingly has not learned anything: it continues to give itself many shocks, i.e., the leg is not withdrawn. In fact it may be "neurotic"; it may be very unteachable now. This is a good control, showing that the simple repetition of stimuli is not causing the leg to be withdrawn.

Furthermore, if the controls are switched and one tries to teach an animal to hold its leg down, punishing it every time it raises the leg, it cannot be done. This is something like Konorski's dogs; there are certain things that cannot be taught them; they will not learn.

That is a preparation which will work in a single segment of the thorax. The head can be cut off—in fact it has to be cut off for good reproducibility—the abdomen can be cut off, and two segments of the thorax, and a single segment be left remaining; it still works. We know the motor neurons involved are of the order of a dozen or so; there are very few motor neurons in these animals. The number of sensory neurons I do not know; but a very limited part of the leg is being stimulated, and there must be only a few score sensory neurons involved. It would probably be quite easy to narrow this down.

The interneurons involved cannot number many hundreds because the entire ganglion has only a couple of thousand cells controlling all the muscles of both sides. This preparation learns quickly. The experiment can be done in the course of an afternoon, including extinction. There is some transfer to the other side and, as I recall, extremely little, if any, to the next segment, anteriorly or posteriorly. This looks like a preparation that might be of interest for classical experimentation.

---

* Unpublished observations.

Luco: At the symposium in Montevideo, Fessard & Szabó (5) considered the possibility that this "spontaneous" activity might be the basis of some learning effects. They said that it was tempting to express the hypothesis that one of the first effects of learning could be the awakening of the pacemaker of some silent neurons.

We have observed "learning" in cockroaches in some experiments on the cleaning of their antennae. The cockroach cleans its antenna with its front legs. As soon as the antenna is stimulated, it holds the antenna with the front legs, pulls it down and cleans it with the palpus. Then, if the front legs are cut, it "learns" to use some other member.

There is an early paper, published in Germany, which describes a careful study of this kind (9). Our observations confirmed just the part of that original work in which we are interested.

We observed the cockroach every day, twice a day, to see how it progressed. We found a beautiful learning curve. What does it learn? It learns to hold the antenna with any other pair of legs in order to clean it. Or perhaps it learns to stand on three legs, if it uses one for the antenna, for then it has to stand on three legs.

What happens with all these reactions *in vitro,* in that case? We have done some experiments already, but I have no records. For the moment we can say that, in the *in vitro* preparation, the reaction of the ganglion seems to appear much more easily than in the hundreds of experiments we have made in normal intact cockroaches. But it is not only quantity we are looking for; it is the qualitative reaction. Are there any of those reactions being modified by the process of learning? That is what we should perhaps have in mind for another conference.

Bickford: May we ask what is the range of stimulation by which you can evoke this pacemaker? You spoke of ten seconds; I was wondering, can you do this, say, every 15 minutes and still get pacemaking? What is the range of times over which cyclic phenomena can be established? If you applied your stimuli every half hour, for instance, would you produce it?

Luco: Half an hour is too long. I have here one example of twenty minutes duration which shows increased activity.

Morrell: I would like to ask Dr. Luco whether, in his opinion, the site of plastic change is postsynaptic or presynaptic.

Luco: As far as I know, the only presynaptic effect that can be considered a trace of the past is the post-tetanic stimulation, but this is not present in our preparation. Fielden at the University of Illinois has confirmed this (6). She can find no post-tetanic reaction in crustacea; she has found no potentiation where the synapses are axo-axonal. So, we think that all of these effects have to be related in some way to the postsynaptic element.

In Figure 71 is a record from a microelectrode placed on the cell of a ganglion *in vitro*. Resting and action potentials of the giant axon from the cockroach have been recorded by means of intracellular microelectrodes by

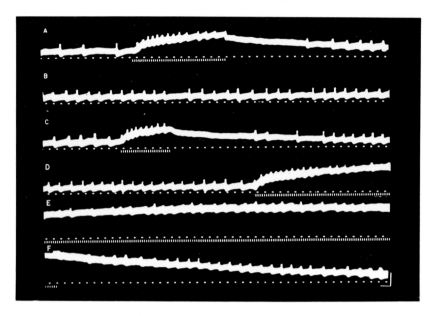

Figure 71. Desheathed metathoracic ganglion *in vitro*. Stimulating electrodes in the abdominal nerve cord; intracellular recording from ganglion. Resting potential: 50 mV. Long-spaced dotted line indicates electrical baseline; short-spaced dotted line indicates period of application of tetanic stimulus at 100/sec. A, B, C, D, E, and F: continuous recording. Calibrations: 10 mV and 0.1 sec. (Luco & Aguilar, unpublished.)

several authors such as Boistel & Coraboeuf (3) and Yamasaki & Narahashi (21). In a recent paper Tauc (19) reported that in *Aplysia* there is a functional discontinuity between the soma and the axon. This portion of the axon appears to have a lower threshold than that of the cell body and acts as a pacemaker when spontaneous activity is present.

On penetrating into the soma, we have observed only small spikes. These small spikes are reminiscent of the abortive impulses observed by Katz (12) and recorded at a point close to the spindle. During a short tetanic stimulation this activity, consisting of small spikes, increases in frequency. After the tetanus there is a silent period (Figure 71, A and C) and after that a new increase in frequency is present (Figure 71B). During a long tetanic stimulation some oscillation in the frequency of these small spikes can be observed (Figure 71, D and E).

To summarize our thinking: The pacemaker activity can be altered by a tetanic stimulation releasing nerve impulses at a frequency different from that existing before the tetanus. This spontaneous activity, modified by the tetanus, may elicit a different response to the same stimulation. This is another kind of post-tetanic potentiation that is probably located in the postsynaptic element.

Henry: I notice that Dr. Bullock commented, and Dr. Luco affirmed, that there is a diurnal rhythm in the isolated ganglion. How long have such rhythms been observed to persist? How long can one keep such a small group of neurons going?

Bullock: In the case I referred to, in *Aplysia,* rhythms in this tidal mollusk have not been maintained over days. I simply meant that this characteristic form of response appears only at a certain hour irrespective of the time of day at which the ganglion was removed from the animal. The preparation can certainly be maintained for eight or ten hours, but it has not been kept for days.

Henry: But the implication is that the rhythm is in some way inherent in that group of cells?

Bullock: Yes, but only to the extent that it does not depend on the preparation being in the animal up to the time it is measured, or in the animal up to a certain time of dissection. One can also recall, in this context, the beautiful demonstration by Janet Harker at Cambridge (8), of a 24-hour rhythm in the subesophageal ganglion of the cockroach, which is very easy to demonstrate. We do not know anything about the nervous correlates, or what is going on in the cells, but she has shown that, if this ganglion is transplanted into another cockroach, the second insect can be timed according to the clock of the first. The clock of the first is set by adjusting the light-dark periods, and then this clock is retained in the isolated ganglion which is transplanted to influence another animal.

Henry: And such a ganglion is of the order of magnitude of only a few hundred neurons?

Bullock: It is a little larger than that, but not more than ten times.

Bickford: Is the influence hormonal?

Bullock: It is usually thought to be neurosecretory.

Reynolds: I wonder whether the phenomenon that Dr. Luco was discussing could be considered as the fatigue of an inhibitory mechanism which was normally active; when stimulated by bursts of stimuli which were inadequate to elicit the motor response but still adequate to stimulate the inhibitory process, this mechanism eventually became fatigued and allowed release of the other response.

Luco: In the labile response, the frequency is so low when there are no responses that it seems impossible that it could be due to fatigue. Besides, an increase of frequency produces the reappearance of the responses. Of course, if the inhibitory synapses were very sensitive to frequency, responding only to certain frequencies, your interpretation would be plausible. But we have no basis on which to judge this.

Feindel: Dr. Luco, how long does this cyclic response continue, once it has been established by intermittent stimulation? Does this go on at the same intervals you used for stimulation?

Luco: When the natural response is being recorded and if, in order to avoid fatigue, stimulation is not at a very high rate, then when stimulation ceases some responses may appear spontaneously at a period similar to that of the previous stimulation. How many times? One or two or three, is all we have observed, but we have not yet made a careful study of this question.

Feindel: Do you think this is some type of change that can be obliterated very easily? This is not the same thing that a segment of the cockroach was doing in the Horridge experiments described by Dr. Bullock, where it really learned something and presumably retained it.

Bullock: Horridge has not studied this preparation overnight, to my knowledge. I believe this learning is pretty well extinguished in a few hours.

REFERENCES

1. ARVANITAKI, A., and CHALAZONITIS, N., Activations du soma géant d'*Aplysia* par voie orthodrome et par voie antidrome. *Arch. Sci. Physiol.,* 1956, **10**: 95-128.
2. ———, Configurations modales de l'activité, propres à différents neurones d'un même centre. *J. de Physiol.,* 1958, **50**: 122-125.
3. BOISTEL, J., and CORABOEUF, E., Potentiel de membrane et potentiels d'action de nerf d'insecte recueillis à l'aide de microélectrodes intracellulaires. *C. R. Acad. Sci.* (Paris), 1954, **238**: 2116-2118.
4. DELAFRESNAYE, J. F., FESSARD, A., GERARD, R. W., and KONORSKI, J. (Eds.). *Brain Mechanisms and Learning.* Blackwell, Oxford, 1961.
5. FESSARD, A., and SZABÓ, T., La facilitation de post-activation comme facteur de plasticité dans l'établissement des liaisons temporaires. In: *Brain Mechanisms and Learning* (J. F. Delafresnaye et al., Eds.). Blackwell, Oxford, 1961: 353-373.
6. FIELDEN, A., Patterns of conduction in the caudal ganglion of the crayfish. *Physiol. Zool.,* 1960, **33**: 161-169.
7. GOMULICKI, B. R., The development and present status of the trace theory of memory. *Brit. J. Psychol.,* 1953, *Monogr. Supp.* **29**.
8. HARKER, J. E., Endocrine and nervous factors in insect circadian rhythms. *Cold Spring Harbor Symp. Quant. Biol.,* 1960, **25**: 279-287.
9. HOFFMANN, R. W., Zur Analyse des Reflexgeschehens bei *Blatta orientalis* L. *Z. vergl. Physiol.,* 1933, **18**: 740-795.
10. HORRIDGE, G. A., Learning of leg position by headless insects. *Nature,* 1962, **193**: 697-698.
10a. ———, Learning of leg position by the ventral nerve cord in headless insects. *Proc. Roy. Soc. London B.,* 1962, **157**: 33-52.
11. JAMES, W., *The Principles of Psychology.* Dover, New York, 1950.
12. KATZ, B., Action potentials from a sensory nerve ending. *J. Physiol.,* 1950, **111**: 248-260.
13. KONORSKI, J., *Conditioned Reflexes and Neuron Organization* (S. Garry, Transl.). Cambridge Univ. Press, London, 1948.
14. LORENTE DE NÓ, R., Circulation of impulses and memory. In: *Macromolecular Specificity and Biological Memory* (F. O. Schmitt, Ed.). MIT Press, Cambridge, 1962: 89-90.

15. Luco, J. V., Plasticity and the natural response of a nervous organization. In: *Perspectives in Biology* (C. R. Cori et al., Eds.). Elsevier, Amsterdam, 1963: 355-360.

16. Pumphrey, R. J., and Rawdon-Smith, A. F., Synaptic transmission of nerve impulses through the last abdominal ganglion of the cockroach. *Proc. Roy. Soc. London*, B, 1937, **122**: 106-118.

17. Roeder, K. D., The nervous system. *Ann. Rev. Entomol.*, 1958, 3: 1-18.

18. Strumwasser, F., Post-synaptic inhibition and excitation produced by different branches of a single neuron and the common transmitter involved. In: *XXII International Congress of Physiological Sciences*, Vol. II (Abstracts of Communications). Excerpta Medica Foundation, Amsterdam, 1962: No. 801.

19. Tauc, L., The site of origin of the efferent action potentials in the giant nerve cell of *Aplysia*. *J. Physiol.*, 1960, 152: 36P-37P.

20. Tauc, L., and Gerschenfeld, H. M., A cholinergic mechanism of inhibitory synaptic transmission in a molluscan nervous system. *J. Neurophysiol.*, 1962, **25**: 236-262.

21. Yamasaki, T., and Narahashi, T., Electrical properties of the cockroach giant axon. *J. Ins. Physiol.*, 1959, 3: 230-242.

STUDIES ON LEARNING AND RETENTION IN PLANARIA

E. ROY JOHN
University of Rochester
Rochester, N.Y.

Several years ago our attention became directed to the potential utility of the planarian in investigations of the biochemical basis of memory. The pioneering work of Thompson & McConnell (14) on the ability of these organisms to acquire conditioned responses, and of McConnell and his associates (11) on their ability to retain and display these responses following regeneration, struck us as most intriguing, if verifiable.

Consequently, William Corning and I endeavored to reproduce the basic phenomena which these workers had described. After some study, it was our conclusion that their observations could be repeated. Other reports of learning in flatworms exist in the literature, and have recently been reviewed by Jacobson (8). No attempt will be made here to review that literature.

In our studies, it became apparent that to condition planarians is rather difficult and requires careful procedure and attention to a number of details. Halas and his co-workers (7) have reported difficulty in their attempts to train planaria. Their subjects were trained in groups rather than as individuals. Testing was carried out in a different apparatus from that used in training, and an extinction procedure was used. The time period which elapsed between training and testing was substantially greater than the time period dedicated to training itself. Perhaps most significantly, the 150 training trials were given as a massed presentation, with trials separated by 30 seconds and a five-minute rest period after trials 50 and 100. Many aspects of their procedure differ substantially from methods which have been found to be successful. These factors may be responsible for the early failure of these workers to obtain significant differences between their experimental group and their sensitization controls. It is my understanding that in later work they have succeeded in reproducing McConnell's early results.

The response obtained with systematic presentation of paired light and shock varies in form from animal to animal. One observes an increased incidence of sharp turns of the anterior portion of the body, head-raising and lateral movement, and abrupt contraction at the onset of the light. If conditioned animals are transected and permitted to regenerate, animals regenerated from tail segments as well as animals regenerated from head segments display the conditioned response as frequently as controls which have been trained and then allowed to rest undisturbed during the period in which the experimental worms were undergoing transection and regeneration.

Since there is cephalad dominance in this organism, the tail sections of conditioned planaria seem somehow to transmit the effects of previous experience to the regenerating anterior portion. The mechanism of this information transfer is obscure, but several possibilities seem to exist: 1. An active process might be involved, in which patterns of nerve impulses in tail tissues transmit information to nervous tissue being formed in the regenerating anterior portion. 2. Another possible active process might be the stipulation by substances in the tail section of the chemical structure of compounds being synthesized to compose the regenerating anterior section. 3. A passive process might be involved in which some intracellular substance which has been modified by the conditioning experience is transferred from the posterior segment where it was initially formed to the anterior segment reconstituted during regeneration. Such transfer might occur (a) due to mitotic activity at the regeneration interface, or (b) due to cell migration. The resolution of these alternatives requires further research, but some data have been obtained which are relevant to these questions.

Abundant data (5, 6) suggest that the neurophysiological mechanism of memory consists of two classes of process: a short-term process, perhaps consisting of reverberatory electrical activity, and a long-term process by which neural excitability patterns are maintained by some sort of structural alteration. In order to reconcile the persistence of memory with the lability of brain chemistry suggested by the high rates of turnover observed in radio-isotope studies, it seemed logical to search for a substance capable of preserving a structural modification by continually imposing an experientially specified configuration on molecules being built in neural tissue. Stability of configuration would thus be achieved, in spite of molecular instability, by stipulation of the invariant form with which new molecules would be synthesized. Imposition of the intuitively reasonable requirement that such a substance be cytoplasmic in locus to be sensitive to synaptic influences impinging on local regions of the cell directed our attention to ribonucleic acid. We attempted, therefore, to devise an experiment to test whether the transfer of information from a previously conditioned planarian tail segment to a regenerating head segment might be based upon the movement or influence of a particular intracellular substance, ribonucleic acid.

We first ascertained that planarian tails could regenerate heads in pond water containing 0.1 mg/ml of ribonuclease. The visible structural anomalies invariably obtained at this concentration indicated clear effects of the enzyme. In our subsequent experiments, ribonuclease concentrations ranged from 0.07 to 0.1 mg/ml, with visible structural anomalies rarely obtained at the lower concentration. Trained animals were then transected and head and tail segments permitted to regenerate in pond water containing ribonuclease, to test whether such treatment would diminish retention of the conditioned response by the regenerated worm. The results of this study are summarized in Table 14.

This study was rather complex because of a number of groups which we included to provide controls for possible effects, on the response levels, of transection, exposure to ribonuclease, or the mere lapse of time. We felt that perhaps the data in our report in *Science* (2) could be presented more clearly, and we have attempted to do so in Table 14. After being subjected to the appropriate conditions, each worm was tested a total of 75 times, 25 tests in each of three successive sessions. For Table 14, we have determined the per cent response of each worm during the 75 test trials, pooled the data for the N worms in each group, and calculated the mean response and standard error for each group. The most relevant comparisons between groups have been evaluated using the t-test. These statistical evaluations are summarized in Table 15.

The central finding of this study can be stated simply: if trained worms

TABLE 14

Condition	Trained transected regenerated				Untrained transected regenerated			
	Enzyme		Pond Water		Enzyme		Pond Water	
Group	I		II		III		IV	
Segment	Head	Tail	Head	Tail	Head	Tail	Head	Tail
N	9	12	12	12	6	6	6	6
Mean %	47.2	19.1	39.4	34.1	15.5	15.6	11.5	12.4
Standard Error	4.5	1.7	5.1	1.9	1.7	1.8	2.7	1.1

Condition	Trained transected regenerated Tested after time lapse				Untrained transected regenerated Tested after time lapse			
	Enzyme		Pond Water		Enzyme		Pond Water	
Group	VII		VIII		V		VI	
Segment	Head	Tail	Head	Tail	Head	Tail	Head	Tail
N	3	3	6	6	6	6	6	6
Mean %	32.1	19.0	29.2	28.9	12.1	12.8	15.3	15.5
Standard Error	2.2	2.6	3.9	5.2	2.7	1.6	2.1	2.5

Condition	Trained intact resting	
	Enzyme	Pond Water
Group	IX	X
Segment	Whole worm	Whole worm
N	6	6
Mean %	51.4	43.5
Standard Error	3.7	, not available

are transected and allowed to regenerate in pond water (Group II), both the head and tail sections perform the conditioned response significantly more than before the initial training, and significantly more (P < 0.001) than head and tail sections from untrained worms which have been transected and regenerated under the same conditions (Group IV). If trained worms are transected and allowed to regenerate in pond water containing ribonuclease (Group I), head sections perform the conditioned response significantly better than before the initial training, and significantly better (P < 0.001) than untrained head sections regenerating under the same conditions (Group III). Trained head sections do not differ significantly whether they regenerate in pond water alone or in the presence of ribonuclease, nor do they differ in their response levels from trained worms allowed to rest intact during the regeneration period.

However, trained tail sections allowed to regenerate in pond water containing ribonuclease perform significantly worse (P < 0.001) than trained head sections regenerating under similar conditions, and significantly worse (P < 0.001) than trained tail sections which have regenerated in plain pond water. Trained tail sections which have regenerated in pond water containing ribonuclease do not display conditioned response levels significantly higher than the response levels before the initial training, nor do they differ significantly from untrained tail sections regenerating under similar conditions. Thus, regeneration in the presence of ribonuclease reduces the re-

TABLE 15

SIGNIFICANCE OF SOME DIFFERENCES BETWEEN GROUPS EVALUATED USING THE t-TEST

Comparison	df	t	P	Comparison	df	t	P
I H vs. I T	19	5.774	< .001	III H vs. III T	10	0.028	N.S.
I H vs. II H	19	1.136	N.S.	III H vs. IV H	10	1.264	N.S.
I H vs. III H	13	6.567	< .001	III H vs. V H	10	1.095	N.S.
I H vs. V H	13	6.691	< .001	III T vs. IV T	10	1.488	N.S.
I H vs. VII H	10	2.986	.02	III T vs. V T	10	1.135	N.S.
I H vs. IX	13	0.773	N.S.				
I T vs. II T	23	5.994	< .001	IV H vs. IV T	10	0.310	N.S.
I T vs. III T	16	1.439	N.S.	IV H vs. VI H	10	1.134	N.S.
I T vs. V T	16	2.755	.02	IV T vs. VI T	10	1.160	N.S.
I T vs. VII T	13	0.036	N.S.				
I T vs. IX	16	8.034	< .001	V H vs. V T	10	0.250	N S.
				V H vs. VI H	10	0.974	N.S.
II H vs. II T	23	0.981	N.S.	V T vs. VI T	10	0.982	N.S.
II H vs. IV H	16	4.875	< .001				
II H vs. VI H	16	4.402	< .001	VI H vs. VI T	10	0.053	N.S.
II H vs. VIII H	16	1.597	N.S.				
II T vs. IV T	17	10.051	< .001	VII H vs. VII T	4	3.861	.02
II T vs. VI T	17	6.042	< .001	VII H vs. VIII H	7	0.648	N.S.
II T vs. VIII T	17	0.958	N.S.	VII T vs. VIII T	7	1.708	N.S.
				VIII H vs. VIII T	10	0.054	N.S.

sponse levels of trained tail sections to levels like those observed in un-trained animals. The fact that these tail sections can subsequently be re-trained with some savings shows that the enzyme has not erased all residual effects of training, nor has it destroyed the capacity of the worm to acquire and perform this response.

Benzer: I think you should state what you are scoring. You are scoring turns? And if so, how many occur spontaneously?

John: We are scoring the total incidence of the three responses which I described: movements of the head, lateral turns of the body, and contrac-tions. Initial levels range from about 11 to 23 per cent. The various sensitiza-tion groups range from 11 to 16 per cent at the end of these procedures, as seen from Table 14.

Calvin: You say "sensitization controls". What does that mean?

John: We were trying to rule out the possibility that animals which are cut and permitted to regenerate in enzyme or in pond water show an altera-tion in response level as a reaction to cutting and regeneration *per se*.

We were also trying to control for whether or not the mere lapse of time in such a situation produces an increase in the response level. We wished to know if any changes observed in our experimental group were due to the specific effect of the enzyme on the conditioned response, and not to some generalized change in the sensitivity of the organism to light because of transection, regeneration, or some unknown irritation from the enzyme.

The reason that so many different kinds of controls were provided stems from the fact that this conditioned response seems somehow less discrete than the more familiar responses with which I personally am used to working, for example, in the cat. There are, as I said, head movements, lateral con-tortions of the body, and contractions. We were trying to find some reassur-ance that any changes we might observe were not an artifact due to the generalized reaction to the ribonuclease or the effects of regeneration.

Calvin: Was there no light or shock treatment, preliminary to enzyme treatment, given to these sensitization controls?

John: These sensitization controls were simply subjected to the manipu-lations, and then the incidence of head turning, lateral movements of the body and contraction to the onset of light was measured.

Calvin: But there was not any unpaired presentation, or anything of this kind to determine whether the animal had been changed by the shock or the light?

John: No, there was not. I should add that so-called pseudo-conditioning controls have been included in other studies, which show that the marked increase in response rate occurs when shock and light are paired but not when they are randomly presented. Sensitization here refers to the effects of the experimental conditions other than shock and light. Response to light was examined as a function of these conditions.

Nirenberg: What is the pH of the water?

John: It is pond water from the Genesee river and tributaries. There are tributaries of the Genesee in which one can find a kind of planarians. They are too small to work with, but the fact they live there indicates the water is all right.*

Bickford: Could we ask how you quantify the response, and by what criteria? Is this observed by someone, or instrumentally quantified?

John: Unfortunately, it is observed. We tried to control for that in a subsequent study by numbering our animals, and then having the experimenter run them blind, not knowing what kind of animal was being observed. This is not an apparatus-measured response; it is subjectively scored. One simply sits there and counts how frequently the animal performs the response. About half the trials in this study were scored by two observers. Their agreement was quite good.

Glaser: The tests are run blind?

John: These were not. Our subsequent study on cannibalism, which I will present later, was run blind.

Bickford: Would it not be possible to quantify this if you had a photocell behind the preparation, or something of that kind to measure the amount of movement?

John: It is not the amount of movement. The animal is gliding along in its usual swimming motion; it is moving. When the light is turned on, there is an abrupt change in its movement.

Mishkin: May I ask whether any reliability studies have been done on recording these responses by two observers or more?

John: We did a small amount of that at the outset, before this study was started, when we were trying to decide if the phenomena described in the earlier papers by McConnell and Thompson and their colleagues (11, 14) could be duplicated in our laboratory. The fact that we went on indicates our satisfaction with this. As mentioned earlier, about half the trials in this study were scored by two judges. Agreement between the two was good.

McConnell: We made a number of reliability studies. The interjudge reliability depends on what period in an animal's training the two judges are observing. At the very beginning of a worm's training, when it is making few really vigorous responses, the reliability may be as low as 80 per cent. Typically, as the animal nears criterion, the reliability rises to 96 or 100 per cent, which is a fairly high reliability.

I might add that some of us have been working for eight or ten years trying to find some objective way of measuring any clear-cut response the worm gives, and that we have not been too successful. This problem is not one we are unaware of—it is merely that we cannot easily automate recording of the worm's responses.

John: Let me summarize Tables 14 and 15. Retention of response by

---

* *Added by Dr. John after the Conference:* The pH is 6.2 ± 0.01.

trained head sections regenerating in ribonuclease (47.2 ± 4.5 per cent) was not significantly different from trained head sections regenerating in pond water (39.4 ± 5.1 per cent), and was essentially identical with response levels observed in trained intact worms which had rested without conditioned response performance during the two-week period required for regeneration (43.5 per cent). In all three of these groups, the retention level was significantly above the initial base rate.

The P value of this retention above initial base rate is significant—at the 0.01 level for trained head sections regenerating either in ribonuclease or in pond water, and at the 0.001 level for trained tail sections regenerating in pond water. However, trained tail sections regenerating in ribonuclease did not display retention levels significantly higher than the base rate before training. These animals performed at the 19.1 ± 1.7 per cent level, which is significantly worse (P < 0.001) than the performance of trained head sections regenerating in ribonuclease (47.2 per cent) and significantly worse (P < 0.001) than trained tail sections regenerating in pond water (34.1 ± 1.9 per cent).

Benzer: How does that 19 per cent vary among the 12 worms?

John: I regret that I cannot carry the distribution of these various groups in my head, but I can say clearly: the fact that those significance levels are at better than the 0.01 level indicates that the standard deviation is not too large.* Table 14, which is for the test trials of this experiment, required some 3500 tests to be compiled.

Benzer: My reason for asking the question was to inquire whether some tails retained perfectly and others were very poor.

John: No, that was not the case. All performed relatively poorly.

Glaser: I am surprised at the number of trials. I thought it was 150 trials for each worm, for each test, or are we counting trials differently?

John: No; it is 75 for each worm, for each test. If you take all the N's, add them up, and multiply by 75, you get a large number.

Glaser: Much larger than 3500. That is why it is important for us to try to see what the standard deviation was, to give the confidence level.† N = 12, that is 1000 trials, or 900; 19 per cent of those give a positive result. So you had 200 positive results to look at, and the standard deviation of that is what—7 per cent?

John: I will add that figure to the record.‡

Deutsch: You have to take the scores done by the same worm independently of each other.

Sinsheimer: If tails are allowed to grow heads in the presence of ribonuclease, can such animals be trained in the usual way?

---

* *Added by Dr. John since the Conference:* The mean was 19.11%. The standard deviation was 5.53%. The standard error was 1.67%. The range for the group was from 14% to 30%.

† *Information provided by Dr. John since the Conference:* On checking, it was found that there were about 9000 test trials.

‡ *Added by Dr. John since the Conference:* The standard deviation for that group was 5.53%.

John: In our original paper we showed that worms which had been transected and permitted to regenerate in ribonuclease would acquire the conditioned response in essentially the same number of training trials as normal worms (2). This is quite important, because the experimental groups were retrained after regeneration to restore their performance to criterion. The fact that they could be retrained indicated that the regeneration in ribonuclease had not destroyed the necessary mechanism.

Deutsch: There seems to be quite a large difference between your heads which were trained and then transected, and regrown in pond water, and the heads trained and transected, and regrown in the enzyme. Would that also be significantly different or not?

John: I will put that in the record.*

Palay: Do you have independent evidence about the time course, the decay of the ribonuclease in your pond water?

John: No, I do not.

Palay: Your only test that it was active is that you found some kind of anomaly in the structure of the animal?

John: Yes, that was our reasoning. We did not have the faintest idea what the stability of ribonuclease was in pond water. So, we used an empirical approach. We used graded concentrations, allowed transected worms to regenerate, and found the minimum concentration which gave us visible effects. We treated that concentration as essentially the threshold dose for gross damage. Whether the effect occurred primarily in the first few hours of exposure or steadily throughout the period, I do not know.

Nirenberg: What was the source of the RNase?

John: Worthington ribonuclease. Attempts were made to provide a number of relevant control groups (see Table 14). Naive animals (Group IV) were transected and permitted to regenerate in pond water, to control for possible sensitization due to the effects of transection. Naive animals (Group III) were transected and permitted to regenerate in the presence of ribonuclease, to control for possible sensitization due to regeneration in the enzyme and for possible effects of the enzyme on structures necessary for acquisition of the conditioned response. The results of these controls showed that transection and regeneration in pond water or in the presence of the enzyme neither produced increased responsiveness due to sensitization nor interfered with subsequent establishment of the conditioned response.

Control for the effects of the time period required for the regeneration, testing and retraining was provided by two groups of worms which were sectioned, permitted to regenerate respectively in pond water (Group VI) or in enzyme (Group V), and then tested for response levels throughout the period in which the experimental animals were observed. The response level

---

* *Added by Dr. John since the Conference:* The t-test for that difference equals 1.136. It does not reach the 0.05 level.

in these groups remained low throughout this time interval, indicating no relevant influences of time lapse or testing *per se* on response levels. Two further groups were trained, transected, allowed to regenerate and rest in pond water (Group VIII) or in enzyme (Group VII) during the time period utilized for regeneration and retraining in the experimental groups, and then tested to see whether the increase in response observed in the experimental groups after retraining was merely a rebound due to the lapse of time after regeneration.

The results indicated that the lapse of time alone did not account for the increment in response observed in the experimental groups on retraining. It is also of interest that the difference in retention displayed by the head and tail segments regenerated from these trained animals in the presence of ribonuclease (Group VII) was significant at the 0.02 level. This group had the primary purpose of serving as a time lapse control. It consisted of trained animals which were transected and allowed to regenerate in enzyme, while other animals were trained and allowed to regenerate in pond water, but an additional time period elapsed in both groups before testing occurred. That time period was the period necessary for the main experimental groups to be retrained. On retesting, the difference between the heads and the tails of Group VII was significant at the 0.02 level.

Feindel: May I ask how long the time lapse was?

John: Fourteen to eighteen days. Finally, trained non-transected animals were kept in pond water containing ribonuclease, and tested at times corresponding to the experimental procedures (Group IX). Comparison of response levels in this control group with response levels observed in trained non-transected animals resting in pond water (Group X) showed no effects of exposure to ribonuclease on retention of response by intact animals.

Thus, these results indicate that conditioned tail sections regenerating in ribonuclease do not retain the conditioned response. The savings scores obtained for retraining suggest that the tails treated with ribonuclease not only possess adequate capacity to acquire and display this response but may retain some residual effects of the prior experience, although they are unable to transmit this residual effectively to the regenerating anterior tissue. The configuration of control data supports the conclusion that the observed deficit in performance is attributable to the presence of the ribonuclease during the period of regeneration, and is due to interference with the process of information transfer rather than to enzymatic perturbation of the anatomical substrate necessary for mediation of the response. The absence of enzymatic effects in intact worms suggests that the action may be localized at the regenerating interface.

These results, then, are compatible with the interpretation that the chemical substance responsible for the presence of conditioned responses in the regenerated animal *may* be ribonucleic acid. It is perhaps necessary to point out explicitly that these results are not sufficient to conclude that the substance responsible for storage of information *is* ribonucleic acid. The results may be due to an unknown effect of the ribonuclease on the regenerating interface, resulting from the general physical properties of ribonuclease rather than from the specific action of ribonuclease on "trained" RNA. These effects may also be due to interference with the anterior migration of cells. Other substances, with no effect on RNA, might possess similar ability to block information transfer to regenerating head tissue. Unequivocal identification of the responsible chemical substance would necessitate demonstration that the common consequence of those perturbations found to be effective for blocking transfer of information consisted *exclusively* of interference with ribonucleic acid. Such a demonstration has not been provided, and presents formidable difficulties.

However, the implication provided by these experiments that RNA is involved in the cellular mechanism of information storage gains strength from a number of corroborating findings, briefly summarized below. Brattgård (1) has demonstrated a relationship between RNA synthesis and stimulation in retinal ganglion cells. Morrell (12) has demonstrated histochemically an increase in RNA concentration of cortical cells which is a result of the prior establishment of a mirror focus. Kreps has reported differentially increased turnover of RNA in the cortical receiving area of the conditioned stimulus after elaboration of conditioned responses in the dog.[*] Eiduson et al. (4) have demonstrated a relation between RNA concentration and the effectiveness of previous imprinting experience in the chick. Dingman & Sporn (3) have shown impairment of maze learning in the rat following interference with RNA synthesis by 8-azaguanine. In earlier work (unpublished), John, Wenzel and Tschirgi observed that intraventricular injection of ribonuclease into trained cats interfered with complex pattern discrimination but not with conditioned avoidance responses. More recently, as we have heard, Hydén has reported changes in the base ratios of amino acids in the nucleus but not the cytoplasm of vestibular cells in rats learning a balancing response, which was not the case in rats subjected to control passive vestibular stimulation. While far from conclusive, this concatenation of results, from multiple species and conditioning situations, strongly suggests the importance of RNA in memory mechanisms.

Some time ago, McConnell et al. (10) reported a finding which may provide a means for more direct evaluation of the role of RNA. These workers reported that cannibal planarians showed a higher incidence of conditioned response following ingestion of fragments of trained worms than after ingestion of untrained worms. Because of the intrinsic interest and possible utility of this observation, an attempt to reproduce this study was carried out by R. Karpick and J. McNabb in my laboratory.[†]

To increase our confidence in the reliability of this work, the animals in

[*] Cited by Palladin & Vladimorov (13).
[†] Unpublished observations.

the study were coded in such a fashion as to ensure that the experimenter could not identify experimental and control animals during experimental sessions. A group of *Dugesia tigrina* was selected; these worms were willing, when food-deprived, to eat fragmented *Dugesia dorotocephala*. These cannibals were then randomly assigned either to an experimental group numbering seven animals, or to a control group numbering six animals. Using the same conditioning techniques utilized in our previous work, a "diet group" of *D. dorotocephala* was then presented with 25 trials per day of paired light and shock, until a criterion of 20 out of 25 conditioned responses was obtained for three successive days. This is a very rigorous criterion. *After each diet worm reached criterion, it was returned to its individual vial of pond water for one day to permit the immediate chemical aftereffects of excitation and stimulation to return to normal.* On the following day it was cut into four equal fragments, each of which was fed to an experimental worm. At the same time, an untrained worm which had been resting in environmental circumstances identical with those of the diet group was cut into the same number of fragments and each fragment was fed to one control worm. A record was kept of the position in the diet worms from which each fragment came, and a distribution of fragments was devised so that each experimental and control worm ingested a total of five fragments, representing all the regions of an entire worm. Training of each of the cannibal worms began after ingestion of the final fragment.

As can be seen from Figure 72, the response level curves in the experimental and control groups of cannibalistic worms do not overlap during the first 12 days. Arrows indicate days on which the differences between the two groups were significant at the 0.01 level or better, using the t-test.

I should say, since I went over these data very carefully before I came here, that I do know the variation in overlap in this group. In the early portion there are two groups which overlap very slightly. Performance of the experimental group began at a high level and increased gradually, whereas the control group began at a comparatively low level of response and gradually increased its response level. The raw data are presented in Table 16.

After 12 days the two curves converged. Eight days later, all the animals were again fed with the appropriate kind of worm fragment. At that time the two curves again diverged sharply, with the experimental group performance showing a significantly greater increment than did the controls.

The outcome of this experiment, supporting the previous report of McConnell and his co-workers (10), suggests that ingestion of some chemical substance in the tissue of the trained worms caused an increase in the response level of untrained worms which was greater than that caused in a control group by ingestion of tissue from untrained worms. At first sight, data of this sort seem incredible because one assumes that, even if an intracellular substance exists which stores information as a macromolecular configuration, it would be destroyed by the digestive system of the ingesting

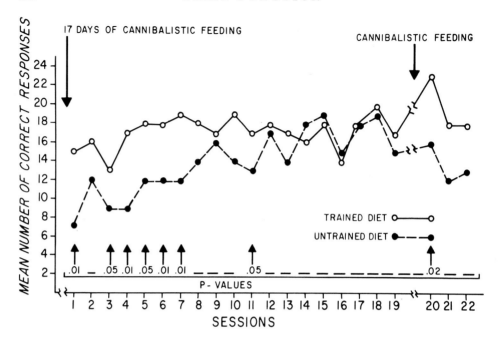

Figure 72. Incidence of conditioned response performance after the onset of training in cannibalistic worms. The experimental group (solid line) had been fed a diet consisting of fragments of trained planarians during a period of 14 to 18 days prior to the onset of training. During this same period the control group (broken line) was maintained on a diet of fragments of untrained resting planarians. Arrows indicate the points at which the performance of the two groups is significantly different as calculated by the t-test. At 20 days after the onset of training, the two groups were again fed the appropriate planarian fragment. Note the subsequent divergence in their performance.
(E. R. John, R. Karpick & J. McNabb, unpublished.)

cannibal. Further consideration, however, generates the possibility that the planarian digestive system may not degrade macromolecules significantly. Current knowledge suggests that large fragments of food are engulfed by parenchymal cells in a phagocytic manner, and degradation of food proceeds to a significant extent inside the cells of the planarian. It is conceivable that macromolecules derived from ingested planarian fragments are utilizable by the cells of the cannibal without the necessity for chemical breakdown before incorporation.

We have difficulty in accounting for the high significance levels of our results without such an assumption. Our data suggest that prior experience has produced a chemical difference in the tissues of the trained animal and that ingestion of this chemical system can alter the response of the cannibalistic worm to light.

Unfortunately, our experimental design was inadequate in that our control group was fed worms which had been resting, instead of worms exposed to randomized light and shock so as to provide a pseudo-conditioning control. It is therefore not possible for us to stipulate that what was transferred

TABLE 16

PERFORMANCE OF EXPERIMENTAL AND CONTROL GROUPS IN CANNIBALISM STUDY

(Number of correct responses made by each subject during a day's training session, consisting of 25 presentations of light paired with shock. P values obtained by t-test.)

Session no.	1	2	3	4	5	6	7	8	9	10	11	12	13	14	15	16	17	18	19	20	21	22	23
Subject																							
Controls																							
C1	7	19	7	10	15	14	12	19	16	12	14	15	11	12	17	16	19	22	11	F	18	16	11
C2	5	15	7	10	11	9	14	15	12	16	13	17	13	19	15	14	17	21	14	E	13	14	13
C3	9	21	12	11	11	9	12	11	18	13	6	17	11	15	23	13	16	19	19	E	20	4	15
C4	9	3	14	4	12	13	12	19	13	18	20	19	13	22	19	23	24	23*	10	D	—	—	—
C5	4	9	5	6	14	10	9	7	17	9	16	16	20	18	21	15	14	9	16	I	12	11	15
C6	6	6	10	15	7	15	12	15	17	13	7	18	17	22	16	9	16	21	22	N	17	17	13
Average	7	12	9	9	12	12	12	14	16	14	13	17	14	18	19	15	18	19	15	G	16	12	13
Experimentals																							
E1	13	15	16	8	23	22	10	23	25	23*	—	—	—	—	18	21	21	22†	—	F	—	—	—
E5	19	21	17	14	20	19	20	18	20	12	19	18	17	13	21	16	20	21	21*	E	—	—	—
E9	9	3	12	19	17	15	22	15	8	21	17	17	22	19	21	19	23	24	22*	E	—	—	—
E11	13	16	11	18	24	17	14	16	17	13	15	15	14	7	16	10	18	16	19	D	22	19	19
E12	16	18	14	19	15	13	22	22	15	23	21	17	16	13	17	6	8	18	1	I	—	22	14
E13	18	21	12	17	14	15	20	20	12	19	20	20	15	24	17	8	10	22	16	N	23	22	15
E14	17	15	10	23	13	23	22	13	22	19	11	20	17	20	14	16	23	19	21	G	24	13	25
Average	15	16	13	17	18	18	19	18	17	19	17	18	17	16	18	14	18	20	17		23	18	18
P =	.01	—	.05	.01	.01	.01	.01	—	—	.05	—	—	—	—	—	—	—	—	—		.02	—	

* Subject reached criterion and was therefore withdrawn from study.
† Retention check.

to the experimental cannibalistic group was *specific* coded information resulting from the systematic pairing of light and shock which led to the establishment of the conditioned response. It is possible that what was transferred was a more *general* increased reactivity to light resulting from the physical effects of light and/or shock unrelated to their paired presentation and, therefore, unrelated to learning. The lapse of a one-day interval between the achievement of criterion by diet worms and their use would seem to provide some assurance that this is not the case. However, the latter explanation would, if true, still not obviate the fact that a long-lasting chemical difference had been achieved as a consequence of stimulation. This in itself would seem to constitute an interesting finding.

We have subsequently attempted and failed to replicate this study with the addition of a pseudo-conditioning control group. While the causes of this failure are not unequivocally clear, review of the course of the experiment suggested a number of possibly important changes from the previous procedure. We are, therefore, currently engaged in a second attempt at replication. If we are successful, we hope to use this preparation to prepare physically and chemically separated fractions of trained planaria; these will then be studied in an attempt to identify a specific fraction which, when ingested, has the same effect on response levels as ingestion of whole fragmented worm. Should such a fraction be found, its chemical analysis might lead to positive identification of the substance responsible for the storage of information about paired light and shock in the trained planarian.

McConnell: I would like to give some data on a study—two studies, really —which some students of mine and I performed this past summer. I have to apologize ahead of time for the crudeness of the study. I will say beforehand that we are repeating the study now, and that what I will present today are significant data from a very badly done study. I hope you will allow me to do this, and that you will put this study away in some mental compartment (encoded with RNA, I presume) and keep the study locked up in your minds until we can report the replication. But please do not really believe the data I am going to give you now until we can confirm them.

Nonetheless, the data I want to report are quite pertinent to this particular Conference. This last summer I had working with me and Reeva Jacobson two medical school students from Stanford, L. Kabat and A. Zelman. In the first run-through of the study, we took untrained planarians and extracted RNA from them. It turned out that in order to obtain enough RNA to do what we wanted, we had to have large numbers of worms. So we used approximately 500 worms in each of the groups I shall describe.

It is not easy to train 500 worms individually. So, we built what might be called a "mass trainer". This is simply an apparatus that delivers light and shock to a large number of worms at a given time. I mention this because we have, consequently, no way of plotting the individual learning curves for each of our animals—the best we could do was to pull out samples of worms from time to time and test them to see how the whole group was responding.

One group of planarians was given about 500 trials of light and shock paired as usual in a classical conditioning paradigm. The second group was given 500 trials of light which were always separated by 60 seconds from the presentation of 500 trials of shock. This is what we would call a pseudo-conditioning group—animals that receive 500 lights intermixed with 500 shocks, with no pairing of light and shock.

We then extracted the RNA from both groups, using essentially the method described by Kirby (9). Within, I suppose, 12 hours after the animals have been sacrificed and the procedure is started, the RNA is ready to be injected into worms that have never received any training whatsoever.

To recapitulate, we extracted RNA from animals that had either been given 500 training trials or 500 trials of pseudo-conditioning. We then injected the RNA into 20 worms that had been randomly selected from our basic stock of planarians (*Dugesia dorotocephala*). These worms were given code numbers, and then the injectees, if I may call them that, were trained in "blind" fashion.

Benzer: Was the injection made with a syringe? And do you simply inject into the body of the worm?

McConnell: We use a micropipette for the injection and plunge it right into the body of the worm. We take a thin glass capillary tube, draw it out to a small point, attach a syringe, and inject under the microscope. We first tried injections using vital dyes, to see whether or not anything we injected into the animal stayed in, and it does. We did not dye the RNA itself.

Now, let me review the data. We will take first the two groups' performances at the end of 25, 50, 75 and 100 trials. At the end of the first 25 trials, the animals that received RNA from conditioned worms responded an average of 16.9 times; the animals that had RNA from pseudo-conditioned worms responded an average of 12.7 times. The difference between these two groups is significant at the 5 per cent level. At the end of 50, 75 and 100 trials, the experimental animals also were superior to the controls, although these differences were not significant past the first day, i.e., the first 25 trials. If you plot the data, though, there is little overlap between the two groups for the entire 100 trials.

The second time we ran the experiment, we had essentially these same two groups but added some more controls. We had the usual experimental group that had about 500 light-shock trials. We had a group of worms that received pseudo-conditioning for 350 trials and then were given 400 trials of light only, to see if we could extinguish any pseudo-conditioning response that might have occurred in the animals. We also had a group of animals that received 500 trials of light only. These are the animals from which we extracted the RNA. We then injected the RNA into untrained animals. We took a fourth group of untrained animals and injected them, not with RNA but with distilled water. So, we ended up with four groups of injectees which then were given 100 light-shock training trials.

The curves were not as pretty on the second run-through as on the first. In general the experimental animals—that is, the worms that had received RNA from the experimental animals—were clearly the superior group. On the second and fourth days of training, that is, at the end of 50 and 100 training trials respectively, the experimental animals were significantly superior to all other groups. These were the only significant differences among any of the four groups. These results are scarcely what could be called clear-cut evidence that the memory was transferred with the RNA, but they are quite encouraging.

Now, I should point out that we made a large number of mistakes. As a matter of fact, I could spend the next half hour outlining the mistakes we made in these experiments. All I can say in favor of these experiments is that we did get some significant differences, that the experimental animals were clearly the fastest learners, and that both experiments were done in "blind" fashion, so that we could not knowingly have influenced the results.

But I must make one further qualification. Our RNA was anything but pure. We certainly had a fair amount of protein mixed in with the RNA, which we did not extract. We are, however, reasonably sure that there was no DNA present in the material that we injected. The best we can say is that we injected something that contained some RNA and some protein and probably a lot of other things, but that whatever it was we injected, it seemed to transfer something to the injectees. Whether what was transferred was "memory", or whether it was something more akin to "sensitization", we do not presently know. But it does look as if we might actually have transferred memories from one animal to another (15).[*]

Deutsch: At the end of Dr. John's presentation he said he had been unsuccessful in repeating the study. I was not quite sure in what way; did he mean that when he did the control he had not, in fact, repeated the previous study, or did he mean that he could not repeat the results of the previous study even on his experimental subjects?

John: Our second cannibalism study was done by an undergraduate student in biology who, a number of times during the experiment, expressed great distress about such things as the fact that it was necessary to move the laboratory. Normally, in our experiments, the animals are in darkness. They are kept in a drawer and pulled out during the experimental sessions. There was a period during her work when, unavoidably, her animals spent a period of time in the light.

The pseudo-conditioning control was added. We had three groups: one group was fed untrained resting worms; one group was fed worms pre-

[*] The research described here was supported in part by Atomic Energy Commission Grant AT(11-1) 825 and in part by Grant MH-2946 from the National Institute of Mental Health.

sented with unpaired, randomized light and shock, and the third group was fed worms which had been conditioned.

When training began after the feeding period, all three groups showed high response levels. The variability in the data was tremendous, in contrast to the previous experiment in which the animals were essentially segregated into two groups, with a little bit of overlap. For unknown reasons, every group started out at a very high response level, including the controls. We obtained no significant differences between groups—not because the response rates were not high, but because all response rates were high.

Thompson: Before we go into the implications, for RNA, of these experiments on planarians, we ought to examine some of the structural peculiarities of this organism which might account for the finding that a trained worm, when split in half, shows retention in both the head and tail sections. First of all, the planarian not only has two specialized eyes located in the head region, but has numerous other photoreceptors scattered throughout its body. There is the possibility, therefore, that the diffuse visual projection system results in a diffuse memory trace. So one would expect retention in both parts of a split worm simply on this basis. The cannibalism work, if substantiated, may show that something else is involved.

A second possibility concerns the type of learning that is being imposed upon the planarian. It must be emphasized that classical conditioning is being observed, not avoidance conditioning. In other words, as far as we know, the animal is not making this turning or contracting response in order to avoid or minimize the shock experience, but rather is making this response in "anticipation" of shock, a sort of conditioned fear. In the rat, for example, after several pairings of light and shock, the animal will squeak or make some other emotional response to the onset of light. The planarian, instead of squeaking, turns abruptly or contracts.

If fear-conditioning is actually involved, then neuroendocrine factors become of great importance, and this is what may be transferred from segment to segment in both the sectioning and cannibalistic studies. I just bring out these possibilities as alternatives to the RNA hypothesis.

Weiskrantz: I wanted to ask either Dr. John or Dr. McConnell a question about the specificity of the learning. The assumption from all of this work is that, in some way, a somewhat specific association is being transported from one system to another. But is there any evidence that if animals are trained on, say, this classical conditioning procedure, then cut or given a cannibalistic procedure, and then trained on quite a different task, the subsequent task is affected? In other words, is it a sort of learning set, rather than a specific habit, which is being transported?

John: I know of no relevant data. Perhaps Dr. McConnell does, since he knows this work very much better than I.

McConnell: I do not think anyone ever trained animals on one task and tried them on another.

Hydén: How is the RNA quantitatively distributed in the planarian with respect to the tissues?

John: I do not know of any data.

Morrell: K. L. Chow, who has studied planaria, has some data. He also has a group in which he did this kind of experiment, regrowing them in the same concentration of ribonuclease; he found no difference in the dye-binding property of cells throughout whatever corresponds to the neuraxis in the planarian.* But the dye-binding ribonuclease or RNase-specific is apparently in the nerve cells, and there is quantitative difference.

Nirenberg: Dr. McConnell, you mentioned the fact that your RNA preparation contained a considerable amount of protein. How do you prepare the RNA?

McConnell: You will forgive me if I point out that I am not a biochemist and that I have to depend on my two medical students for information on this point. The extraction method we employed is a modification of one first described by Kirby (9). I will outline it briefly, although you may well be familiar with Kirby's method. First we homogenized the animals and added phenol; then we removed the phenol with ether and centrifugation; then we evaporated the remaining mixture, and presumably what was left was RNA—in our case, RNA with some protein and probably some other things, too. Then we dissolved the mixture in distilled water for injection.

Benzer: Did you analyze the preparation for polysaccharides?

McConnell: I do not know whether my colleagues tested for polysaccharides. I can refer you to the studies we reported (15). I am not at all certain that they ran any test for polysaccharides, but I could be wrong about that.

Bullock: I would like to ask what reason there may be to believe that the RNase still retains any enzyme activity if and when it gets inside the animal, which has merely been swimming in it.

Hild: I have some experiments in which I very naively also tried to introduce ribonuclease into nerve cells. I started out with Worthington ribonuclease and added various concentrations in the medium, expecting that perhaps something would enter the cell. But, from what we have heard now, there are various kinds of ribonucleic acid. If this enzyme preparation from Worthington is capable of interfering either with polymerization or depolymerization of RNA of various kinds, and if it goes into a cell, how does it act?

Our results were at first striking but they are not reproducible. I have reported this at another meeting. What I thought was this: an ordinary neuron stained with basic dye shows staining of nucleolus and Nissl substance, the two sites where the ribonuclease is concentrated. At a concentration of 1:1000 enzyme, left on the cell for three hours or so, in some

---

* Personal communication.

cases there was a very striking non-staining of the nucleolus, whereas Nissl substance at no time was affected.

So I thought, "Now I have something," and tried to repeat it, but I could never produce the same result again. So the question, of course, is, does the enzyme go into the cell, whether it is planarian cell or culture cell? If it goes in, how is its effect tested?

Nirenberg: I have, actually, very few remarks to make, except for one note of caution, and that is that RNase preparations, by and large, even crystalline preparations, all contain many other enzymes. They are usually prepared from pancreas. I think you will find they contain DNase, and some proteolytic enzyme and, very probably, a number of other substances. This should really be taken into consideration.

Calvin: I know that the question raised by the cannibalistic experiment, at least that of cell regeneration of the fed pieces within the worm, has been taken into account, although not actually mentioned. This is certainly an item which has to be considered as a possible way in which the RNA, or hormone, or whatever is being transferred, may be transmitted, namely that it is in terms of a cell itself, an intact cell, rather than a chemical. The experiment described by Dr. McConnell would, of course, answer that question if it were successful.

Benzer: I agree with Dr. Calvin in worrying about the ribonuclease. As I understand, the experiments were done at a concentration of ribonuclease only 30 per cent less than one which induces definite monstrosities in regenerating worms. Just lowering it 30 per cent can produce pre-monstrosities that one does not see. Also, other enzymes should be tried. Ribonuclease is famous for being contaminated with trypsin, for instance.

There is one basic point that bothers me very much about the whole story. Having run a few worms myself, I am even more aware of this. That is, the worms are quite nervous. The response that one scores is something that they are doing all the time, more or less. Something that is impressive in the data we have seen this morning is how much this background varies from one experiment to another. In Dr. John's early experiments (2) he had about 15 per cent spontaneous response. In his later data on cannibalism, the worms that had eaten naive worms show about 30 or 40 per cent spontaneous response. Now, in McConnell's work it looks like around 80 per cent. To what extent has general nervousness of the worm been excluded as a factor?

McConnell: A correction. You cannot really say the spontaneous rate in the latter study was 80 or 90 per cent, because these are animals that have had something done to them.

Benzer: Precisely; they are nervous. This is shown by the fact that without even shining the light on them, you get 50 per cent response.

McConnell: There is not always time to present all the controls that have been run.

Glaser: I was concerned about the statistical significance of the criteria applied. In Thompson & McConnell's first paper (14), I recall the background rate quoted was 30 per cent, and the trained responses were about 40 per cent. In the more recent results, criterion of 23 out of 25 is often quoted, which is 92 per cent, while in the experiments on cannibalism, 50-53 per cent was considered a very successful score. I do not know how to compare these different numbers.

There seems to be great variation from experiment to experiment in what is background and what is acceptable effect. You not always seem to tune to the same criterion in the same experiments. It is a little hard to judge the technique.

John: Let me take the last point first. In the cannibalism experiment, the question we were asking was, "Do the two groups show differences?" We did not train to a particular criterion, but simply trained and observed the worms. Perhaps we should have continued training instead of feeding again when the two groups had converged.

We wanted to know if we could make the two groups diverge. We had to decide which question we wanted to ask. The variability in base rate which is observed comes, I think, from the question of the intensity of the light which is used. Some workers use a 100-watt bulb. We use a 7.5-watt bulb. The difference in response level to the lower intensity of light is very striking, when compared with the higher intensity.

I would like to make a general remark about this entire domain, if I may. Frankly, the first time we took a look at this preparation, we took our look in disbelief. It seemed a very interesting thing which was probably not true but which would be very useful, and certainly was intriguing if it turned out to be true.

I am a little embarrassed, except I suspect people often proceed this way when they are entering an area which is strange to them. When we went into the ribonuclease experiment, we did not question the purity of Worthington's ribonuclease, not realizing this was a question. Chemists are reliable people. We simply bought some ribonuclease and chucked it in.

After we finished the study, we realized there had been an enormous amount of work involved, compared to what we expected.* Worms are very little and cats are very big. We worked with cats for many years. You kind of assume that this is a little animal, therefore it is a little project, but that does not follow at all. It is just as much hard work with planarians as with cats—even a little bit more, because you are more unsure about it.

This ribonuclease study, if we were going to do it again, would be designed in a different way. We came out with some findings that were statistically significant. I have sympathy for Dr. Hydén when somebody suggests, "Why don't you do thus and such?" His first reaction is shock. There

---

* *Added by Dr. John after the Conference:* That study required over 30,000 training trials and over 9000 test trials.

are lots of things we could think of doing to improve that first study, but it is a lot of work.

When we finished the cannibalism study, again after a tremendous investment of time and effort, we realized that we did not have a pseudo-conditioning control. It is very distressing to finish a study and find that you left out a control you should have been smart enough to think of. You might consider taking another group, and treating it alone as a pseudo-conditioning control, but you must worry about all the environmental variables that may differ, since controls must be run at the same time you run the experiment. In that case, you are faced with the necessity of doing the whole thing over. We have not repeated the experiment because perhaps, if we can work it out, there might be better and more convincing ways to ask these questions. Then, when we were finished, we would really be convinced. Whether it is apparent or not, we have some skepticism built in, also.

These are important questions that are being asked, and one wants to be sure they are asked properly. What is needed is a technique to establish a differentiated response, where a planarian makes one kind of a response to one stimulus and another kind of response to another stimulus which is basically similar to the first one. Each animal then provides his own control with respect to the question of sensitization and pseudo-conditioning.

If one had such a differentiated response and one could show with a cannibalistic procedure that transfer really did occur, there could be no question but that what had been transferred was specifically coded information relating to the differentiation between two similar events. Thinking along these lines, some people have been utilizing the maze, trying to establish whether maze learning would transfer through the cannibalistic procedure and whether the specific effects of ribonuclease could be obtained in a maze training situation. That was not the direction we chose. We decided to try to differentiate an avoidance response to two different lights, between flicker and steady light. For the past year we have been pursuing this approach without success.

REFERENCES

1. BRATTGÅRD, S.-O., The importance of adequate stimulation for the chemical composition of retinal ganglion cells during early post-natal development. *Acta Radiol.*, 1952, Suppl. **96**: 1-80.
2. CORNING, W. C., and JOHN, E. R., Effect of ribonuclease on retention of conditioned response in regenerated planarians. *Science*, 1961, **134**: 1363-1365.
3. DINGMAN, W., and SPORN, M. B., The incorporation of 8-azaguanine into rat brain RNA and its effect on maze-learning by the rat: an inquiry into the biochemical basis of memory. *J. Psychiat. Res.*, 1961, **1**: 1-11.
4. EIDUSON, S., GELLER, E., and BECKWITH, W., Some biochemical correlates of imprinting. *Fed. Proc.*, 1961, **20**: 345.

5. GLICKMAN, S. E., Perseverative neural processes and consolidation of the memory trace. *Psychol. Bull.*, 1961, **58**: 218-233.

6. GOMULICKI, B. R., The development and present status of the trace theory of memory. *Brit. J. Psychol.*, 1953, Monogr. Supp. **29**.

7. HALAS, E. S., JAMES, R. L., and STONE, L. A., Types of responses elicited in planaria by light. *J. Comp. Physiol. Psychol.*, 1961, **54**: 302-305.

8. JACOBSON, A. L., Learning in flatworms and annelids. *Psychol. Bull.*, 1963, **60**: 74-94.

9. KIRBY, K. S., Ribonucleic acid from rat liver. *Biochem. Prep.*, 1958, **6**: 79-82.

10. McCONNELL, J. V., JACOBSON, R., and HUMPHRIES, B. M., The effects of ingestion of conditioned planaria on the response level of naive planaria: a pilot study. *Worm Run. Dig.*, 1961, **3**: 41-47.

11. McCONNELL, J. V., JACOBSON, A. L., and KIMBLE, D. P., The effects of regeneration upon retention of a conditioned response in the planarian. *J. Comp. Physiol. Psychol.*, 1959, **52**: 1-5.

12. MORRELL, F., Lasting changes in synaptic organization produced by continuous neuronal bombardment. In: *Brain Mechanisms and Learning* (J. F. Delafresnaye et al., Eds.). Blackwell, Oxford, 1961: 375-392.

13. PALLADIN, A. V., and VLADIMIROV, G. E., The use of radioactive isotopes in the study of functional biochemistry of the brain. In: *International Conference on the Peaceful Uses of Antomic Energy*, Proceedings, Vol. 12. United Nations, New York, 1955: 402-408.

14. THOMPSON, R., and McCONNELL, J. V., Classical conditioning in the planarian, *Dugesia dorotocephala*. *J. Comp. Physiol. Psychol.*, 1955, **48**: 65-68.

15. ZELMAN, A., KABAT, L., JACOBSON, R., and McCONNELL, J. V., Transfer of training through injection of "conditioned" RNA into untrained planarians. *Worm. Run. Dig.*, 1963, **5**: 14-21.

MODIFICATION OF RNA AS A RESULT OF NEURAL ACTIVITY*

FRANK MORRELL
Stanford University School of Medicine
Palo Alto

In this presentation I shall argue that certain features of the pathophysiology of epilepsy may afford insights into the neural mechanisms which underlie learning and memory. I shall suggest that the so-called "secondary" epileptogenic lesion may be viewed as an analogical model of cellular "learning". This suggestion may seem surprising to those of you who know that for many years our laboratory has studied the manner in which epileptogenic lesions *interfere* with the more orthodox types of learning, not to mention those who consider epilepsy as a purely pathological event having nothing to do with normal cerebral physiology.

We know a good deal about the normal pattern of electrical activity generated within the brain of man and many species of experimental animals. Figure 73 illustrates a normal electroencephalographic tracing in an adult male subject. Note the relatively rhythmic, regular and smooth oscillations. Note also that the electrical pattern is different in different parts of the head—and, most particularly, that symmetrical points on the two hemispheres exhibit a striking similarity in frequency and morphology of electrical waveform.

It is not especially surprising that such electrical similarity should occur, since homotopic regions in each hemisphere generally resemble each other not only in terms of function, anatomic organization and connectivity with periphery or other neural systems but, in addition, are specifically interconnected (point-to-point) by the great cortical commissure, the corpus callosum. The importance of the corpus callosum for transfer of information (such as might be involved in a learned behavior) from one hemisphere to the other has been demonstrated in most elegant detail by Sperry (16), Myers & Sperry (13), and Stamm & Sperry (17).

Callosal transfer of information has proved to be an equally important concept in a context quite separate from the behavioral study of learning. Indeed, the material I wish to present derives from investigations into the pathophysiology of experimental epilepsy. Initiation of these particular ex-

* This work was supported by USPHS Grant B-3543.

periments resulted from the desire to learn more about a relatively common clinical observation.

For those unfamiliar with electroencephalographic (EEG) tracings, Figure 74 illustrates the pertinent clinical observations. The record is that of a ten-year old boy who has an epileptogenic lesion in the left parieto-occipital cortex (channels 3 and 4). The typical electrical configuration of an epileptogenic lesion is shown in channels 3 and 4, where the large, sharp, so-called "spike" potentials stand out prominently and are easily distinguished from the normal potential pattern as seen in Figure 73 or in channels 1 and 2 of Figure 74. Such spikes occur frequently, repeatedly and apparently spontaneously (or at least in the absence of known stimulation).

At this time let me state explicitly the first of the assumptions required if our analogical model is to hold: that the "behavior" of a population of nerve cells may be characterized, at least in part, by the electrical oscillations generated therein. It then follows that the ganglionic network comprising an epileptogenic focus exhibits a form of behavior quite different from that of a non-epileptic population (compare channels 3 and 4 with channels 1 and 2 in Figure 74).

Now, as noted above, the *primary* epileptogenic lesion in this child is located in the left parieto-occipital region. However, a glance at channel 8 (Figure 74) reveals that typical "spike" potentials also appear in the homotopic region of the right hemisphere. Most often such evidence of contra-lateral discharge is not seen immediately after onset of the clinical disorder but rather tends to appear much later, many months or years after the primary focus is well established. For that reason, and also because the contralateral focus almost invariably arises in the cortical site to which the

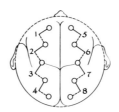

Figure 73. Electroencephalogram of a normal adult male. Derivations are as indicated in the diagram. Calibration: 50 μV and 1 sec.

callosal fibers from the primary focus project, we assume that it represents a *secondary* focus, i.e., that somehow the contralateral discharge is caused by continuous bombardment through the callosal pathway from the abnormal cells of the primary focus. Nevertheless, in the human disease the evidence is far from compelling because one can never be sure that the contralateral cortex was not independently injured by the same (or another) agent which caused the primary focus.

In order to clarify this mechanism we initiated a study in experimental animals. After developing a technique (8) for inducing small chronic epileptogenic lesions by local freezing of a 2-4 mm area of cortical surface, we produced unilateral lesions in a large series of cats and rabbits. Great care was taken to insure that the homotopic, contralateral cortex was not damaged.

Figure 75 illustrates two electroencephalographic tracings from a rabbit

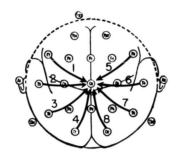

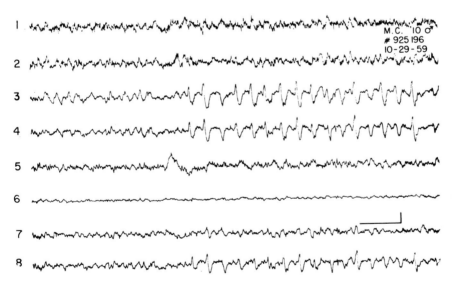

Figure 74. Electroencephalogram of a ten-year old boy with a history of chronic focal seizures. Seizures invariably began with an aura of bright flashing lights appearing in the right visual field. At the age of three years he had sustained an injury in the left parieto-occipital region. The primary focus is seen in channel 4. Calibration: 50 μV and 1 sec.

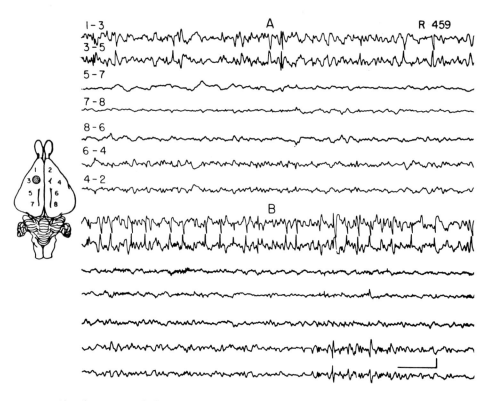

Figure 75. Electroencephalogram of an unanesthetized rabbit 24 hours (A) and three days (B) after production of an ethyl chloride lesion. The site and extent of the lesion are indicated by the cross-hatched area on the diagram. Derivations are bipolar from implanted electrodes over the indicated regions. Calibration: 50 µV and 1 sec. (From Morrell, 9.)

in which a left-sided epileptogenic lesion had been produced. Figure 75A represents the tracing taken 24 hours after producing the lesion. The abnormal discharge (primary focus) may be seen in the upper two channels. Simultaneous tracings from the opposite hemisphere and from other areas in the same hemisphere reveal no abnormality. After a time varying from a few days to three weeks, one may observe (Figure 75B) the development of similar paroxysmal activity in the opposite hemisphere at a point homotopic with that of the primary focus (lower two channels).

At first the secondary discharge was clearly dependent upon the primary one in the sense that spikes only occurred in temporal conjunction with those in the primary lesion, had a measurable latency following the primary spike (Figure 76), and disappeared altogether after excision or neuronal isolation of the original focus. The configuration of activity in the secondary area is that of an evoked potential; it looks like a "reflection" of the primary spike and thus has earned the colloquial name of "mirror focus". However, if the primary lesion is not excised or isolated within a few days to a few weeks, the secondary discharge becomes independent and persists in-

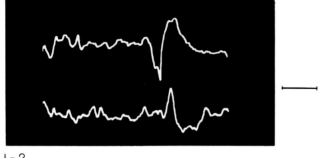

Figure 76. Characteristics of the dependent mirror focus. In the ink-written tracing the upper two channels record the primary focus and the lower two channels the mirror focus. The ethyl chloride lesion is indicated by cross-hatching. Calibration: 100 μV and 1 sec. In the oscilloscopic record, the upper channel records the primary region and the lower one the secondary region; calibration: 100 msec. (From Morrell, 9.)

definitely despite ablation or neuronal isolation of the primary focus. Figure 77 shows the continuing epileptiform discharge in the secondary focus (upper two channels) although the primary focus (lower two channels) ceased to fire after surgical transection of all incoming and outgoing pathways.

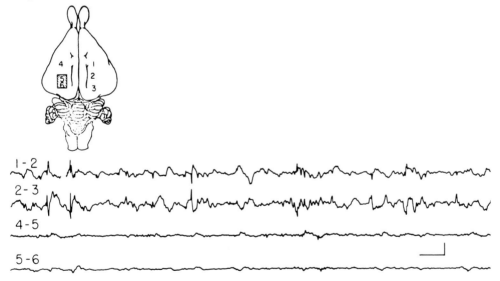

Figure 77. Independent discharge in a secondary epileptogenic focus. The secondary focus (upper two channels) continues to fire despite cessation of discharge in the primary lesion (lower two channels). Further explanation in text. Calibration: 100 μV and 1 sec.

TABLE 17

EFFECT OF EXCISION OF PRIMARY LESION ON RESOLUTION OF SECONDARY FOCUS

Number of animals	Age of lesion	Result*
12	24 hours	12/12 (100%)
14	72 hours	14/14 (100%)
12	7 days	8/12 (66.5%)
10	14 days	8/10 (80%)
15	21 days	4/15 (26.6%)
12	30 days	1/12 (8.3%)
13	90 days	2/13 (15.4%)
88 Total		

* Proportion of animals with complete resolution of 2° focus six months after placement of the ethyl chloride lesion.

To demonstrate the time-course through which a secondary focus is transformed from the dependent to the independent status we performed excisions or callosal transections at various stages after establishment of the primary discharge in a large series of animals. The criterion for evaluation was simply the presence or absence of epileptiform activity in the secondary region as seen in an EEG tracing taken six months after induction of the primary lesion. Table 17 indicates the results of excision; Table 18, the effect of callosal transection. In both groups the likelihood that the secondary focus will disappear drops precipitously if more than one or two weeks are allowed to elapse before the surgical intervention is carried out.

Brazier: After your surgical interventions, what is the general level of excitability in that hemisphere, elsewhere than at your mirror focus?

Morrell: The general level of excitability is not measurably altered.

Now we may proceed to an extension of the assumption stated above. The primary epileptogenic lesion was produced by local freezing with ethyl

TABLE 18

EFFECT OF CALLOSAL TRANSECTION ON RESOLUTION OF SECONDARY FOCUS

Number of animals	Age of lesion	Result*
12	24 hours	12/12 (100%)
15	72 hours	11/15 (73%)
10	7 days	6/10 (60%)
12	14 days	3/12 (25%)
12	21 days	0/12 (0%)
10	30 days	0/10 (0%)
11	90 days	1/11 (9.1%)
82 Total		

* Proportion of animals with complete resolution of 2° focus six months after placement of the ethyl chloride lesion.

chloride. On the other hand, the secondary or mirror focus developed in an area which had never been injured or acted upon by any foreign physical or chemical agent. It represented a population of initially normal nerve cells, connected with a chronically discharging zone by massive commissural tracts, which gradually developed a new and independent pattern of electrical behavior as a consequence of the sustained alteration of its afferent input. The new pattern of electrical behavior was long lasting and survived the complete elimination of the neural signals by means of which it had been originally evoked. We have suggested that the permanent alteration in cellular behavior exhibited by the mirror focus may be viewed as an example of cellular "learning" (12). Since the population of neurons comprising the mirror focus was limited to a small and easily defined area (defined by plotting the "field" of the abnormal electrical potentials with closely spaced electrodes), it seemed reasonable to examine such tissue more closely for signs of structural or molecular changes related to the newly acquired "behavior".

Indeed, some changes were found. Qualitative histochemical techniques revealed marked increases in the binding of a basic dye by ribonucleic acid.

In general the following method was employed. After preliminary electrical studies had clearly indicated the extent and distribution of both primary

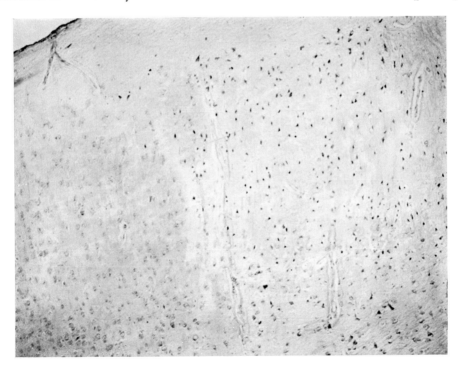

Figure 78. Section through region of the mirror focus. Note the collection of densely stained cells to the right of the photomicrograph compared with the characteristic staining of normal cortex to the left. Methyl green pyronin stain.
$\times$ 75

and secondary discharging areas, the animals were sacrificed and brains perfused *in situ*. Serial whole brain sections were prepared and stained with methyl green pyronin (or in later series with aqueous azure B bromide or gallocyanin at acid pH). Zones of primary and secondary foci were compared with electrically normal regions. In sections passing directly through the foci comparisons between normal and epileptogenic areas could be made on the same slide.

Figure 78 demonstrates a nest of darkly stained neurons in a section taken at the border of the electrically defined mirror focus. The area of secondary discharge is on the right and the adjacent normal cortex on the left. Although no cellular detail is visible at this low magnification, one can easily see the gross difference in dye-binding properties between normal and abnormal cell populations. In this particular animal the intracellular pyronin-dense material was fairly uniformly scattered throughout all cortical layers. In another animal (Figure 79) the pyronin-dense cells were confined to the IVth layer and part of the IIIrd (the discrete band extending from the upper left to the lower right corner of the figure). More superficial cells (upper right) show no increase in dye-binding, nor do those of the Vth and VIth layers, except for a few scattered pigmented cells deep in the VIth layer (lower left). In the extreme lower left corner one may see the fiber pathways of cortical white matter.

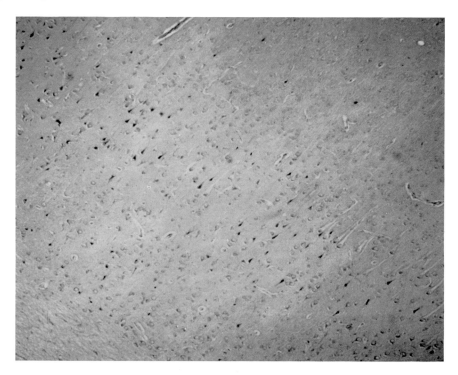

Figure 79. Histochemical staining of the mirror focus in another animal. Here the pyronin-positive cells are mainly in the IIIrd and IVth cortical layers. Further description in text.   × 85

It is important to point out that considerable care was taken with respect to techniques of fixation, of staining and sectioning of tissue so as to minimize any possibility of technical artifact (10). As mentioned above, the original findings have been replicated with two other histochemical methods for identification of RNA (azure B and gallocyanin). Staining specificity was routinely checked with ribonuclease extraction (Armour, crystalline, 1 mg/ml adjusted to pH 6.5 with NaOH, 60 min. at 25°C.) which invariably eliminated the dye-binding. On the other hand, pretreatment of slides with deoxyribonuclease (Worthington, crystalline, 0.2 mg/ml in 0.003 M magnesium sulfate, pH 6.5) for 90 minutes at 25°C. did not eliminate dye-binding. Removal of DNA was further checked by loss of Feulgen stainability. To eliminate observer bias the slides were coded and were read independently by two experienced histologists, neither of whom knew the results of the electrical studies used to determine the location and extent of primary and secondary foci prior to sacrifice. The site of the primary lesion was varied from animal to animal; location of the secondary focus varied accordingly, thus excluding the possibility that a particular cell type or grouping might have been inherently sensitive to basic dyes. The brains were perfused with fixative while the animals were under deep anesthesia but still alive. This procedure minimized cell changes due to poor fixation. Moreover, it seems highly unlikely that fixation artifact would vary in location from animal to animal in a manner precisely concordant with variations in the site of electrical discharge. There remains one argument, which may be valid at least for the primary lesion, that the dark cells are simply partially chromatolysed neurons. Yet the same sort of cells is seen in the mirror focus, an area untouched by the experimental procedure, the cortex remaining unexposed until the brain itself was removed. Neither can one account for these findings on the basis of retrograde degeneration, for such histochemical changes are not seen contralateral to a simple cortical excision.

In the past two years we have attempted to obtain a more quantitative estimate of the alteration in dye-binding by using microspectrophotometry and visible light. Measurements were made of the RNA-azure B binding with the two-wavelength method of Patau (15) and Ornstein (14). Slides were mounted with a matching refractive index oil. The aperture was kept small enough to subtend an area of cytoplasm 5 μ in diameter. Under these conditions analysis of absorption curve characteristics indicated Beer's law to hold. Section thickness was measured directly at a magnification of 1500 × from folds in areas adjacent to the cells under study. Thus, although the variable geometry of these cells precluded accurate determination of RNA-azure B amounts per cell, the method did provide an objective estimate of relative RNA concentration. Observations were made at wavelengths of 508 and 540 mμ and all values were corrected for distributional error to 540 mμ according to the formula of Patau (15), using the table given by Swift & Rasch (19). Two hundred cells were sampled on each slide; 100 from the electrically abnormal mirror focus and 100 from a cortical region which had shown no electrical disturbance. Four values were taken for each cell. In addition, at least two whole brain sections through the mirror focus were measured in each animal; the tabulation now being complete for nine of the sixteen animals in the present series. So far the data seem best expressed as mean extinction, or optical density, per micron section thickness. A preliminary calculation, based only on the nine completed cases, indicates an average increase (over control values in adjacent normal cortex) of 35-50 per cent in azure B binding by cells of the secondary epileptogenic region.

The second explicit assumption is that the alteration in RNA is specifically related to the epileptiform cellular "behavior". Although the general areas of electrical and chemical alteration coincide, our present techniques do not permit us to say that any given pyronin-dense cell has actually participated in the epileptiform activity.

Now, before commenting on the possible significance of these findings, I should like to mention briefly some additional experiments which are relevant to the interpretation of the histochemical data. Since most of these experiments have been published elsewhere (9, 11) I shall omit details or demonstrations at this time.

As was noted in the discussion of Professor Hydén's paper, when performance of a particular behavior pattern is used as the measure of "learning", it is sometimes difficult to know whether an associated change in neuronal chemistry is related to learning *per se* and not the concurrent motor activity. Even though our own model does not involve behavior of the animal, in many ways it has similar drawbacks. Thus, since the mirror focus was itself discharging spontaneously, one might argue that the permanent alteration of excitability as well as the increased RNA was dependent upon continuous self-reexcitation rather than upon structural or molecular factors. To evaluate this possibility it was necessary to abolish spontaneous discharge in such a way as to make it possible, later, to test for retention of abnormal, hypersynchronous and paroxysmal responses to stimulation. Complete neuronal isolation of the secondary region was carried out, taking care to preserve the pial blood supply to the isolated cortical slab. This procedure resulted in disappearance of spontaneous epileptiform discharge and such isolated epileptic slabs remained quiescent for the several months of observation. At the end of the observation period, microelectrodes inserted into the slab failed to disclose spontaneously firing units, but when seizure discharges were elicited in surrounding normal cortex by electrical stimulation or topical placement of metrazol (with care to prevent spread of the drug itself), after considerable delay the paroxysmal activity jumped the neuronal gap so that independent self-sustained discharge enveloped the isolated region and was reflected in massive unit firing. In our experience and that of many other workers, such evidence of ephaptic activation does not occur in chronically or acutely isolated non-epileptic tissue. This fact was taken to indicate that increased excitability had persisted in the mirror region despite the long period of inactivity.

Thus the second aspect of the mirror focus model which seemed analogous to behavioral learning was the evidence that the altered responsiveness persisted throughout a period in which spontaneous paroxysmal activity was abolished and self-reexcitation, as judged by the unit record, was absent. The mirror focus had not only "learned" to behave in terms of paroxysmal discharge but "remembered" this behavior even after months of inactivity. By excluding reverberating circuits as the basis for the long-lasting change in cellular behavior, the isolation experiment gave further support to the notion that molecular or structural alterations were responsible. Cells in the isolated mirror focus exhibited pyronin-dense staining characteristics which were indistinguishable from those in the intact secondary region except for the presence of obviously damaged cells around the borders next to the zone of surgical trauma.

The two assumptions listed above have been stressed not because they are considered unreasonable or far-fetched but simply to make quite clear those elements of the argument for which the evidence is not yet conclusive. The third and last assumption is unnecessary to the general thesis but bears upon interpretation of the histochemical findings in the isolated mirror focus. We noted that dye-binding properties were "indistinguishable" from those in intact secondary regions. But we do not have definite proof that such similarity in appearance indicates that exactly the same chemical change has taken place. If we *assume* that the same chemical alteration is present under these two conditions, then the isolation experiments, by eliminating the factor of concurrent neural activity, afford much more crucial evidence linking the histochemical data to the neuronal "memory" of past experience and, hence, to the information responsible for the acquired behavior. Unfortunately, many factors contribute to some uncertainty on this matter. To mention only one: an increase in dye-binding may represent a non-specific neural reaction to a number of processes. For example, if there is any such thing as regeneration (even abortive) in the mature central nervous system, the cells of an isolated area may exhibit increased RNA synthesis as a consequence of an increased demand for the protein needed for growth. However, regeneration and axonal sprouting cannot explain the entire picture since non-epileptic isolated cortex does not show a similar pyronin-dense pattern. On the other hand, it is conceivable that epileptic cells have a greater tendency to regenerate than do normal cells. Until we can decipher the code, or, at least, be sure that the RNA of epileptic cells is different from the RNA involved in ordinary metabolic activity, we will be unable to resolve this uncertainty.

Even if we exclude the special problems associated with surgically isolated cortical slabs, interpretation of the histochemical data is not easy.

Many variables may operate to upset the stoichiometry of nucleotide-dye mol binding necessarily assumed for quantitative evaluation of RNA levels by visible light microphotometry (3, 18). Although we have tried (especially in our current efforts at quantification) to eliminate the more obvious sources of error, we are still unable to conclude anything about absolute *amount* of RNA even from the best of measurements on dye-binding. The latter could equally well be influenced by changes in polymerization and possibly by submolecular factors involving charge distribution. Nevertheless, we do feel the evidence on hand is sufficient to indicate that there is *some* change in neuronal RNA associated with development of a secondary epileptogenic lesion. In turn, since the cells and cell systems of the mirror focus have been shown to exhibit many of the attributes of learning and of memory, it seems reasonable to consider the possibility that some form of ribonucleic acid complex may provide the molecular substrate for information storage in nerve cells.

The last statement has been deliberately phrased as a generalization, although I am well aware that my concrete evidence, if related to information storage at all, pertains only to a very abnormal kind of "information" producing a very specific and abnormal type of behavior. The analogy of the mirror focus may seem whimsical and even paradoxical. Nevertheless, an epileptic lesion, like a viral infection or a cancer, is established by the taking over of pathways and processes ordinarily used in more physiological transactions. Normal metabolic cycles may be altered in tempo, direction, or by accumulation of unusual by-products in disease states, but I am aware of no clinical disorder which represents a new biological principle. A mutation, which could conceivably have this effect, is almost always lethal. For this reason it seems likely that transfer and storage of abnormal information such as occurs in secondary epileptogenic lesions may differ in degree rather than kind from that which occurs normally. Certainly, the investigation of this preparation has yielded some interesting and provocative findings. At the very least we are now in a position to study clear-cut and permanent changes in the properties of single cells and cell populations which arise as a direct function of the previous exposure of those same cells to a known stimulation.

To begin the discussion, I would like to make two comments concerning the central theme of this conference. That theme, as I understand it, is the possibility that the permanent record of individual experience is stored in the form of a modification of nucleic acid molecules. I have chosen to interpret the term "individual experience" as meaning the "experience" of a single nerve cell. Only in this very special and restricted sense do the observations just described bear upon the central theme at all. Under these conditions I believe one can conclude that epileptic activation of nerve cells results in an increase in the number of anionic binding sites on intracytoplasmic RNA of about 35 per cent. We do not know whether the increased dye-binding reflects a change in the total amount of RNA or simply a change in secondary structure such as to make additional reactive sites available on the same molecule. Nor do we have any information on base sequence which might suggest an interaction with the genetic code. Thus even within the context of the private life of a single cell we have a great deal still to learn about the intimate details of RNA makeup and metabolism.

My two comments are cautionary and questioning. By limiting ourselves to the "experience" of a nerve cell we may be quite beyond the realm of the interactions which underlie learning. So far as I know no one has shown that behavioral learning requires an intracellular storage mechanism in the first place. Many would argue that behavior is a stochastic phenomenon emerging from random constellations of neural elements and not identifiable from the characteristics of any given unit. Then, of course, our model of cellular "learning" is simply not relevant to the issue at hand.

The question concerns the manner in which the concepts of molecular biology are employed in neurophysiology. For example, excluding the RNA viruses, the bulk of experimental evidence is consistent with the notion that the nucleotide sequence in RNA is specified by genetic information in DNA. Were this shown to be generally valid, it would pose great difficulties for the hypothesis of Hydén (4, 6), wherein the nucleotide sequence responsible for a "memory" is presumed to be originally established as a consequence of ionic flux induced by nerve impulses. By analogy with immunological specificity this would correspond to an "instructive" rather than "selective" mechanism of antibody synthesis. If the DNA-RNA specification system were susceptible in a random way to ionic fluxes, the ordinary metabolic machinery of the cell would be rapidly undone. Fortunately, metabolism continues despite learning. Obviously these genes and their corresponding RNA and enzymes required for metabolic activity are unharmed by nerve impulses. Perhaps, then, only certain special-purpose molecules are sensitive to ionic flux. If such molecules are conceivable, there seems no particular reason to strain the imagination still further with the requirement that they be "experientially stipulated" in a Lamarckian manner. Previously "informed" molecules (for example, with the code for synthesis of a neurohumor) might be selected or released by a particular pattern of impinging synaptic activity. The latter supposition is more in keeping with current genetic theory. Generation of a particular behavior (motor, sensory, etc.) still depends on classical connectivity, i.e., which particular cells and pathways are activated. The nerve cell need only use its molecular code to store a change in excitability to a particular impulse pattern. This would account for storage and could account also for retrieval or recognition based upon properties of cell surfaces (as occurs in antigen-antibody reactions and in embryogenesis).

However, one of the most difficult aspects of this particular proposal is the requirement that an electrical current induce a molecular rearrangement which is thereafter irreversible and immune to further perturbations of its electrical surround. We know that once a memory is stored one can do virtually anything with the electrical activity of the brain and not influence that storage.

Benzer: I do not understand the difficulty. There are two problems. One is, how do you change electrical impulses to a nucleotide sequence? The second problem is, how does that nucleotide sequence become immune to loss? What I am saying is that the second part is easy. Once you have created nucleotide sequence, it can be self-replicating and proliferate in large numbers, completely ignoring further electrical impulses.

Morrell: Fine, except that we require electrical impulses to alter the molecule in the first place.

Feindel: Not necessarily. That is an assumption, is it not? That you see electrical activity as an aspect of nerve cell activity does not mean it is the fundamental method by which any RNA might be changed within the cell. I think one has to keep an open mind about that. If you were a biochemist, you might be recording something in the chemical area rather than the electrical area which would manifest the change equally well.

McConnell: There are at least two other possibilities to consider. First, there might be a correlation between the pattern of incoming impulses and the changes one gets in the RNA, so that one RNA molecule could actually code a number of things, depending on when and with what pattern these impulses arrived. That is one possibility, if you simply want to look at a single cell. The second possibility is that a given input could make a change in a large number of cells drawn from a much larger population. In this case, the input would make the same change in every cell. The next input could change a large number of cells too, also drawn randomly from a larger population. Each input would "erase" all previous inputs. But as long as one cell retained the input, the specific memory, this might be enough.

Mommaerts: At this point, we have one half of a working hypothesis, if it were agreed that, due to the pattern of stimulation, one gets a change in the cyclic nucleotide content. The second half of the working hypothesis is in the form of a question only: could these cyclic nucleotides, in turn, influence the synthesis of nucleic acids?

Bickford: To return to the lesion, Dr. Morrell, you did mention something that perhaps ought to be brought into your model. If I understood you rightly, you said that, if this secondary focus is undercut, it will not develop a mirror focus; there has to be communication beneath as well as across. I do not think you mentioned that again, as to how you explain it and how it fits into your model.

Brazier: I understand that a very important step in your working hypothesis is that there is an afferent bombardment of the mirror focus. This presumably is not only inference but has been checked by electrodes in the corpus callosum. My question is: why do you use an abnormal bombard-ment? Why are you using a pathological situation? If I understand you correctly, your electrodes are on sensory cortex. Why not perform an experiment in which you bombard that sensory cortex in a set of rabbits, with a loud noise going on for many, many days, and then compare their brains with those of their litter mates? Why introduce a surgical problem with degeneration and all the highly pathological changes that take place as a result? In your hypothesis, should my suggestion work or should it not?

Morrell: I suppose that it might work. Remember that our original ex-periment was not designed to study mechanisms of learning or memory, or anything of the sort. We were studying secondary epileptogenic lesions. Among a series of observations came those of pyronin-dense cells. Only later, as we began to think about the electrophysiological features of the mirror focus as a prototype of cellular "learning" did we consider the histo-chemical data in the same context. Then, of course, we wondered if we had hit upon a way actually to visualize educated neurons! And having hit upon an easily reproducible phenomenon which fit most of the rules of a model, we decided to explore it thoroughly and quantitatively before turning to other things.

If prolonged sensory stimulation results in a similar chemical "tag", as the experiments of Hydén (4) and Brattgård & Hydén (2) indicate is in fact the case, it should be even more useful than the mirror focus. I suspect that the more usual types of behavioral training would leave more scattered traces and would not involve a small area of the nervous system so heavily as to be detectable with presently available techniques. At the moment our probing is done with a crowbar rather than a scalpel; we hope the difference is quantitative and not qualitative.

Brazier: Lying behind my question is whether you have to have an ab-normal discharge in order to obtain your histochemical changes, or whether accumulation of normal discharges would also produce them.

Hydén: An important question here is whether or not what you observe is an increased amount of RNA per cell.

Morrell: I think that that may well be so. Most of the histochemists with whom I have talked about this feel that is the case. However, I think it would probably be safe, and perhaps even more interesting, to consider that the increase in dye-binding with a basic dye reflects an increased avail-ability of protein-bound anion in the nerve cell.

Hydén: It would be desirable to determine the volume of the nerve cells. A volume decrease could simulate an increase of RNA. A volume increase could give the impression of a decreased amount of RNA. Therefore, such controls are important.

Morrell: I agree. We have made attempts to measure the volume. This is not easy to do in a cortical section.

Hydén: By X-ray microspectrography and using a scanning micro-photometer it is possible to obtain accurate values of cell volumes, irrespective of their shape (5).

Fox: The absorption maxima of many dyes, and I think this is particularly true of some of the basic ones like pyronin, change as they are bound by polymers. If you measure the absorption due to pyronin without having some framework of reference as to the way in which the absorption maxima are changed by reaction not only with RNA but, as you suggest yourself, with proteins, it makes it extremely difficult, I think, to draw any quantitative inference.

Morrell: Quite so. But I do not believe that shifts in absorption maxima contribute any substantial source of error in our newer technique.

Nirenberg: Would it be possible to do a relatively short-term experiment in the presence of P^{32}, and look for differences between stimulated and nonstimulated tissue? In other words, look at the focus?

Morrell: Radioautographic studies are now under way to settle precisely that question, but there are not enough results yet to warrant any statement.

Nirenberg: Is not the whole point of the discussion that you found an increase in the amount of RNA in this part of the brain?

Morrell: Not necessarily.*

John: I have some questions about the basic phenomenon, ignoring the interpretation of what the changed density is to be attributed to. As I understand the experiment, you have the possibility that the changed dye-binding may be due to the fact that this is an independent mirror focus, that it is a region which was stimulated, or that it is a region which was under-

---

* *Added by Dr. Morrell after the Conference:* It seems to me that the point of this discussion is related to the fact that we have unequivocally demonstrated *some* change in RNA associated with development of a mirror focus. Furthermore, the alteration is not in the direction of a *decreased* amount. The weight of evidence certainly suggests that there is a net increase in amount of RNA—but as I have said before, we still do not regard the evidence as crucial, since an increase of dye-binding by RNA might also occur from a change in secondary structure such as to make available additional anionic binding sites on the same RNA molecule. Until now we have not had the necessary technical facilities to allow a clear distinction between the possibilities. Final interpretation of the increase in dye-binding by RNA of these cells should be withheld until direct chemical analysis provides us with unambiguous answers. Nevertheless, the rigorous biological and enzymatic controls employed in these studies are adequate, in my opinion, to indicate a definite chemical change in cells of a mirror focus and to implicate RNA as a participant in this change. Incidentally, the magnitude of the histochemical alteration is considerably greater than the increase of RNA shown by Hydén (6) in cells of Deiters' nucleus after vestibular stimulation. This latter fact may explain why it was measurable at all with our crude techniques and may also be relevant to Dr. Brazier's question concerning the use of more physiological forms of sensory bombardment. For example, electrical responses to acoustic stimuli may be recorded from many areas of the brain quite distant from "primary" auditory cortex. There is no reason to assume that chemical modifications resulting from such stimulation would be confined to the classical auditory system. Certainly, it seems unlikely that the chemical modification would be confined to a circumscribed clump of nerve cells which could be compared with unaltered nerve cells on the same histological section.

Let me emphasize again that there is no intent to imply any quantitative concordance between these observations and the presumed chemical substrate for information storage in the nervous system. Our observations are relevant to the central theme of the Conference only if they direct the attention of the biochemist and cytologist to a particular molecular species in which changes associated with more orthodox behavioral learning might be discovered by applying the more refined techniques of Hydén and others.

cut and isolated. I am not sure what the control is to which you were referring your mirror focus stain. If you look at the staining of the mirror focus before it has become independent, after it became independent, and also study a recently stimulated, chronically isolated cortical slab which has not been an independent mirror focus, how do these compare to the slab which you showed us? I would also like to know how much time elapsed from the time you convinced yourself that this was a region which had a sustained excitability and would propagate in or out, in contrast to the normal isolated slab, before you took it out to test the RNA staining. If you recently stimulated and took it out, you would expect a higher RNA turnover.

Morrell: I realize that. Our basic histochemical data are based on the *intact* mirror focus in more than 100 animals and *isolated* mirror foci in about 50 animals. The isolated mirror focus was studied electrophysiologically in another series of 270 animals. It was impossible to interpret the staining properties of the isolated slabs which had been probed with microelectrodes and exposed so as to allow the stimulation and recording procedures described. Thus, the chemical and physiological measurements were made on different experimental populations. However, we have no reason to suspect that the populations differ in any way which might invalidate the correlation. It would be especially nice if we could perform intracellular microelectrode studies and simultaneous cytochemical determinations on the same nerve cell but, so far, one method of analysis seems to exclude the other.

John: Does tissue from a dependent mirror focus look different from this?

Morrell: Yes.

Bickford: Could vascular factors be important anywhere in the genesis of this mirror focus? I seem to remember in your early work you used fluorescein. Did this relate to vascular changes in the mirror focus area?

Morrell: Yes. There is some evidence of sodium fluorescein staining in the area of the mirror focus, which appears shortly after the development of the mirror focus, and later on disappears. We have not looked at this day by day but we have looked at it after a week, three weeks and three months. It certainly is not there at three months. There is no sustained change in blood-brain barrier, if that is what the sodium fluorescein indicates, although there may be a change at the beginning of its development.

Feindel: Have you made any effort to study the glia in this area in comparison with the neurons? Is there no change in staining?

Morrell: We have had no success. With the particular techniques we have used we have not been able to demonstrate altered staining properties of glial cells.

Thompson: I realize you cannot investigate all problems within a couple of years, but have you determined whether or not a subcortical focus is formed in your cortical experiments, perhaps in the thalamus?

Morrell: That is a good question. Such studies are presently under way but there are not sufficient data to report as yet.

Bickford: In regard to the subcortical pathway, Mattson in our laboratory has some evidence that, if you strychninize two homologous areas in the cat, obtain spiking in one hemisphere driving spiking in the other, and then cut the corpus callosum, this desynchronizes the connection between the two. However, if you deepen the anesthesia, the system will resynchronize again in spite of the fact that the corpus callosum is entirely cut. This indicates that under these conditions some other pathway comes into action. I suppose this may be the same path that has some effect in your nerve fibers.

Mishkin: Have you never seen any induction of an epileptic focus in the same hemisphere? There are many rather strong and long connections within the hemisphere. I would suppose the same thing could be observed if it were looked for.

Morrell: There are two answers to that question. The first is that there is some tendency for local enlargement of the primary lesion over long periods of time.

Brazier: Do you feel that is due to new bombardment in additional fibers?

Morrell: I cannot be sure whether or not the mechanism is ephaptic or synaptic through "U" fibers.

Dr. Mishkin is probably more interested in the long intrahemispheric pathways of which the most prominent, perhaps, is the occipito-frontal radiation. The animal studies have not shown any induction of secondary foci which could be ascribed to those pathways. At least with respect to the parameters we have measured, they appear to be largely inhibitory in function.

Reynolds: What happens to the RNA in the original lesion?

Morrell: That is really hard to estimate, because of exactly the problem Dr. Hydén raised. The cells are dark; they are small. They look chromatolytic. They are too damaged to test.

Reynolds: If the area enlarges, would this be true of the neighboring cells which were incorporated in this enlarged area source?

Morrell: Yes, it would.

Weiskrantz: I have two questions, which perhaps are related. If you look at RNA content in a slab that remained isolated for some time, is there reduction in RNA? Do you find a sort of negative mirror focus phenomenon?

Morrell: Yes.

Weiskrantz: The second question is really a point of information: I seem to remember, in reading some of the work of Brattgård (1) on retinal RNA as a function of stimulation, that, at least depending upon the age of the animal, a large amount of stimulation can produce relatively irreversible changes. So that in giving a great deal of stimulation to a mirror focus a change may be induced therein which, even when the animal is deprived of further stimulation, may produce relatively irreversible effects. I am not sure whether you were proposing that your phenomenon was somehow different from what we know about stimulation in other regions with respect to increase of RNA.

Morrell: If I am not mistaken, irreversible changes of that sort are found in newborn or young animals during the maturation period. Thereafter, stimulation produces a transient increase in the ribonucleic or ribonucleoprotein fraction, which disappears with return to rest.

Weiskrantz: Are those the only cases of irreversible changes in developing organisms, or are there others?

Hydén: Some studies have been done in Uppsala by Leksell et al. (7) on a heavy dose of irradiation, but those are the only ones I am aware of.

REFERENCES

1. BRATTGÅRD, S.-O., The importance of adequate stimulation for the chemical composition of retinal ganglion cells during early post-natal development. *Acta Radiol.*, 1952, Supp. **96**: 1-80.

2. BRATTGÅRD, S.-O., and HYDÉN, H., The composition of the nerve cell studied with new methods. *Int. Rev. Cytol.*, 1954, 3: 455-476.

3. GLICK, D., ENGSTROM, A., and MALMSTROM, B. G., A critical evaluation of quantitative histo- and cytochemical microscopic techniques. *Science*, 1951, **114**: 253-258.

4. HYDÉN, H., Biochemical changes in glial cells and nerve cells at varying activity. In: *Biochemistry of the Central Nervous System*, Vol. III (O. Hoffmann-Ostenhof and F. Brücke, Eds.). Pergamon, London, 1959: 64-89.

5. ———, Quantitative assay of compounds in isolated, fresh nerve cells and glial cells from control and stimulated animals. *Nature*, 1959, **184**: 433-435.

6. HYDÉN, H., and PIGON, A., A cytophysiological study of the functional relationship between oligodendroglial cells and nerve cells of Deiters' nucleus. *J. Neurochem.*, 1960, 6: 57-72.

7. LEKSELL, L., LARSSON, B., ANDERSSON, B., REXED, B., SOURANDER, P., and MAIR, W., Lesions in the depth of the brain produced by a beam of high energy protons. *Acta Radiol.*, 1960, **54**: 251-264.

8. MORRELL, F., Experimental focal epilepsy in animals. *Arch. Neurol.*, 1959, 1: 141-147.

9. ———, Secondary epileptogenic lesions. *Epilepsia*, 1960, 1: 538-560.

10. ———, Lasting changes in synaptic organization produced by continuous neuronal bombardment. In: *Brain Mechanisms and Learning* (J. F. Delafresnaye et al., Eds.). Blackwell, Oxford, 1961: 375-392.

11. ———, Information storage in nerve cells. In: *Information Storage and Neural Control* (W. S. Fields and W. Abbott, Eds.). Thomas, Springfield, 1963: 189-229.

12. MORRELL, F., SANDLER, B., and ROSS, G., The "mirror focus" as a model of neural learning. In: *XXI International Congress of Physiological Sciences* (Abstracts of Communications). Buenos Aires, 1959: 193.

13. MYERS, R. E., and SPERRY, R. W., Interhemispheric communication through the corpus callosum. *A.M.A. Arch. Neurol. Psychiat.*, 1958, **80**: 298-303.

14. ORNSTEIN, L., The distributional error in microspectrophotometry. *Lab. Invest.*, 1952, **1**: 250-265.

15. PATAU, K., Absorption microphotometry of irregular-shaped objects. *Chromosoma*, 1952, **5**: 341-362.

16. SPERRY, R. W., Cerebral organization and behavior. *Science*, 1961, **133**: 1749-1757.

17. STAMM, J. S., and SPERRY, R. W., Function of corpus callosum in contralateral transfer of somesthetic discrimination in cats. *J. Comp. Physiol. Psychol.*, 1957, **50**: 138-143.

18. SWIFT, H., Quantitative aspects of nuclear nucleoproteins. *Int. Rev. Cytol.*, 1953, **2**: 1-76.

19. SWIFT, H., and RASCH, E., Microphotometry with visible light. In: *Physical Techniques in Biological Research; Vol. III: Cells and Tissues* (G. Oster and A. W. Pollister, Eds.). Academic Press, New York, 1956: 353-400.

IMPAIRMENT OF LEARNING AND RETENTION FOLLOWING EXPERIMENTAL TEMPORAL LOBE LESIONS

L. WEISKRANTZ
University of Cambridge
England

Since we are going to be dealing with rather complex phenomena, I want to make a few introductory comments.

I think that it is undeniable that there is currently a fashionable urge to study the neurology of memory, but it would be ridiculous to suggest that experimental neurologists in the past, using conventional techniques of lesions, stimulation and recording, could have studied discrimination, emotion or learning without thereby studying memory.

There is a further difficulty, not unrelated, and that is that while we have broad descriptive categories such as memory and discrimination and arousal, these are very rarely matched to actual descriptions of the behavior itself, but only to rather indirect inferences drawn from behavior. That is, we never see pure discrimination, pure memory, or pure arousal, or even, for that matter, pure lever-pressing (though that is a different sort of impurity). Not all psychologists believe any longer that these categories are useful. I do believe they are useful, but I think we have to keep in mind how indirect our inferences are when we talk about behavioral changes relating to memory. Some of these difficulties have already become apparent in the discussions here. If you are describing a given behavioral situation, it is often extremely difficult to know whether you are talking about memory or learning or changes in input, for instance, to take one example that came up earlier.

However, I do not think experimental neurologists are in a special category here. It is exactly the position that everyone is in who is interested in studying the effect of a given treatment on behavior. Whether you are launching an animal into space, or giving it a drug, or winking at somebody's wife, you have a very complex set of inferences to go through in order to measure the behavioral changes. I do not really think that psychologists have worked out the general experimental logic that applies to these situations.

Coming to the question of memory, it is obvious that somewhere within the organism there have to be events that outlast any particular input. And whatever these events are, or wherever they are, there is ample evidence that either they do not remain fixed and stable, or their accessibility does not remain unchanged. The evidence which relates to this part of the phenomenon, namely the change which occurs with time, is sometimes called "consolidation". But I am not going to talk much about this for it has recently been reviewed by Deutsch (9), and I am sure a certain amount of the material is familiar to you. But, in any case, sooner or later, these events must lead to relatively enduring states which are independent of large changes in electrical activity as normally measured. This is the point Dr. Morrell touched on. When one is considering the effects of lesions on behavior, one has to try to characterize them at least in some very rough way. I shall take a very simple analogy, really much too simple, but I think perhaps it helps us to classify certain changes that we obtain when we make a brain lesion. Then the further question is, can we affect different parts of our analogy experimentally?

If we imagine correspondence coming into any office (Figure 80), it is going to turn up fairly soon in an "in" basket on someone's desk, and sooner or later some of the material in the basket is going to end up in someone's relatively permanent filing cabinet. On some occasions it is going to be necessary to refer to material either in the "in" basket or in the filing cabinet. We can imagine that in either of these locations (A and D in Figure 80) there is some sort of fading or strengthening that goes on with time; or we can imagine there is some sort of fixed and minimal delay in the transfer stage (C).

When we say that following a lesion something is wrong with memory, obviously there is a number of places in such a system where the defect could have occurred. B could be near a drafty window and its contents be blown out. Or we can imagine that the "in" basket consists of the entire office and there is no other file. Nothing is lost but we just cannot find it! I do not have to press this analogy.

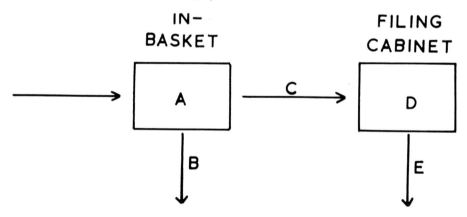

Figure 80. Diagram illustrating handling of incoming information. A: Temporary storage; C: transfer stage; D: permanent storage; B and E: retrieval from storage.

I would like to look at some clinical phenomena. If we consider the stage marked "E" in Figure 80, which represents getting something out of the permanent file, there are clinical cases of this kind that are quite dramatic. These are the typical cases of amnesia, where somebody has forgotten who he is, where he comes from, and suddenly something happens and it all comes back. It is obvious the file was there all the time but its accessibility had altered.

I think it is extremely difficult, on the basis of neurological material, to point to changes within the file itself. It is here, presumably, that one invokes, if not RNA, then some sort of change at the molecular level. Blockage at C is, I think, easier to discover.

One but not necessarily the only way of characterizing the evidence relating to consolidation might be to say that when information comes in, it is available to the animal for the moment, but it takes time to get through to D. Some rather devastating events like shock or anesthesia can prevent any further transfer of this material from A to D.

Even more convincing, in my opinion, are some cases which have been described by Penfield and Scoville, in collaboration with Milner (22, 24). I want to spend a fair amount of time on the kind of cases they described. Such persons have no difficulty in remembering material over a short period of minutes, but once they turn to something else the original material simply vanishes; it is as though the experiences had never taken place. They can, however, remember events that occurred some time before the operation. In a less dramatic way, the same sort of defect is seen in Korsakoff's psychosis. Obviously the complete filing system has not been destroyed since pre-traumatic material is still available. The story is not as simple as that, because such cases sometimes show a certain degree of retrograde amnesia, but at least a block at C is strongly suggested. Such cases are usually described as having an impairment in "recent memory". According to the present analogy, that is a particularly misleading label. In fact, the impairment is not in recent memory, but in getting the information into the long-term store.

Disturbances at A and B, where it is really appropriate to use the term "recent memory", are more difficult to isolate in the clinical literature. Some of the really extreme Korsakoff cases might belong there, but they are quite generally debilitated by this stage.

Feindel: What do you mean by A, in terms of what we ordinarily speak of in memory function? What would your A correspond to, clinically?

Weiskrantz: I do not think I know of any really clear-cut clinical cases. I am going to come to this, in a sense, in animals. There are certain lesions which, in animals at least, produce difficulty in delayed alternation and similar tasks. I personally believe that, in that sort of case, the difficulty is at B. But various people have entertained the hypothesis that with such lesions the material in A decays abnormally rapidly.

Feindel: You mean there is a lot of wind-blowing-in-the-window so that the material cannot be sorted and filed?

Weiskrantz: Yes. Actually, leaving neurology, we know how we can experimentally alter such events in man. These are the typical experiments on retroactive inhibition, and the ingenious experiments of Broadbent (3) and others of putting separate inputs into the two ears. It has been shown that if the person attends to material in one ear, material in the other ear tends to decay. So the material in A can be manipulated experimentally.

What we have been concerned with in some of our work is trying to affect these stages differentially. Much of the work I am going to present is preliminary. The question is whether or not the experimental design is suitable for pursuing this kind of an interest.

Before turning to the temporal lobe cases, I would like at least briefly to present some of our work on the frontal lobe because I think it may illuminate the general experimental rationale. It has been known for a long time that lesions in the dorsolateral portion of the frontal lobes produce a deficit in delayed response or delayed alternation performance. This is the sort of task in which an animal watches the experimenter hide a piece of food in one of two positions, but is prevented from responding by the lowering of a barrier. A few seconds later it is allowed to respond. This is repeated for many trials, the position of the bait being varied according to a random schedule. A normal animal can perform quite well at, say, five seconds delay but animals with frontal lesions have very great difficulty in doing it.

Morrell: Is it important that the barrier be opaque?

Weiskrantz: Some of the work of Dr. Mishkin's laboratory (1) has shown that if there is no barrier at all, at least in one situation, no deficit is found. Actually, in their experiment it was a delayed alternation situation, which is slightly different—it was not a question of using food for the bait. That is a situation where the animal has to go first to the right and, after a delay, to the left, then to the right, and so on. They found an opaque screen produced a deficit. I hope I am quoting this correctly. I am sure Dr. Mishkin will correct me if I am wrong. A transparent screen produced a partial deficit in the animals with frontal lesions.

We have been interested to see if we can produce a reversible frontal deficit by means of stimulation, rather than the usual permanent surgical defect. We had already published a brief report of this some years ago (34) but the complete report appeared only a few days ago (33). Probably it has not reached this country yet. There are various other people who have been concerned with exactly the same sort of technique. Stamm (25), for example, has been looking at a similar phenomenon, and Chow (6) has been concerned with similar effects in the temporal lobe.

The technique is to put a grid of electrodes over the frontal lobes (Figure 81). The photograph does not show the actual electrode points but markers to indicate their positions. The points are all electrically independent of each other, and we can stimulate between any two tips. We are particularly concerned with stimulation around the sulcus principalis. We know from the lesion work that a lesion there produces more of a deficit than one elsewhere in the frontal lobe.

This turned out to be, in our hands at least, surprisingly easy. Not everyone has found it so. I think we have been fortunate in our choice of parameters, which are: 100 cps, square wave, monophasic, 0.2 msec. The amplitude was set for each animal to be always two volts below the threshold for obtaining any observable motor effect; we measured it from time to time, it remained quite constant but was different for each animal. We stimulated for one second out of four, irrespective of what the animal was doing.

We had three animals trained to do delayed alternation and performing at roughly the level that would be expected of normal animals in such a situation, i.e., around 90 per cent. The effect of the stimulation is not ap-

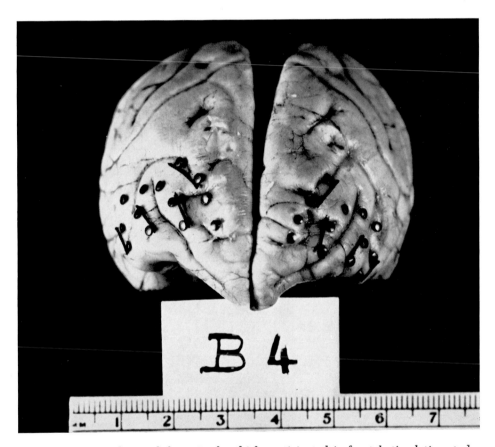

Figure 81. Brain of one of the animals which participated in frontal stimulation study. Markers in photograph are about 2.5 times the size of the actual electrode contacts, which were 0.8 mm in diameter. Lines ventrally adjacent to pairs of contacts connect sulcus arcuatus stimulation points; lines dorsally adjacent connect sulcus principalis stimulation points. (From Weiskrantz, Mihailović & Gross, 33.)

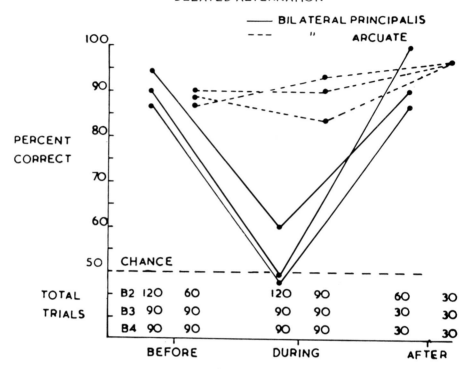

Figure 82. Graph showing reversible effect of sulcus principalis stimulation on delayed alternation performance, with no effect from sulcus arcuatus stimulation. (From Weiskrantz, Mihailović & Gross, 33.)

parent at all in the general behavior of the animal. Yet the delayed alternation performance falls quite radically; in fact, in two animals it fell to the chance level (Figure 82). Immediately after the stimulation had been terminated, the animal returned to a good performance level. That was without any break at all in the experimental session.

The dotted lines show the effect of stimulation outside this focus—still in the frontal lobes, but outside the principalis focus. You can see there is no appreciable effect. It is fairly clear, from a lot of work that we have done, that this is quite a specific change.

Bickford: Can you tell us where the stimulation point is? I am not familiar with this terminology. Is this ahead of the motor cortex?

Weiskrantz: This is quite anterior to the motor cortex; it is prefrontal.

Feindel: How far ahead of the arcuate is that? Is it the convolution in front?

Weiskrantz: It is anterior to the arcuate and lying near the principalis. This is in the monkey.

Feindel: You do not get any motor effect at all?

Weiskrantz: No, it is absolutely clear-cut. There is an amusing story about this. We put this performance on film, with some sham stimulation sessions intermixed with the real stimulation ones. The question was, could people, by looking at the film, tell the difference between real stimulation and sham stimulation? We lost the key to this, and we ourselves literally could not tell which was sham and which was real. The best way we could tell when we were actually stimulating was to note whether the animal could do delayed alternation.

Bickford: Do you have evidence of electrical discharge? Does this set up epileptic discharge in the animal, or not?

Weiskrantz: It produces an afterdischarge which persists for a few seconds. The question as to whether or not it is essential to have that afterdischarge, we could not answer in these particular animals because, unfortunately, there was no electroencephalograph where we were working. Stamm (25), however, has some information on this, which suggests it is necessary to have an afterdischarge.

Concerning the question of specificity, if the animal has been trained to do some quite different task, such as discrimination between two auditory inputs, there is no appreciable effect either on arcuate or principalis stimulation (Figure 83). And there are other tasks which show no effect. The stimulation effects are quite specific.

Feindel: Is the auditory test one where the animal has to do something with its hands, to make a choice?

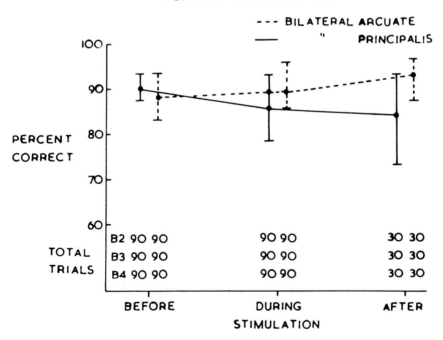

Figure 83. Graph showing lack of effect of sulcus principalis or sulcus arcuatus stimulation on auditory discrimination performance. (From Weiskrantz, Mihailović & Gross, 33.)

Weiskrantz: Yes. In that test there are two auditory stimuli and two responses it must perform, one for one stimulus and another for the other.

In our stimulation experiments, the same animals had electrodes in the hippocampus. We caused hippocampal afterdischarges and tested behavioral effects. This was unilateral stimulation.

What we found with hippocampal stimulation was a slight decrement on practically any test. Figure 84 shows auditory discrimination and delayed alternation performance. These are medians for three animals. There was a large variety of other tasks that we tried. In all cases we found a slight effect, nothing specific.

Feindel: There were no bilateral stimulations?

Weiskrantz: No. One of our collaborators, Mihailović, set up bilateral discharges through unilateral stimulation, but we have no evidence there were such effects in these three animals.

Mishkin: How were these trials given? That is, was there a day of stimulation and a day of no stimulation, or were they intermixed within the day, or what?

Weiskrantz: This was done in a very complex way to balance order effects. Some days the animals had 20 or 30 trials with stimulation, followed by 20 or 30 without, and another day it was reversed. Some days we had no stimulation at all to test whether there were any sequential effects with time.

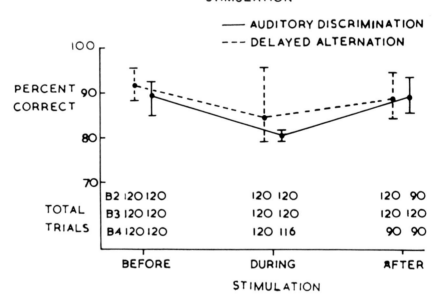

Figure 84. Graph showing slight effects of unilateral hippocampus stimulation on both auditory discrimination and delayed alternation. (From Weiskrantz, Mihailović & Gross, 33.)

Mishkin: Were these the same techniques that were used to obtain a positive result on delayed response, in which you were stimulating for one second out of four?

Weiskrantz: Yes.

Bickford: Was that unilateral or bilateral stimulation that produced the change in delayed alternation shown in Figure 82?

Weiskrantz: In Figure 82, the big drop was caused by bilateral stimulation. There is a very considerable drop with unilateral stimulation but not as great as with bilateral.

The drop in auditory discrimination during hippocampal stimulation is more than we obtained with the frontal stimulation. Even so, it is still a slight effect.

I want to look at this in another context. I think it is fairly obvious that this technique could have advantages for behavioral analysis, especially where we are concerned with memory function, because one of the great difficulties in analyzing lesion material is that we are dealing with irreversible effects; we cannot, with irreversible phenomena, make distinctions between changes in the store and changes in retrieval, for example. One must be able to return the system to a normal state before one can test what happened while it was in the abnormal state.

We tried to use this to see if we could affect the short-term storage. It is known that frontal lesions do not interfere with conventional visual discrimination. These are problems which normally require a few hundred trials for learning and, therefore, they cannot ever be administered within a single session. I think the next figure shows a typical example of this kind of test.

Figure 85 shows one of the animals with implanted electrodes, working on a pattern discrimination problem. A peanut is under only one of the two patterns, and the position of the two patterns is varied from trial to trial. The animal's task is to find the peanut reliably. This, typically, would take two, three, four hundred trials. We found this kind of a learning task was not affected at all by stimulating animals day after day while they were learning. What we tried to do in these animals, in order to look at the short-term retrieval, was to see whether quite fresh and new discriminate information is less useful for them (as compared with controls) than older information. We tried to exploit the learning set phenomenon and train animals so they could solve simple discriminations within a few trials. So that, in this kind of situation, the animal only has information available to it which is specific to that task, which is a few seconds or at most a few minutes old.

Figure 86 shows the sort of discriminanda, for example, two simple toys. This kind of technique will be well known to many of you. If you train animals on a long series of such rather simple tasks, they perform better and better, and accordingly you can produce an animal which will learn at

Figure 85. Animal confronted with visual pattern discrimination problem.

whatever speed you wish, including one-trial learning, depending on the amount it has had of "learning to learn" (12).

This was the situation we used: we had animals with a learning set; we gave them problems which they could learn very quickly. We found that, while no effects of our stimulation on difficult pattern discriminations could be seen, they were very apparent in these situations. The stimulated animals did learn these simple situations but they took an average of one and one-half to two times as long as they did when not being stimulated. Brush and co-workers (4) have found similar evidence, although they do not interpret it this way but in terms of perseveration. I think one can say that typically on difficult discriminations, frontally stimulated animals are not impaired, whereas on simple ones they are.

Again, one of my colleagues, Dr. Gross (11), has shown that retention for this kind of discrimination twenty-four hours after it is learned is very good. In fact, it is slightly better than normal, but reversal of discrimination within a day is rather impaired. I think that can be interpreted similarly. We now know, also, from more recent work in our laboratory, that reversal *between* days is not affected. There would be violent disagreement among people working in this area as to whether it is memory disorder or not. *If* it is memory disorder, it must be characterized as one at stage B in our diagram (Figure 80), that is, retrieval from the "in" basket.

Turning to the temporal lobe, I have already mentioned the cases which have been described by Milner. There are other cases described by other writers, Walker (32), for example, and Dr. Victor (31), who has described a case in some detail.

I would like to ask three questions about these cases in relation to the

Figure 86. Animal confronted with visual object discrimination problem.

present discussion. First of all, what are the critical anatomical structures? Second, since the answer to that is probably going to involve animal experiments, what sort of behavior must be studied in an animal which we suspect has a similar defect, in order to detect the deficit? Third, what is the nature of the mechanism? That is, why should this particular pathology lead to this particular consequence?

Going to the first question, the bitemporal lesions carried out by Scoville (24) in man (either for the relief of epilepsy or for attempted therapy in schizophrenia) involved the hippocampal formation and tissue surrounding it laterally and ventrally, as well as the pyriform and amygdaloid tissue which is anterior to it. It was possible, from his work, to show removal of the material from the hippocampal formation was not by itself critical. The possibility remains that the removal of the anterior tissue, the pyriform cortex, is necessary but not sufficient for the defect. But, then, I think this is unlikely from the report of Dr. Victor and his collaborators (31).

Penfield (22) carried out surgery in a rather different way. His lesions were unilateral lesions, they were made from a more lateral approach, and they were essentially deep removals which approached lobectomies. Even though the lesions were unilateral, Penfield argued that there was some evidence of electrical abnormality on the other side which, in effect, produced a patient with bilateral pathology. Only a small percentage of cases with unilateral removal showed this rather devastating memory defect. Walker (32) does not agree with this interpretation of Penfield's about unilateral lesions really being bilateral lesions. I am not going to be concerned with the question of whether it is unilateral or bilateral, but just emphasize, as far as the human material is concerned, that the hippocampal formation was involved in all the cases which showed this kind of memory defect, that is, adequate short-term storage but no transfer of the short-term store to the long-term one.

Feindel: Would you like to say what you mean by hippocampal formation? Do you include hippocampal gyrus?

Weiskrantz: It was involved in these cases.

Feindel: I think this is rather important because one of the difficulties, as you know, has been that these terms have been used somewhat differently by different writers or groups studying the problem. I think that if you use the term we should be told what you include.

Weiskrantz: What I tried to say is that what was involved in the lesion was the hippocampal formation itself, Ammon's horn plus much else; Ammon's horn was involved in all the lesions I mentioned.

Feindel: I take it you used "hippocampal formation" to mean what we would say anatomically is hippocampus proper.

Weiskrantz: Yes. Going back to Penfield and Scoville's findings, in Penfield's cases (22) they were deep lesions which invaded the white matter plus the neocortical tissue, for, by making this lateral approach, he was invading the hippocampus and a great deal of adjacent tissue as well.

Scoville's approach (24) was quite different. He tried to slip in medially; in other words, he approached the hippocampus by going under the frontal lobes and making medial resections of the temporal lobe. We do not have the reconstructions. We do not know what he took out. All we have are very elegant drawings of what he did—his section would involve all of the hippocampus, and it would also involve the tissue surrounding it, but not going up very far on the lateral surface.

Benzer: Which is your procedure?

Weiskrantz: This is not my procedure at all. All I am trying to say is, in all of the human material, this structure, the hippocampus, has been included. That other tissue was also included does not mean the hippocampus was not implicated. There is at least agreement among the examiners of the human cases that that structure is included in the pathology which leads to this particular kind of memory defect.

Benzer: Does the pathological effect require damage on both sides?

Feindel: The conclusion in the series Dr. Weiskrantz is quoting was that these cases have to have bilateral involvement to show the defect at all. That was the point of the question I raised when he was describing stimulating the hippocampus on only one side in the monkey; I do not think this is valid in comparison.

Weiskrantz: No, I would not like to claim that it is conclusive.

Victor: Dr. Feindel, are you making an unqualified statement that the lesions have to be bilateral?

Feindel: No, only in the two series of cases he is referring to. I was going to discuss some of this later, because I think Walker's series (32) was not studied in quite the same way and there is no detailed information.

Bickford: I think you can obtain suppression of recent memory from uni-lateral stimulation. This is stimulation I am talking about, not ablation. In case the implication is that there must be biliaterality, I think we have some evidence that unilateral stimulation could do it.

Feindel: I agree, we do too. I was just referring to these two series of surgical cases that were published. Both of those claimed bilateral dam-age.

Weiskrantz: The point is that there have been many statements about the human material, saying that the hippocampus seems to be involved in this kind of memory pathology. It seems that in all of these cases the hippo-campus has been damaged.

In cases of Korsakoff psychosis, a phenomenon you see, for example, in alcoholics, a rather similar sort of memory defect occurs as in the temporal lobe cases (2, 26). Here there has been implication of pathology in the re-gion of the mammillary bodies and tissues surrounding it. In fact, in one series of 70 post-mortems on Korsakoff cases, I gather there was pathology in the mammillary bodies in over 90 per cent of the material, and also damage in other structures as well, the dorsomedial nucleus for instance (14). Much of this material is very unsatisfactory. There were no controls, and it is not known how often regions that look abnormal are found in supposedly normal material. I think this is a very important point.

In any case, there has been some suggestion of a system here which involves the hippocampus and one other major part of the brain, namely that part of the hypothalamus or mammillary bodies which is related to the hippocampus in perhaps several ways but at least via the fornix, a tract which emerges from the hippocampus and circles around and descends to the mammillary bodies. So, it looks as if we have a fairly neat sort of pic-ture.

Feindel: I would like to say it is not neat.

Victor: No, indeed, it is not this simple at all.

Weiskrantz: I do not wish to say that the reality is neat. Some people have implicated in a fairly simple way some system of this sort.

When we turn to animal work and we look into the effect of the hippo-campal lesions, it is true that some authors have claimed hippocampal lesions affect rate of maze learning in rats (13, 27). But when we turn to the monkey work, the anatomical homologies are somewhat more obvious. I think the story is not clear-cut. We can go back to earlier work of Mishkin (18, 19), for example, which compared the effect on visual discrimination learning of lesions in the hippocampus (made in one of two ways) with neo-cortical lesions in the inferior temporal region.

The conclusion which emerged from his study was that this neocortical lesion produced a rather greater defect in both learning and retention of visual patterns than was caused by lesions to the hippocampus. An attempt has been made by Orbach and collaborators (20) to produce in monkey the kind of lesion that Scoville produced in man. They came out with a very complicated picture. There was a variety of effects, including deficit in retention for pre-operatively acquired habits, and deficit in relearning. But one of the most severe deficits was in delayed alternation, which we have always been associating with frontal effect. It does not look as if this is a parallel to the human material. Furthermore, it is difficult to know whether to ascribe the discrimination-learning deficits to neocortical damage, since the authors admit that it was possible that there was some undercutting of temporal neocortical tissue in almost every case. So, we are in a difficult situation. Also, and this appears to me to be very important, the animals with temporal neocortical lesions (in their series they had some neocortical controls) consistently showed a deficit in the retention of post-operatively acquired material, whereas the animals with hippocampal lesions were variable in this regard.

So, from this it is difficult to tell whether a neocortical lesion is, in fact, not more severe than a hippocampal lesion in producing a relative defect. I think other people have also made hippocampal lesions or have stimulated the hippocampus and have had some difficulty in producing kinds of effects that would be predicted (6, 10).

Chow (6), for example, set up hippocampal afterdischarges. It is difficult to know exactly what he meant by that. There was no histology. He compared those with neocortical temporal afterdischarges. He found that the neocortical afterdischarge did produce a serious effect on learning and retention, whereas the hippocampal one did not.

I think it is at this point that we have to stop and ask some fairly serious questions. That is, in these animal experiments, what is it that we are looking for as parallels to the human material? There is no doubt that we ought to ask some question about learning and retention. But I suspect, if we were to administer the sort of tests to human cases that we administer to our animals, we would have a rather muddled picture.

Therefore, what I would like to do—I do not think this has been done quite this way before—is to start from the human experiments and see if we can construct some sort of appropriate analogue.

Just to repeat the human case again, according to Milner (17) the temporal lobe cases could perform adequately over short periods of time, if they continued to be occupied on the particular task in question. Once they left that task, they could not remember ever having been exposed to it. So, what we require is a task which is sufficiently short so that the animal is not likely to shift spontaneously from it to something else. If we are interested in studying retention at some later time, it has to be a task that involves some measure of learning. If we were confident of a large effect, we could study instances of one-trial learning, but if we want to have a sensitive measure of a partial effect, the one-trial learning situation is, of course, not very good, because the score can only be zero or one. That is one thing we need—a task of learning which can go on rather quickly, but not so quickly that our measure of retention is not a sensitive one.

As a second requirement, we need tasks which are sufficiently numerous so that retention can be studied day after day, and systematic variations can be made in exploring the two factors which are likely to be important here, namely temporal interval and interference effects between tasks.

I think that if you examine the learning set paradigm I have already talked about with the frontal animals, you will find it meets some of our requirements because, by suitable manipulations both in the experience of the animal and the properties of the objects, one can find tasks that are learned at almost any desired speed.

We have tried to adjust these two factors, that is, the task difficulty and the experience of the animal, so that the tasks require somewhere in the neighborhood of twenty trials, or less. We can deliver one trial, say, every ten seconds, so that these tasks can be delivered to the animal over a period of a few minutes.

We have presented these tasks in a variety of combinations. On the first day the animal gets two tasks; the first we call task A, a pair of objects, one of which has the peanut under it. When the animal has learned that to a criterion, it gets the second task, B. On the next day, it gets the same task as it had last, B, plus the new task, C. The third day, C and D; the fourth day, D and E, and so forth, going generally to, say, 48 days or something of that sort. So there is each day a measure of retention over 24 hours for a task, and a measure of new learning for a task requiring only one or two minutes to be completed. One can ask whether these two kinds of measures can be dissociated as a function of the various brain lesions.

What we found in our stimulation study on frontal lobes (33) (although we did not do it in exactly the way just outlined) was that there was definite impairment of the new learning, and from our lesion work we know that there definitely is *not* impairment of retention of such tasks over 24 hours.

There are various other combinations as well. We have, for example, ABC, BCD, CDE, and so forth, or, to study retention within a day as contrasted with retention between days, ABA, BCB, CDC, DED, and so forth. There is, as you see, a number of ways of arranging these rather simple problems, so that one can look at different effects.

We have not yet done very much with this; the work is preliminary, and the question is whether it seems worth continuing.

We, in fact, have a number of animals being run at the moment, with a variety of lesions, but what we started with were animals with inferotemporal lesions. The reason we did this was that they happened to be available from another study. Also, I think from one point of view, it is the obvious first place to look.

Mishkin: Just to make it clear, these lesions do not involve the hippocampus?

Weiskrantz: These are neocortical lesions, not involving the hippocampus. The lesions do not involve deep structures at all; they are bilateral.

Green: Do they involve the entorhinal cortex?

Weiskrantz: No. Let us examine what is known about the effects of this lesion. From the studies of Mishkin, Chow, Pribram (5, 18, 19) and a number of others, we know the following: when animals are given visual patterns to learn to discriminate, if they have lesions in this part of the brain bilaterally, they learn rather more slowly than animals which have no lesions, or animals which have lesions elsewhere. I think we have good evidence, which I will not go into now, that this deficit is one of discrimination learning rather than one involving a change in sensory capacity. We have measured the visual fields of these animals. Wilson & Mishkin (36) also have produced strong evidence supporting the same position. Auditory discrimination learning is not impaired. Somesthetic discrimination learning is not impaired. There is some suggestion from other work that these other kinds of discrimination learning can be impaired by lesions elsewhere (23, 34, 35). So it seems as if we have a number of modality-specific regions concerned with perceptual learning.

Feindel: Is there any evidence that the monkeys used in those experiments had visual field defects?

Weiskrantz: There is very clear evidence they did not. These animals are still alive, but it is known that the deficit occurs without lateral geniculate degeneration. Dr. Cowey, in our laboratory, has devised a method of studying visual field defects in monkeys quite precisely. We can really say, with some certainty, that the inferior temporal lobe lesion produces no change in the visual fields that we can detect (7, 8). I think this is really clear-cut. We can, of course, pick up changes in the field with lesions in the classical visual system.

We have this question of learning defect. What does learning defect mean? When we give animals problems which require several days for learning, we cannot distinguish between the acquisition of material over a relatively short period of time and retention over a longer period of time. All we have are lumped scores for problems requiring, as a rule, a few hundred trials spread over a few days or a week. These lumped scores are consistent with the kind of defect we are looking for, but are not sufficient to demonstrate it.

What I would like to show now are some preliminary results that Mrs. Iversen has obtained in the Cambridge Laboratory with temporal, frontal, and normal animals.

Figure 87 shows results for the AB-BC-CD-DE sequence I first outlined. We can plot retention in terms of a ratio, $L - R/L + R$, where L is the number of trials the animal required the first time it was given the task to perform, and R is the number of trials it required the second time. This ratio would be zero if the animal showed no savings from the first occasion to the second occasion. If it showed savings, the score would be positive, with a maximum of 1. If it took longer to learn than it did on the first occasion, the ratio would be negative. The two animals with temporal lesions in this sort of test certainly look different from the other animals, and show no savings. The two with frontal lesions are, in fact, better than the normals, which confirms our earlier observations.

The figures below the bars show the proportion of negative ratios that entered into this median. Figure 88 presents the median L and median R for each animal for all problems. This is simply plotting the same data in a somewhat different way. One of the two animals with temporal lesions does seem to take, on the average, longer than any of the others, but the other seems to be within control range. It is learning more quickly, on the average, than the normal.

If you look at the normal, J-10, you can see it requires fewer trials, on the average, to relearn the problems. This is generally true of the control animals, the temporal animals requiring, if anything, slightly more. So, it looks as if one could study, in this way, retention measured independently of learning.

Mishkin: May I ask if you took an average? You said 48 days of testing. Is that 48 problems, 48 comparisons?

Weiskrantz: Yes. This is median, actually, not average. We had to exclude some problems. There is always a difficulty in this sort of thing, because

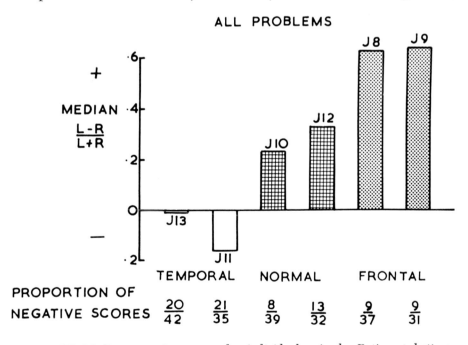

Figure 87. Median retention scores for individual animals. Ratios at bottom refer to numbers of negative scores, i.e., number indicating negative savings, relative to total number of scores.

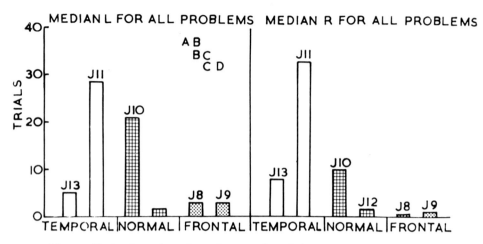

Figure 88. Median L and median R plotted for each animal. See text.

from time to time you cannot get your problems exactly right, and you are going to find some tasks for some animals that are learned in zero trials on both occasions, in which case your retention measure is meaningless.

Deutsch: Did you train the animals to a certain criterion each day?

Weiskrantz: Yes, to a criterion of 18 correct responses out of 20. I now want to show that this defect is different from the human temporal lobe defect. When we look at the ABA-BCB-CDC paradigm (Figure 89), we have both a measure of 24-hour retention and of retention within a single session—that is, retention over a period of five minutes or so. You will see

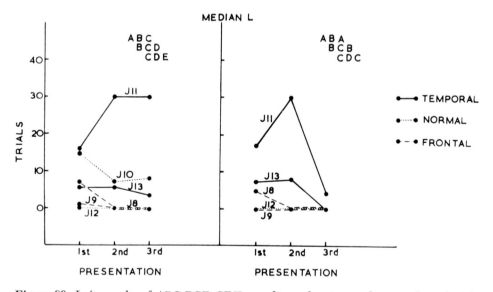

Figure 89. *Left:* results of ABC-BCD-CDE paradigm, showing median number of trials required for learning on first, second and third presentations of the same problem. *Right:* similarly, for ABA-BCB-CDC paradigm. This paradigm involves retention both within days and between days.

that the animals with temporal lesions again show the 24-hour retention defect which we found in the AB-BC-CD arrangement, but they demonstrate very good retention *within* a single session. This is different from the human cases, where we would expect that as soon as there was a switch to a new problem retention of an earlier one would be poor.

Morrell: These are inferotemporal lesions; they are not hippocampal, and thus are not comparable anatomically to the human cases.

Weiskrantz: I am saying they are not comparable in their memory defect, nor anatomically. But I have presented some reasons why I think it was worth testing the effect of inferotemporal lesions before going to the hippocampus. The results indicate that the deficit caused by the inferotemporal lesion in the monkey is not the same as that in the temporal cases in man. Of course, there are other differences. For example, the inferotemporal monkey deficit is modality-specific.

Again, and I think this is a fairly interesting finding, one would not expect in the human material that task difficulty had anything to do with this situation, and yet in our material task difficulty turns out to be quite an important variable.

In Figures 90 to 95 we have plotted savings as a function of initial learning score (L). Actually, our measure of savings here was L-R/L, which

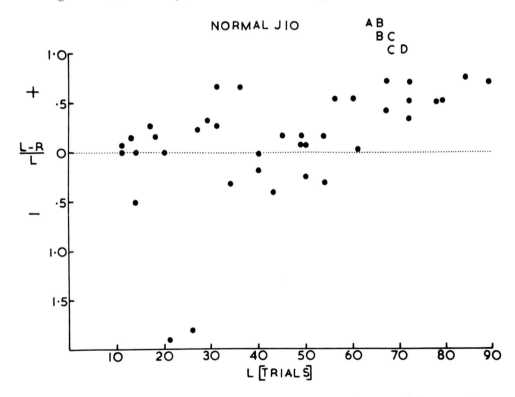

Figure 90. Distribution of retention scores for one animal as a function of the original score for each problem, using the AB-BC-CD paradigm.

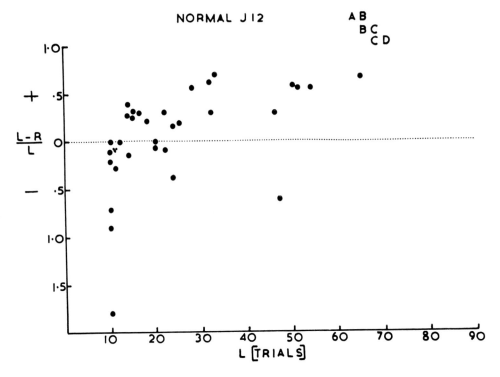

Figure 91. See Figure 90.

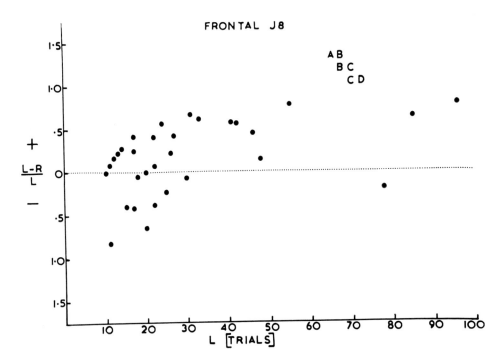

Figure 92. See Figure 90.

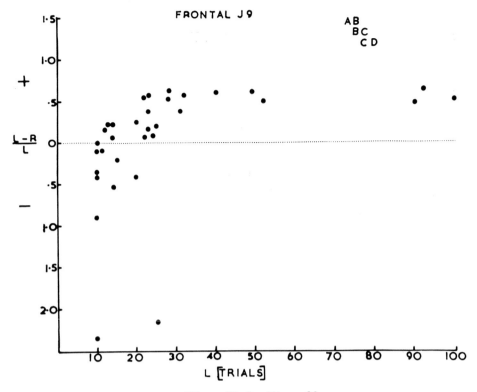

Figure 93. See Figure 90.

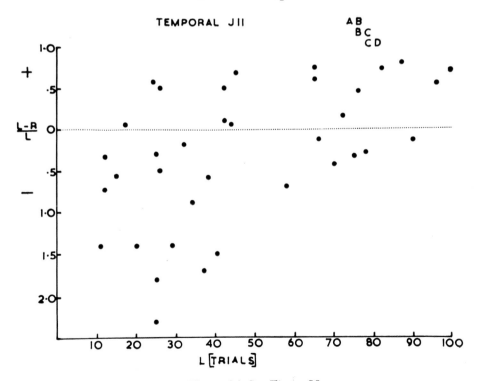

Figure 94. See Figure 90.

is not quite the same as our earlier measure, but for these graphs that could not at all change the relationship plotted. You will see that retention increases as the number of trials required for initial learning increases, for all animals. The plots for those with temporal lesions are simply displaced downwards, as they would have to be, of course, in view of the results we have discussed earlier, but the shapes of the distributions are much the same. These animals, too, are more likely to retain material presented for more trials than for fewer trials. This is reminiscent of other results with temporal lobe lesions in monkeys, showing that pre-operatively overtrained habits are less affected than habits trained only to criterion. I do not think our results would be expected if the defect were similar to that in man. There are various other predictions which do not hold up. For example, the performance of inferotemporal animals does not drop between daily sessions in a difficult discrimination learning task which requires several sessions.

Deutsch: Certainly, for normal human material, it has been found that the greater the difficulty of the task, the better the retention.

Weiskrantz: I think that Milner, in her clinical reports on the bitemporal cases (22, 24), has very good evidence that even if you present material over and over again to such cases, you cannot get it through to the store.

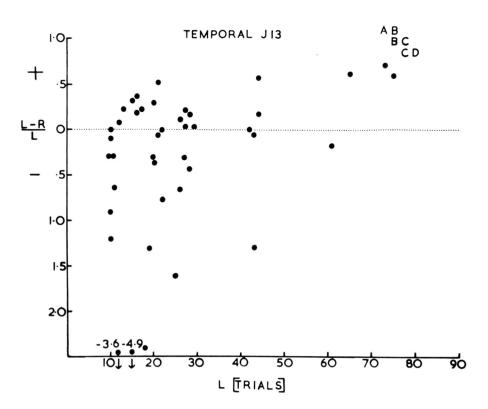

Figure 95. See Figure 90.

Feindel: I think she mentioned that one of the two patients from the Montreal series could learn something after very high motivation (16, 17). I am just trying to paraphrase what she said. I am not quite sure it is as black and white as you make it.*

Weiskrantz: What I want to ask is, what sort of lesions should one try next? First of all, it might be that there is an interaction among these several modality-specific regions that are going to present in combination a much more severe deficit than we see in any single modality.

It is also possible that a combination of neocortical and hippocampal tissue will produce a critical defect. Actually, if you look at the animals in Mishkin's early paper (18), the two most impaired animals, if I remember correctly, were ones which were supposedly control animals; that is, controls for hippocampal damage, but ones which inadvertently received neocortical plus hippocampal damage. I think this is very likely here.

All I want to say at this stage is that the sort of impairments we obtain from lesions and stimulation experiments very rarely, if ever, seems directly to involve a difficulty of disturbance of the actual contents of the store. We can block the transference of material from one stage to another, but it is very rarely that we ablate the contents.

In conclusion, by using techniques of this type, one at least might be able to dissect out a rather gross change in learning disability, or something of that sort, into the appropriate sort of boxes in which one wants to put these things. So, I think that the technique shows promise although the results for the temporal lobe are still only very preliminary.

Mishkin: I would like to emphasize just one thing. As Dr. Weiskrantz has said, the evidence on animals to date simply does not compare with what has been reported in certain cases of temporal lobe damage in man. This kind of severe "memory" impairment has never been reproduced in animals. I think his point is very good, though. The tests which have been used, the kinds of behavior that have been studied, are perhaps not the ones that we would think now, on the basis of Dr. Weiskrantz' analysis, would be the most appropriate. The experimental design he is using, specifically asking the question about interference during the daily learning session, seems to me to be one that would be especially worth investigating.

Morrell: Why is the defect in the hippocampal region in humans supposed to be an impairment in registration between the store of memory and experience or record of experience? Would you not expect to find an impairment in simple conditioning to a new problem?

Weiskrantz: We have found an impairment in simple conditioning, if you include pattern discrimination learning as simple conditioning. But the point is, if the conditioning is so simple that it should go on quickly, with-

---

* *Dr. Feindel's note after the Conference:* Dr. Weiskrantz is quite correct in saying that repeated testing with the same material failed to produce any improvement with practice in the patient with the temporal lobe memory deficit, according to Milner's findings. On the other hand, she points out that in the two cases studied the loss of recent memory was not absolute and that there was some improvement in the first few years after excision.

out interruption over a short period of time, you would not predict, from the human material, that there would be any defect.

Mishkin: There is one other possibility which should not be overlooked. I think it would be worthwhile attempting to produce a discharging lesion in the hippocampus as opposed to the kind of damage or interference we have been working with. There is, I suppose, at least some reason to believe it is not only the locus but the type of pathology that is important.

Adey: I hope to speak later about the question of drug-induced discharges in the hippocampus and their propagation in relation to the interruption of performance. I think you have a good point.

Weiskrantz: I do not know whether you accept Chow's evidence (6) or Flynn's work (10) on this as being relevant. There have been attempts to set up hippocampal discharges.

Mishkin: These are not chronic pathologies; these are afterdischarges.

Bickford: I just wanted to raise the question of whether your results with the frontal discharge could possibly be a distraction or affect of some kind. Since you cannot communicate with the animal, I wondered if it felt discomfort or anything like it during stimulation, which would cause its performance to deteriorate.

Weiskrantz: I think it is very hard to argue that it could be discomfort of the sort that would affect only one kind of performance.

Bickford: This is a prolonged type of performance, is it not, where this type of distraction might be important?

Weiskrantz: No. In fact, the most serious case of prolonged stimulation to the frontal lobes was when we gave these animals the difficult pattern discrimination; the animals were stimulated throughout the whole session, 50 trials per day for several days, and showed normal learning curves. Also, they actually remembered better than normals on the next day.

Morrell: I would like to say, in the animals we studied with pathological discharging unilateral lesions in the medial temporal lobe, there was a pronounced deficit in formation of conditioned responses to auditory, visual and tactile signals, with auditory being most affected. The deficit disappeared with ablation of the discharging lesion, even though the ablation included more tissue than was involved in the discharging area.

Adey: I find it very difficult to see why people become so excited about the differences between comparable lesions in subhuman primates and in man, since, quite obviously, the complexity of the projections of the hippocampal system into subcortical structures is something which has evolved with man himself, as a part of a phyletic sequence. And the vastness of the subcortical connection of the hippocampal system in man has probably no real rival in the histology of the brain of the subhuman primate, as far as we can determine it. One would be, I think, very rash at this stage to conclude that the specificity of a hippocampal lesion was, in fact, the determining factor in the subsequent deficit in performance. It seems to me much more likely the modulating influence of the hippocampus on a whole series of subcortical systems, and perhaps even on the subcortical systems in the primary sensory pathways, may be the influence that determines the laying down of the memory trace.

I think it is well to recall, as Penfield (21) pointed out so very elegantly and so very definitively, that there is no reason to conclude that the hippocampus itself is the actual site of the memory trace or the memory function. Thus, one may proceed with infinite elegance to the performance of restricted hippocampal lesions, or lesions in the entorhinal cortex, for example, without, I think, any ultimate hope of unraveling this particular problem.

Weiskrantz: In reply to Dr. Adey's comment, it seems to me it is perhaps unnecessarily nihilistic. If one wants to do any refined analysis, probably one is going to go to animal work, because it is rather difficult to get these cases for post-mortem, and rather difficult to get the kind of pathological case that allows very careful dissection, anatomically.

Therefore, it seems to me to be worth the try at least to look for parallels in the animal experimentation. Furthermore, this question of whether the hippocampus is that much more evolved in man than in monkey—

Adey: You apparently missed my point completely, in that I was trying to point out that it is the interrelations of the hippocampus with subcortical systems through which the phenomenon of storage of information, and so on, probably manifests itself.

Weiskrantz: I would accept that, although that is a matter of interpretation.

Adey: Yes, the diencephalon of man is presumably vastly removed from the diencephalon of the monkey in its complexity. It has nothing more than the broad skeleton of similarity.

Weiskrantz: I think the first place one would look would be in similar places in man.

Adey: I agree.

Weiskrantz: The kind of memory defect that you see in the human cases, I think, is somewhat rare, in that it permits a rather clear, not absolutely clear, but a rather clear specification. This would seem, in terms of how we conceptualize neurology of memory, to fit in at a fairly natural stage, that is, it would involve blocking at a discrete point in this sort of model. Therefore, if this is the case, it would seem to be particularly worthwhile to try to find the same kind of thing in animals.

Adey: Possibly that is the case. However, looking at the whole gamut of hippocampal lesions, as they have been experimentally inflicted over the last twenty-five years, and the apparent lack of clarity in the results, it is necessary to consider investigations such as those which I hope to discuss later, where a simple subcortical lesion produces both a memory defect of the kind frequently described as being typical of temporal lobe damage and, at the same time, the electrical cortical activity in the hippocampal system is deranged. The recovery of performance occurs *pari passu* with the recovery of hippocampal activity. Therefore, I think the question of the reciprocity of interrelations between the hippocampal system and the sub-cortical organs with which it is connected, directly and indirectly, is the more fruitful way of looking at this problem rather than trying, in a sense, to find some angel on a pin's head within a hypothetical critical area of the hippocampus.

Thompson: If the hippocampus is important in recent memory, then one might expect that most of those neural structures related anatomically to the hippocampus should be involved in it, too. Our recent-memory test for rats consists of a task called, in psychological terms, the successive reversal of a position habit, and is related to alternation performance.

The apparatus involves a T-maze. What the animal must learn to do is to avoid that side from which a shock to the feet had been administered 30 seconds previously. To illustrate, the animal is placed in the start box and is allowed to choose either the left or right arm. If it goes to the left, it receives a shock. The animal then turns around and goes to the right arm in order to enter the goal box. This constitutes an "informing trial". Thirty seconds later it is returned to the start box for a test trial. Virtually all control animals will go to the right arm. Those operated animals I described as showing a loss do not do that. They may continue to go to the left on several successive test trials, each time receiving a shock, before a reversal response is made. Then, on later tests, the animal is given an informing trial in which a response to the right arm is punished, and subsequently given test trials.

Mishkin: Is it one trial reversal?

Thompson: We reversed them when they made one correct response.

In our initial experiment (28), we tested the effects of lesions in the mammillary bodies, mammillothalamic tract and anterior thalamus. It was found that bilateral destruction of either of these subcortical structures significantly impaired the animal's ability to perform on the reversal task.

We have since made lesions in many other cortical and subcortical areas. Damage to the hippocampus, of course, gave us significant deficits in performance. In addition, discrete lesions invading either the anterior limbic region, septal nuclei, lateral preoptic area, lateral hypothalamic area, substantia nigra or the tegmentum immediately superior to the interpeduncular nucleus also interfered with the learning of this task.

Perhaps even more interesting are those lesions which failed to affect reversal learning. They include the prefrontal cortex, posterior cingulate area, caudate nucleus, amygdaloid complex, medial thalamus, posterior thalamus, lateral subthalamus, pretectal area and the central gray.

It is immediately apparent that all of the structures critical for the performance of the task are related to the hippocampal-fornix systems, but not all structures having hippocampal connections are involved. For instance, a lesion confined to the postcommissural fornix fibers gave negative results. This was also true for the stria medullaris and the parafascicular nucleus.

For the moment, at least, the main question is whether or not the losses observed on this task reflect a disturbance in recent memory. These data could equally well be interpreted in terms of a loss in response inhibition, such as that developed by McCleary (15).

Green: I would like to address a question to Dr. Thompson about what strikes me as a most remarkable and interesting finding. He finds, I gather, that—as a nonpsychologist, forgive me if I do not use the right words— short-term retention is abolished or severely damaged by lesions of path- ways which go to the hippocampus and involve the hippocampus itself, and pathways which lead from the hippocampus to the rest of the brain. In addition, he finds that control lesions made very extensively elsewhere in the brain do not interfere with this kind of activity.

I would like to ask him whether the conclusion that one should draw from this is that the hippocampus itself probably is not concerned with the engram, since what we are seeing is an interference of in-going fibers, the main part of the brain to which they are going, and the fibers that go out from that part of the brain. In other words, this may be very important for retention, but probably is not the place where it is actually occurring.

Thompson: I did not mention a number of things. For example, we found very clearly that the magnitude of the deficit we obtained in our operated animals, whether it resulted from lesions in the hippocampus, septum, mammillary bodies or preoptic area, was a function of the size of the lesion. The larger the lesion, the greater the loss.

If, however, we consider only those cases with virtually complete destruc- tion of a given structure, we find that the extent of the loss of performance was independent of the site of damage. In other words, the hippocampal lesion was not producing a greater deficit than was a septal lesion or a mam- millothalamic tract lesion.

I also neglected to mention the point that most of the critical lesions examined in this reversal experiment have no disturbing effect on the post- operative retention of a brightness discrimination (29, 30). Possible excep- tions to this are the lateral hypothalamic and the hippocampal lesions.

So, long-term memory is probably not localized in these structures. What specifically their function is in recent memory is difficult to say at this time.

REFERENCES

1. BATTIG, K., ROSVOLD, H. E., and MISHKIN, M., Comparison of the effects of frontal and caudate lesions on discrimination learning in monkeys. *J. Comp. Physiol. Psychol.*, 1962, **55**: 458-463.
2. BRIERLEY, J. B., Clinico-pathological correlations in amnesia. *Geront. Clin.*, 1961, 3: 97-109.

3. BROADBENT, D. E., Immediate memory and simultaneous stimuli. *Quart. J. Exp. Psychol.*, 1957, **9**: 1-11.

4. BRUSH, E. S., MISHKIN, M., and ROSVOLD, H. E., Effects of object preferences and aversions on discrimination learning in monkeys with frontal lesions. *J. Comp. Physiol. Psychol.*, 1961, **54**: 319-325.

5. CHOW, K. L., Further studies on selective ablation of associative cortex in relation to visually mediated behavior. *J. Comp. Physiol. Psychol.*, 1952, **45**: 109-118.

6. ———, Effect of local electrographic after-discharges on visual learning and retention in monkey. *J. Neurophysiol.*, 1961, **24**: 391-400.

7. COWEY, A., The basis of a method of perimetry with monkeys. *Quart. J. Exp. Psychol.*, 1963, **15**: 81-90.

8. COWEY, A., and WEISKRANTZ, L., A perimetric study of visual field defects in monkeys. *Quart. J. Exp. Psychol.*, 1963, **15**: 91-115.

9. DEUTSCH, J. A., Higher nervous function: the physiological bases of memory. *Ann. Rev. Physiol.*, 1962, **24**: 259-286.

10. FLYNN, J. P., and WASMAN, M., Learning and cortically evoked movement during propagated hippocampal afterdischarges. *Science*, 1960, **131**: 1607-1608.

11. GROSS, C. G., Discrimination reversal after lateral frontal lesions in monkeys. *J. Comp. Physiol. Psychol.*, 1963, **56**: 52-55.

12. HARLOW, H. F., The formation of learning sets. *Psychol. Rev.*, 1949, **56**: 51-65.

13. KAADA, B. R., RASMUSSEN, E. W., and KVEIM, O., Effects of hippocampal lesions on maze learning and retention in rats. *Exp. Neurol.*, 1961, **3**: 333-355.

14. MALAMUD, N., and SKILLICORN, S. A., Relationship between the Wernicke and the Korsakoff syndrome. *A.M.A. Arch. Neurol. Psychiat.*, 1956, **76**: 585-596.

15. McCLEARY, R. A., Response specificity in the behavioral effects of limbic system lesions in the cat. *J. Comp. Physiol. Psychol.*, 1961, **54**: 605-613.

16. MILNER, B., Psychological defects produced by temporal lobe excision. *Res. Publ. Ass. Nerv. Ment. Dis.*, 1958, **36**: 244-257.

17. ———, The memory defect in bilateral hippocampal lesions. *Psychiat. Res. Rep.*, 1959, **11**: 43-52.

18. MISHKIN, M., Visual discrimination performance following partial ablations of the temporal lobe. II. Ventral surface vs. hippocampus. *J. Comp. Physiol. Psychol.*, 1954, **47**: 187-193.

19. MISHKIN, M., and PRIBRAM, K. H., Visual discrimination performance following partial ablations of the temporal lobe: I. Ventral vs. lateral. *J. Comp. Physiol. Psychol.*, 1954, **47**: 14-20.

20. ORBACH, J., MILNER, B., and RASMUSSEN, T., Learning and retention in monkeys after amygdala-hippocampus resection. *Arch Neurol.*, 1960, **3**: 230-251.

21. PENFIELD, W., Functional localization in temporal and deep Sylvian areas. *Res. Publ. Ass. Nerv. Ment. Dis.*, 1958, **36**: 210-226.

22. PENFIELD, W., and MILNER, B., Memory deficit produced by bilateral lesions in the hippocampal zone. *A.M.A. Arch. Neurol. Psychiat.*, 1958, **79**: 475-497.

23. Pribram, H. B., and Barry, J., Further behavioral analysis of parieto-temporo-preoccipital cortex. *J. Neurophysiol.*, 1956, **19**: 99-106.

24. Scoville, W. B., and Milner, B., Loss of recent memory after bilateral hippocampal lesions. *J. Neurol. Neurosurg. Psychiat.*, 1957, **20**: 11-21.

25. Stamm, J. S., Electrical stimulation of frontal cortex in monkeys during learning of an alternation task. *J. Neurophysiol.*, 1961, **24**: 414-426.

26. Talland, G. A., Psychological studies of Korsakoff's psychosis: VI. Memory and learning. *J. Nerv. Ment. Dis.*, 1960, **130**: 366-385.

27. Thomas, G. J., and Otis, L. S., Effects of rhinencephalic lesions on conditioning of avoidance responses in the rat. *J. Comp. Physiol. Psychol.*, 1958, **51**: 130-134.

28. Thompson, R., A note on cortical and subcortical injuries and avoidance learning by rats. In: *The Frontal Granular Cortex and Behavior* (J. M. Warren and K. Akert, Eds.). McGraw-Hill, New York, 1964: 16-27.

29. Thompson, R., and Hawkins, W. F., Memory unaffected by mammillary body lesions in the rat. *Exp. Neurol.*, 1961, **3**: 189-196.

30. Thompson, R., and Massopust, L. C., The effect of subcortical lesions on retention of a brightness discrimination in rats. *J. Comp. Physiol. Psychol.*, 1960, **53**: 488-496.

31. Victor, M., Angevine, J. B., Mancall, E. L., and Fisher, C. M., Memory loss with lesions of hippocampal formation. *Arch. Neurol.*, 1961, **5**: 244-263.

32. Walker, A. E., Recent memory impairment in unilateral temporal lesions. *A.M.A. Arch. Neurol. Psychiat.*, 1957, **78**: 543-552.

33. Weiskrantz, L., Mihailović, L. J., and Gross, C. G., Effects of stimulation of frontal cortex and hippocampus on behavior in the monkey. *Brain*, 1962, **85**: 487-504.

34. Weiskrantz, L., and Mishkin, M., Effects of temporal and frontal cortical lesions on auditory discrimination in monkeys. *Brain*, 1958, **81**: 406-414.

35. Wilson, M., Effects of circumscribed cortical lesions upon somesthetic and visual discrimination in the monkey. *J. Comp. Physiol. Psychol.*, 1957, **50**: 630-635.

36. Wilson, Jr., W. A., and Mishkin, M., Comparison of the effects of inferotemporal and lateral occipital lesions on visually guided behavior in monkeys. *J. Comp. Physiol. Psychol.*, 1959, **52**: 10-17.

HIPPOCAMPAL MECHANISMS IN PROCESSES OF MEMORY: THOUGHTS ON A MODEL OF CEREBRAL ORGANIZATION IN LEARNING*

W. ROSS ADEY
Brain Research Institute
University of California
Los Angeles

What I would like to discuss is, first, the system organization of the hippocampus, as we have studied it in animals with ablation and drug studies; second, the computer analysis of various aspects of the wave processes during discriminative learning; third, the more direct monitoring of the physicochemical changes in learning, as we have studied them in a variety of behavioral performances by the application of impedance measuring techniques to the learning process.

Much of what has been said earlier has, in essence, concerned itself with something which is not universally accepted in the neurophysiological and particularly in the psycho-physiological community, namely the question of equipotentiality in the cortex, in relation to mechanisms of learning, and storage of information.

It was made apparent in a number of the presentations, and in particular in Dr. Weiskrantz's, that the frontal and temporal regions of the cortex are those which appear to have some relationship to the storage of information, or at least to its recall under appropriate circumstances.

I do not wish to discuss any aspect of the frontal lobe problem except to emphasize that, as Dr. Deutsch remarked, the question of the changes following frontal lobe lesions may also be a discriminative problem in sensory systems as well as having aspects of a problem in recent memory.

It would be easy to assume, as has, indeed, been commonly done over the past fifty years, that there is an essential equipotentiality between cortical regions in the processes of storage of information. Much has been written and many studies have been performed in support of the theme that, with the exception of the primary receiving areas, the cortical mantle functions as a whole in processes of storage of information, and that performance defects ensuing upon regional ablations relate essentially to the volume of

* The work described in this paper was assisted by Grants B-1883 and M-3708 from the National Institutes of Health, and by Grant AFOSR AF 61-81 from the U.S. Air Force.

cortex removed, rather than to its location on the cortical mantle (45).

Slowly, evidence has accumulated that there may be at least two major cortical zones having a special relationship to the laying down of the memory trace or, at least, to the recall of the information under appropriate circumstances. Lesions in prefrontal cortex have been shown to interfere with tasks involving recent memory, but the possible relationship of the defective performance to modifications in mechanisms of sensory discrimination rather than to a specific defect in memory function has been emphasized by Rosvold & Mishkin (54). The dramatic memory defects resulting from interference with temporal lobe structures, as first described in the monkey by Klüver & Bucy (44), have been duplicated and confirmed in many studies since that time, and have been the subject of symposia and reviews (2, 16, 19, 33).

The role of the temporal lobe, and the effects of stimulation, ablation, and so on, is even more complex. The question that I would like to discuss first is the comparative anatomy of the hippocampus; this discussion will be focused on the hippocampal structures.

As Edinger (31) showed some time ago, in a figure which is historically quite interesting, if one looks at the temporal lobe in cross section, the hippocampus has two palisades of closely arranged cells forming two main structures. One is an arch of pyramidal cells, and at the other end it is enclosed by a smaller "U", the layer of dentate cells. In each case there is a very definite palisade arrangement. This is something we will come back to and discuss repeatedly. The hippocampus exemplifies something common to all cortical structures, in that the dendrites are very closely adjacent and overlapping. The cell borders are extremely close in the hippocampus, closer in fact than in other cortical structures; in the hippocampus they may be only a few angstroms apart, 100 to 200 Å, I believe, from Dr. Green's studies (36). The implication is that this proximity may be sufficient in degree to allow some interaction between the nerve cells.

When one reviews the input and output arrangements of the hippocampal system, one of the earliest schemes came from Elliot Smith (57) on the basis of studies of the whole gamut of vertebrate brains, suggesting that on the dorsomedial side of the hemisphere is the primitive hippocampal cortex. He noted that the input arrangements come from an adjacent bulge which he called the paraterminal body, and which we call the septum. The input is from neurons in the deeper parts of the forebrain and the thalamus.

The output, on the other hand, is a bundle (the fornix) running without interruption down into the tegmental region of the midbrain. Elliot Smith thus proposed an essentially simple input-output arrangement. He conceived the fornix as being one of the first major motor systems in the mammalian forebrain. We do not now consider the hippocampus as a motor organ, but the interesting observation has been made by Eckhard Hess (39) of Chicago that if one damages this dorsomedial region of the avian hemisphere young birds fail to imprint. This failure of imprinting appears to be one of the most characteristic features of lesions on the medial aspect of the hemisphere.

The final point that I would make about the hippocampus and the hippocampal cortex is that essentially through the whole scale of vertebrate creatures, and certainly throughout the mammalian scale, there is a uniformity of structure in this palisade arrangement of cells in the hippocampus itself. It also has very extensive reciprocal relations with subcortical structures. They are not reciprocal on a one-to-one basis that would allow reverberation, but there is a quite extensive input to the hippocampus from virtually all thalamic areas and from the rostral midbrain. If one considers hippocampal projection systems through multisynaptic pathways, there is a very wide distribution through the diencephalon with, perhaps, some focusing of the output in the dorsal part of the thalamus and in the region between thalamus and hypothalamus. We will come back to the latter again, because this appears to be a significant zone through which many of the effects of hippocampal stimulation make their way to subcortical levels.

Attention has been focused on the allocortical structures of the amygdaloid and especially the hippocampal systems in the laying down of the memory trace. The great antiquity of the hippocampal system in the evolution of the brain and the essential stability of its basic structure in the face of immense evolutionary changes in the remainder of the cerebral mantle are in themselves a challenge to seek a fundamental comprehension of its functional role. If our understanding of the homologies between the avian and mammalian brain is accurate, it would appear that damage to the hippocampal cortex in the newborn chick leads to defective imprinting behavior (39). Despite this and other strikingly suggestive evidence for participation by the hippocampal system in essential processes of memory even in simple brains, many persisting difficulties in such an easy interpretation have demanded a cautious attitude. For example, the memory trace may be laid down outside the hippocampal system (50), but integrity of its interrelations with these seemingly unrelated cortical and subcortical regions may be vital to the appropriate recall of previously learned discriminative habits (15).

Very importantly, not all learning requires the integrity of this system, and many classical conditioned reflexes involving the cardiovascular and respiratory systems persist after large diencephalic lesions disrupting major connections between the cerebrum and more caudal levels of the brain stem (29). A variety of partial lesions in the hippocampal system of the rat (43), the cat (42), monkey (49) and baboon (1) have produced varying decrements in ability to achieve new learning, but often with a high retention of old learned habits, including those involving discriminative tasks. Two main contributing factors may be responsible for sometimes incompatible and even contradictory findings reported in these studies. The complexity of hippocampal connections with other structures makes it difficult to assess effects of simple transection, or limited resection; and the apparent relationship of hippocampal integrity to aspects of recent memory and directed attention involving discriminative choice emphasizes the importance of experimental paradigms aimed at the selective testing of these functions. The effects of overtraining in relation to post-operative retention of learned habits are discussed below.

In broader perspective, we may ask whether a careful examination of the hippocampal system and related structures in the course of learning a discriminative task would reveal changes in patterns of electrophysiological activity closely correlated with acquisition of the learned task and, more fundamentally, whether such changes in electrical patterns would reveal anything about the fundamental nature of the processes by which information is stored in cerebral tissue. Such changes have been detected in our own studies by the application of a series of increasingly refined computing techniques (6, 12, 13). Some of the more recent results in this area will be presented here, since they would appear to provide additional supporting evidence for the basic importance of the wave process in the handling of information in cerebral systems, and to invite earnest consideration of the neuron in the cerebral system as a phase comparator of the patterns of waves which, arising both intrinsically and extrinsically, sweep across the neuronal surface in complex spatiotemporal patterns. Such a frame of functional organization would assist in defining the possible uniqueness of integrative processes in cortical systems, characterized by dendritic overlap in a palisade arrangement of cells, and with wave phenomena as a concomitant of electrotonic processes in dendritic structures.

The increasing sophistication of analytic technique used in these studies has served to emphasize that, at least insofar as we may monitor the transactional mechanisms in cerebral tissue in the learning process, the wave processes have the requisite criteria for this function, and would appear considerably removed from the category of a mere noise in the cerebral system. Nevertheless, the recording of patterns of electrical activity in the course of a learned performance seems unlikely to reveal essential aspects of the permanent physicochemical changes associated with the deposition of the memory trace.

For this reason, we have directed our attention to the possibility of a more direct approach to the long-term changes in the state of cerebral tissue in the course of learning. We have developed a technique for measuring impedance in small volumes of hippocampal tissue with implanted electrodes (9). In its application to the changes appearing during acquisition of a discriminative habit, it has revealed substantial but transient impedance shifts confined to the period of the discriminative performance (8, 10), and only after the behavioral performance has risen appreciably above chance levels. The findings have suggested a model of the cerebral system in which these changes may result from ionic exchanges involving the glial compartment, with the glial tissue acting as a varying and probably non-linear load on the electrotonic processes in dendritic structures responsible for the wave activity in cerebral tissue. The site of the "memory trace" may thus be sought at the functional interface between neuronal and glial tissue.

It is proposed to present certain aspects of recent studies on the participation of the hippocampus in mechanisms of discriminate learning before turning to the application of impedance measurements.

Let us therefore pass quickly to some of the studies which we have performed in cats, monkeys and, recently, in chimpanzees, indicating some of the behavioral test situations.

The most common situation which we have used for the cat is the one involving a modified T-maze discrimination for food, on the basis of a visual cue. The animal has many electrodes implanted in deep structures. The records are generally free from artifacts, and the movements of the animal do not interfere with them in any way. The modified delayed response situation requires that the cat sit on a pedestal. Food is concealed under one of two identical cans. After a delay period, from 5 to 20 seconds, the bridge is lowered and the animal can make its approach. In the monkey we have extensively utilized a visual discrimination task in which projected symbols appear. On the basis of a correct decision the animal receives a food pellet reward. Basically, the records which we have analyzed are those which come from the reticular formation, the dorsal hippocampus, the pyriform cortex, the entorhinal area and the visual cortex.

During the discriminative task, as the animal makes its approach in the T-box, the EEG records show a series of rhythmic wave discharges which are most regular in the hippocampal system. Concomitant discharges appear in the reticular formation and, to some extent, in the visual cortex. We make between 60 and 100 of these records every day, and have done so six days a week for the last four years. I can assure you this is no isolated phenomenon occurring occasionally. It is a uniform aspect of the record that one finds during the performance of the discriminative task.

1. EFFECTS OF RESTRICTED DIENCEPHALIC LESIONS ON LEARNED DISCRIMINATIVE BEHAVIOR AND CONCOMITANT HIPPOCAMPAL ELECTRICAL ACTIVITY

Restricted diencephalic lesions in the cat, centered in the subthalamic region but not strictly confined to the subthalamic nucleus, produced a major reduction in the excitability of single units in the rostral midbrain reticular formation. There was also reduced amplitude of evoked potentials to peripheral stimuli in the sciatic nerve (11, 47). In both cats and monkeys, these lesions were accompanied by curious modifications of behavior, including a lack of awareness of environmental stimuli such as food rewards, and conditional avoidance stimuli.

In a subsequent study we have examined the effects of similar but smaller lesions on a T-maze discriminative task and delayed response performance in cats with chronically implanted electrodes in the dorsal hippocampus, entorhinal cortex, amygdala, midbrain reticular formation, and primary sensory cortical region, including visual and sensorimotor (15). This study was based on the premise that at least some of the effects resulting from sub-thalamic lesions might be due to a disruption of the normal functional in-terrelationships between the hippocampal system, including the entorhinal cortex, and subcortical regions extending as far caudally as the rostral mid-brain reticular formation (1, 7).

After a unilateral subthalamic lesion, a striking defect was noted in the animal's relationship with the environment in the opposite half of its visual field (Figure 96). In an approach to food in a modified T-maze on the basis of a visual cue, the animals consistently failed to approach rewards placed in the visual field on the side opposite to the lesion, although rewards placed in the ipsilateral half of the visual field were correctly detected. This de-fective performance was temporary, and recovery occurred after seven to ten days. A second similar lesion in the remaining undamaged subthalamic zone was also followed by a profound temporary defect in discriminative performance, this time again on the side opposite to the lesion.

Thompson: This is delayed response?

Adey: No, this is the T-box test, but the results were identical, as I shall explain. Chance performance is 50 per cent.

Morrell: Evidently the animal's performance was poorer than 50 per cent.

Adey: I want to refer to that. The bottom graph in Figure 96 shows the analysis of the effects of this lesion inflicted first on the left side. The animal was able to make about 100 per cent correct performances after the lesion to rewards placed on its left side, but rewards placed on its right side were followed by a very severe decrement in the performance.

When the second lesion was made on the right side, a reversal in the be-havioral defect occurred. Now, with a right-sided lesion, the animal was unable to secure rewards placed on its left side, although it performed very appropriately for right-sided rewards. This was a very interesting finding. We went into it quite carefully, in both the T-maze and the delayed re-sponse situation, and found that it appeared to be a condition in which the animal was unable to retain or remember information coming from the op-posite half of the visual field. In delayed response tests, it was noted that these animals would closely watch concealment of the food reward in the contralateral visual field but that, even with delay periods as short as two seconds, they would immediately ignore this side of the environment and make an incorrect approach to the ipsilateral test area. It may be empha-sized that at no time did these animals display major defects in general motor performance outside the test area, nor was there any evidence of compulsive circling.

The EEG records from hippocampal structures accompanying the discriminative performance were greatly modified in the period of reduced behavioral capability. The characteristics of control records in both T-maze and delayed response tasks have been described in detail elsewhere (4, 5, 6, 15, 41). The period of the discriminative performance was characterized by a very regular burst of "theta" waves at an essentially single frequency around 5.5 cps. In the cat, this activity maximized in the dorsal hippocampus and in the entorhinal area of the pyriform cortex. In the epoch of alerted behavior preceding the discrimination, there was a wide spectrum of

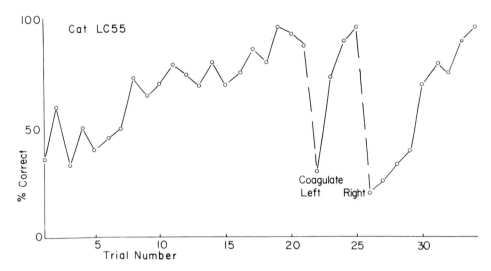

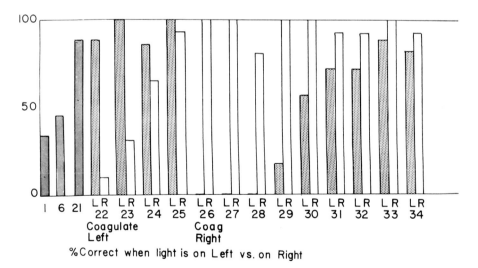

Figure 96. *Above:* training record in T-maze learning, with effects of successive coagulation of left and right subthalamic areas. *Below:* poor score with right-sided reward placements after coagulation of the left subthalamus, and converse performance after a right subthalamic lesion. (From Adey, Walter & Lindsley, 15.)

activity from 4 to 7 cps, but predominantly at about 4 cps. Similar but less regular trains of waves appeared during the discriminative performance in subcortical structures, including the subthalamus and midbrain reticular formation. Computed analyses of phase and spectral patterns in these wave trains will be discussed below.

The effects of bilateral subthalamic lesions on these regular 6 cps bursts during attempted discriminative performances in the T-maze situation are shown in Figure 97. Rhythmic 6 cps waves in hippocampal structures in the control record (Figure 97A) were replaced by irregular slower waves during attempted approach three days after the lesion was completed (by coagulation of the remaining undamaged subthalamic zone 15 days after electrolysis of the first side) (Figure 97B). At this time the behavioral performance was gravely impaired for approach to rewards in the visual field opposite to that of the more recent lesion. Tests at this time often resulted in a rapid exit from the start box on presentation of the situation, but ended with the animal halting in confusion, without reaching either the right or the wrong side of the T-maze. Partial recovery of behavioral performance in the period 20 to 30 days after the second subthalamic lesion was accompanied by recovery of many aspects of rhythmic discharges during performance of the T-maze task (Figure 97C). In tests made three days after a bilateral lesion, the behavioral performance had declined to 23 per cent, and the records in the hippocampal system show only relatively irregular discharges. After 27 days, most of the regular activity had returned in the hippocampal system and, at the same time, the performance was coming up again to around 65 per cent.

Bickford: Could you comment on Figure 97A? It looks as though there is more activity before the discrimination is made than afterward, or am I reading it incorrectly?

Adey: What you are seeing is the typical aspect of the alerted animal prepared to make its run, and the spectral analysis does show a great deal of high amplitude waves, with dominant frequency at 4 per second. During discrimination there is a speed-up to 5 to 6 per second. The spectrum is narrower, faster, than in the record from the pretest period.

In the delayed response situation, control records prior to subthalamic coagulation showed the typical 5.5-cycle burst during the approach (Figure 98). Two days after completion of bilateral subthalamic coagulation, one sees only a much lower-amplitude, irregular type of slow wave. Certainly, it does not have the regularity in the approach period that characterizes the control. At this stage, the performance was 45 per cent correct. Twenty-two days later, with performance at 80 per cent correct, this wave activity returned during the approach period. I show this to illustrate the fact that lesions which are not in the hippocampal system but are apparently in its projection pathways can grossly interfere with the electrographic activity in the hippocampus.

In delayed response tests (Figure 98) immediately following electro-

CAT WL-8

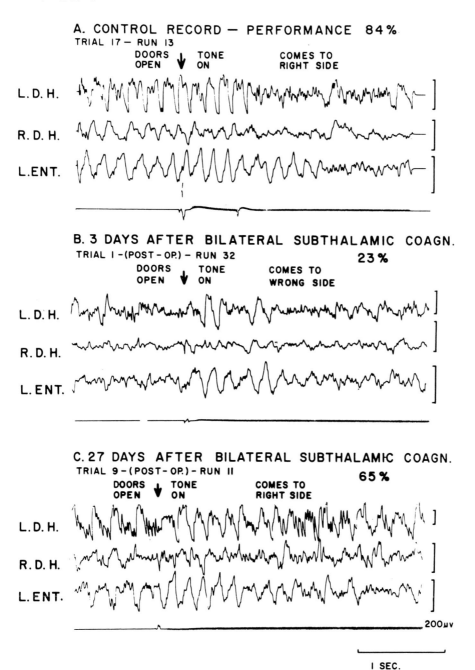

Figure 97. Recovery from effects of bilateral subthalamic coagulation lesions, with correlated EEG records during T-maze performance. Rhythmic 6 cps waves in control record (A) were replaced by irregular, slower waves during attempted approach three days after completion of lesion (B), but much of this activity had returned 27 days after lesion (C). L.D.H.: left dorsal hippocampus; R.D.H.: right dorsal hippocampus; L. ENT.: left entorhinal cortex. (From Adey, Walter & Lindsley, 15.)

coagulation of the second subthalamic area, failure to approach rewards in the visual field opposite to the more recent lesion occurred consistently. Even slow and studied placement of the food reward on the affected side under the attentive gaze of the animal did not improve the performance. As soon as the food was concealed, the cat's attention wandered, or was easily diverted by minimal intercurrent stimuli. After the coagulation, the duration of the slow wave trains was considerably reduced, the rhythmicity was absent, and the amplitude of the slow waves was decreased. Moreover, there was no acceleration of the slow waves as the animal made the approach response. Recovery of performance from 45 per cent two days post-operatively (Figure 98B) to 80 per cent twenty days later was associated with the return of major hippocampal slow wave components in the waiting period and their acceleration in a normal fashion during the discriminative approach (Figure 98C). It should be emphasized that, even when discrimination was most gravely impaired, there was no interference with classical conditioned motor responses in the test situation.

Feindel: I am not quite clear from your comment of what you were interpreting in regard to unilateral, ipsilateral or bilateral activity. I see that on

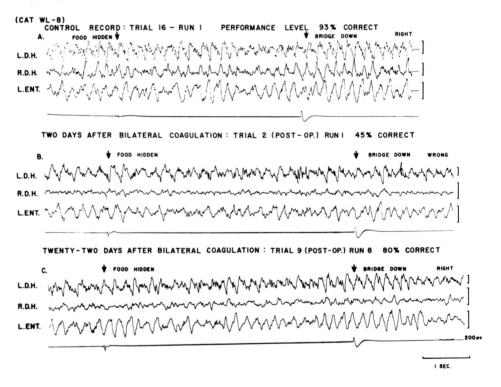

Figure 98. Correlation of recovery of delayed response performance following bilateral subthalamic lesion, with reappearance of normal 6 cps bursts during approach (A). Two days after lesion this activity was essentially abolished (B), but returned after 22 days (C). L.D.H.: left dorsal hippocampus; R.D.H.: right dorsal hippocampus; L. ENT.: left entorhinal cortex. (From Adey, Walter & Lindsley, 15.)

your lower record (Figure 98C), for example, you seem to have very little in right dorsal hippocampus as compared to left. What is the cause?

Adey: Although these lesions are shown as bilateral, they were not inflicted simultaneously on both sides. In this case, the second lesion was the one on the right side, in the right subthalamic area. At the 22-day mark, the recovery had not proceeded as far in the right side of the system as on the left. Later, the right side recovered in much the same fashion as the left. The left- and right-sided lesions were inflicted 10 to 15 days apart.

These findings would support the hypothesis of a close relationship between the presence of certain clearly specified patterns of wave activity in the hippocampal system and the ability to make a discriminative motor performance. In this study, the disruption of hippocampal wave activity was achieved by damage to diencephalic zones with which the hippocampus is functionally related, probably on a reciprocal basis. In an endeavor to establish further the nature of these interrelations in the processes of memory and recall, we have examined the effects of graded doses of psychotomimetic and hallucinogenic drugs on learned behavior, and on concomitant electrical activity in hippocampal structures and in subcortical regions.

2. Effects of Psychotomimetic and Hallucinogenic Drugs on Hippocampal EEG Records and Learned Behavior

Certain cyclohexamine derivatives, extensively tested as analgesic agents in human surgery, were found frequently to produce severe disorientation, including death experiences. We have tested two of these substances, 1-(phenyl cyclohexyl) piperidine monohydrochloride (Cl-395, Sernyl), and n-ethyl-1-phenyl-cyclohexylamine monohydrochloride, in cats (5). It was found that, within a few minutes of intraperitoneal injection of a 2 mg/kg dose, discriminative T-maze performance was rapidly disrupted, and that simultaneously the slow-wave activity in the hippocampal system was replaced by high-amplitude, seizure-like discharges, often triggered in long trains of spikes by sudden stimuli, such as a light flash or a hand clap. Moreover, examination of thalamocortical conduction characteristics in a "non-specific" system revealed little effect attributable to the drug.

These seizure discharges increase and persist for many hours. Even eight hours after the dose, the record is very different indeed from the control. In the behavioral test performance, one finds a gross distortion of the pattern in the hippocampal system, beginning as early as five minutes after the drug administration. In the control records there is the pre-approach type of activity at 4 to 5 cycles. On presentation of the situation there is a speed-up, and the computer shows a regularization at 5 to 6 cps. Five minutes after the drug, a similar T-box test shows no aspect of modification of the record by the presentation of the situation, and the animal goes to the wrong side. After 20 minutes there is no behavioral response, and 24 hours after the drug the hippocampal wave burst appears typically during the approach to the food, but the latency is quite long. In fact, the animal made more mistakes than usual. The performance was down to about 70 per cent. Here within the hippocampal system are thus quite fine correlates of the ability, or the modification of the ability, to make a visual discriminative performance.

The profound changes induced by these drugs in the hippocampal system, in the absence of major effects in other cortical-subcortical systems, encouraged our investigation of hallucinogenic drugs, including lysergic acid diethylamide, psilocin and psilocybin (4). With these drugs, an orderly progression in the origin and spread of seizure-like electrical episodes was clearly apparent. Doses of lysergic acid of the order of 25 µg/kg in the cat produced brief seizure-like episodes in a quiet environment. They seemed critically dependent on reduction of visual and auditory sensory influences. These episodes were maximal in amplitude and longest in duration in dorsal hippocampal and entorhinal cortex, and appeared variably in the thalamus and midbrain reticular formation.

A dose of 50 µg/kg of LSD produces in cats a typical picture, with the animals lying purring, with paws extended; often, when sitting, pawing at invisible objects; standing with the tail erect, and moving with a broad-based gait. They spread their hind legs, and quite often stand with fur erect for long periods, apparently staring at some hallucinatory experience. We found that, if one places the cat in a dark environment, the hippocampal system exhibits apparently "spontaneous" seizure-like discharges. At this stage it is possible to see those discharges occurring primarily in the hippocampal system, without involvement of other cortical or subcortical structures. The seizures are seen at that dose level only with the animal in a dark, quiet environment. It is necessary to reduce the level of sensory input in order to see this type of seizure.

Larger doses of lysergic acid, in the vicinity of 100 µg/kg, caused these seizures to persist in a well-lit environment. At this dose level they were sustained for as long as five seconds in the hippocampal system, and propagated into the amygdala and thalamic nucleus ventralis anterior. Concurrent slow wave discharges occurred in the primary visual cortex, and intermittently in the rostral midbrain reticular formation.

Doses of lysergic acid in the range 75 to 100 µg/kg caused intermittent seizure discharges to persist even under the stimulus of discriminative test situations. In delayed response testing, seizure episodes during the delay period had no effect on the subsequent correct discriminative performance. When, however, the seizure episode encroached on the period in which a discriminative performance was required, the animal staggered about in an aimless fashion, often failing to complete the approach, or making a slow incorrect approach. These findings were presented in detail in the previous volume of this series (3).

The records indicate that the seizure episode associated with the disrupted performance involved subcortical structures, including thalamic nucleus ventralis anterior and midbrain reticular formation. The sampling of subcortical systems with chronically implanted electrodes must obviously be relatively incomplete, but our findings suggest that the disruption of focused attention induced by these drugs is fundamentally related to the propagation of the disturbance into subcortical systems. Whether focal disturbances confined to the hippocampal system are also associated with disrupted discriminative behavior remains uncertain, although the studies of Andy & Akert (17), Andy, Chinn, Allen & Shawver (18), and Holmes & Adey (41) have shown that electrically induced seizures confined to limbic structures are compatible with many normal behavioral patterns not requiring discriminative capability.

Feindel: Is the failure of any repetitive discharge in the amygdala of any significance?

Adey: We have considered this, and the findings appear to be that involvement of the amygdala is not clearly related to the loss of performance. There need not be seizures in the amygdala in the course of tests in which the animal is unable to make the performance.

Bickford: Could we ask you why you call these seizure discharges? We avoid the term in the human electrogram. I wonder if it clarifies anything.

Adey: I have been using "seizure-like" but I thought it pedantic, so I gave up the "like". They are electrographic seizures. In this case, the episodes of generalized phenomenon of this kind are associated with *absenses* of a psychomotor type. So perhaps there is some justification for calling them "seizures". I think your point is very well taken; one should be careful about the use of the word "seizure".

Feindel: Does the animal show any behavioral change?

Adey: Staring and maybe pawing at something immediately following.

Feindel: So it was a seizure.

Adey: Seizure-like.

Brazier: May I follow up a question of Dr. Feindel's? Do you put importance on the fact that these electrographic seizure-like discharges are bilateral? What is your opinion about the importance of these having to be bilateral?

Adey: We have had a good deal of experience with cats that had implantations for, say, six to nine months. At that stage, a true epileptic focus appears in one of the leads, as a result, presumably, of scarring and irritation. This focus can show tremendous localized seizure discharges with no disruption of performance until such time as it becomes bilateral. At that stage, within 24 hours, the animals usually die in status epilepticus. The seizure process becomes general. Certainly, the unilateral focal discharge is not associated with any behavioral disruption. These are seizure discharges occurring during the testing period.

Feindel: Is this true, also, of some of the task performances? You find no change in performance?

Adey: No change in the performance level. If the discharge spreads widely within the hippocampus on one side, occasionally, very occasionally and usually at that stage, it becomes generalized.

Feindel: Are you considering whether the spread is, as it were, straight across, or down deep and back up? Do you have material on that?

Adey: One of the difficulties with the implanted electrode technique is that one is looking at the ocean from a limited number of points on the seashore. When the discharge finally does turn up at one of the subcortical electrodes, I think there is reason to assume it has already probably progressed to other places. We have tried to span the most important projection areas like ventralis anterior, subthalamus and midbrain reticular formation. I would not suggest that we had a sufficient number of electrodes.

Brazier: Have you a special reason for choosing the dorsal hippocampus? Compared with the cat, man is so poorly endowed with this structure. Possibly this accounts for man's relative poverty in hippocampal theta activity as well.

Adey: The reason the dorsal hippocampus was chosen is that the regularity of the theta and its distribution in relation to performance is very different from that in the ventral hippocampus.

In summary, the results of our lesion and drug studies support the view that the hippocampal system in its normal reciprocal interrelationships with certain subcortical systems is vitally concerned in the continued capability to make a discriminative performance involving the integrity of both recent and long-term memory functions. We have observed that apparently stable patterns of rhythmic hippocampal electrical activity are constant concomitants of this discriminative behavior even in circumstances of considerable overtraining, and that temporary disruption of the behavior by lesions and drugs leads to a deterioration of these electrical patterns. Their reappearance proceeds *pari passu* with the recovery of the behavioral performance. We have also found lysergic acid to be a useful diagnostic tool in its selective enhancement of spike discharges in patients with temporal lobe epilepsy (23).

At this stage we may briefly consider the question of overtraining in relation to the essential role of the hippocampal system in learning. There is evidence that overtraining followed by a variety of hippocampal and temporal neocortical lesions in the rat, cat and monkey may cause little disruption of learned performance, but that similar lesions in the course of learning lead to major defects in learned performance (24, 43, 49). This is, indeed, a particularly challenging finding which permits no ready explanation. Our findings in studies of phase-locked wave disturbances during behavioral discrimination in the course of repeated training with successive reversal of cues (12) suggest that, over a period of many months of such cue reversals, a progressive decline in the rhythmicity of average response computations appears in subcortical regions such as the midbrain reticular formation. We have not detected similar adaptive phenomena in computa-

tions of the rhythmic trains of hippocampal slow waves. We have interpreted those results as indicative that the essential information necessary
to the discriminative performance may have reached minimal proportions,
and that the indubitable behavioral sophistication engendered by such long
training enables an appropriate behavioral performance with little more
than fleeting attention to the behavioral cues.

Our computed results, to be summarized below, suggest that in overtraining a high scatter may again appear in phase patterns of successive records, but having certain subtle differences from the irregular patterns in
early training. Speculatively, the less regular pattern in the sophisticated
animal may still contain key aspects of information, and represent a form
of "shorthand". The decline of such rhythmic phase-locked averages in
subcortical structures during overtraining, and their concomitant persistence
in the hippocampal system, may indicate a gradual decline in functional in-
terdependence between hippocampal structures and those subcortical zones,
such as the subthalamus and midbrain reticular formation. The introduction
of novelty into the training situation has been found to reestablish potently
aspects of shared rhythmic processes in widely separated cortical and subcortical structures (6, 12).

In order to study the intrinsic organization of the hippocampus and its
wave of processes during these behavioral performances, we sampled the
dorsal hippocampus, the ventral hippocampus, the pyriform cortex or entorhinal cortex behind and, incidentally, almost always the amygdala and
midbrain reticular formation.

Feindel: What part of the amygdala?

Adey: Usually the junction between the basal and lateral nuclei in the
more ventrolateral zone. This is the region in the cat characterized by the
40 per second burst discharges.

3. COMPUTER ANALYSIS OF HIPPOCAMPAL EEG PATTERNS IN DISCRIMINATIVE LEARNING

The foregoing discussion has examined the role of the hippocampus in
its complex interrelations with subcortical structures in the course of discriminative learning. It is now proposed to summarize extensive computed
analyses of phase patterns in the wave trains within the hippocampal system in the course of discriminative performances. The evidence from these
studies of consistent phase patterns in hippocampal wave trains has strongly
supported the hypothesis of conveyance of information on the basis of
graded analog wave processes and has, in turn, provided a powerful link
in the chain of investigations leading to the application of impedance measuring techniques to hippocampal functions in the learning process.

We have examined frequency, phase and amplitude relations between
the wave trains recorded simultaneously in different parts of the arch of
the hippocampal formation, and in adjacent zones of the pyriform cortex,

including the entorhinal area. With closely spaced implanted electrodes, it has been possible to examine phase relations between adjacent regions, such as zones CA 4 (adjacent to the dentate granule cells) and CA 2 (in the hippocampal pyramidal cell layer), hopefully revealing the nature of intrinsic patterns of organization within the hippocampus in a particular region, and changes in these patterns associated with learning (3, 6, 12, 13).

Initial studies with crosscorrelation analysis indicated that, in the course of correct responses, there are consistent phase patterns in the regular 6 cps wave trains accompanying the discriminative performance. In early training, this phase pattern indicated a sequence from the dentate granule cells to the region of the hippocampal pyramidal cell layer in CA 2, thence to the posterior superior pyriform cortex, or entorhinal area. While evidence from such computed phase analyses can never establish a functional synaptic sequence in anatomical pathways, it may be pointed out that there is a close resemblance in these patterns to the classical anatomical pathways proposed for activation of the hippocampal cortex by Elliot Smith (57) and Herrick (38). Subsequent examination in identical circumstances in the fully trained animal indicated a complete reversal of these phase patterns, with activity in entorhinal cortex leading in phase the activity in the CA 2 pyramidal cell zone, and with the latter showing a lead in phase over the wave trains in the dentate granule cell zone. These results suggested a prior activation in the trained animal of connections between the entorhinal cortex and the pyramidal cell layer, consistent with conduction through the powerful temporo-ammonic tracts of Cajal. The dentate granule cells, on the other hand, were activated somewhat later in the trained animal. We have considered these results in the frame of the convergence on the dendritic trees of the pyramidal cell zone of these two clearly defined anatomical influxes, the one coming from the entorhinal cortex via the temporo-ammonic tracts, and the other through the short axons of the dentate granule cells. The latter are activated from septal areas and other zones accessible to "arousing" influences ascending through the reticular system. In this frame of organization, we have considered the possibility that the dendritic arborizations of the pyramidal cells may be sensitive in the trained animal to the relative times of arrival of influxes from entorhinal cortex and dentate granule cells. Speculatively, the dendritic trees might function as phase comparators for the graded analog wave processes sweeping across their surfaces in complex spatio-temporal patterns. This concept will be elaborated below.

Figure 99 shows the result of a crosscorrelation in records from the hippocampal system in early training. The crosscorrelation and autocorrelation techniques, introduced to EEG studies by Dr. Brazier and her colleagues (22), offer the advantage of allowing assessment of phase information. If, for example, a record is taken from the dorsal hippocampus and another from the pyriform cortex, the essential mathematical procedure is to multiply them together. In so doing, any inherent or hidden rhythmicity will be demonstrated. The phase information is retained by measuring the positive-going peak closest to zero time and noting its position in relation to zero time. The channel which carries that peak is the one which is leading; in the example shown in Figure 99 the amount of the lead is 35 msec. In a second example, the value, 20 msec., is the lead between A2 and the entorhinal cortex. On the basis of this analysis, one can say what is the lead or lag between these closely spaced leads.

By contrast, records from the same channels in the same animal late in training show reversal of these phase patterns. If we sum the three phase angles, the closure of the phase pattern is quite narrow. By the use of such a "triangulation" calculation between three leads, one can establish a fair degree of reliability from such a computation.

We have been encouraged to extend the application of crosscorrelation techniques to an examination of phase patterns in wave trains within the hippocampal system during correct and incorrect responses in the fully trained animal (13). These studies have disclosed highly consistent patterns of phase relations between dorsal hippocampus, entorhinal area and ventral hippocampus in correct responses in the fully trained animal. Examination of phase relations between dorsal hippocampus, entorhinal area and ventral ferent test days, has indicated reversals in phase patterns as compared with correct responses, with good consistency in each of the two groups of phase and pattern analyses. Surprising as these results are, they have been amply supported by much more extensive examinations, including a variety of cross-spectral analyses.

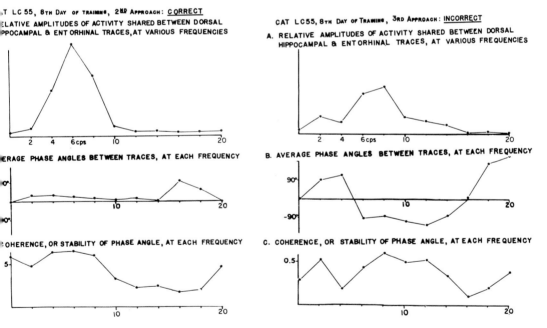

Figure 99. Cross-spectral analyses of shared amplitudes (A), average phase angles (B), and phase angle coherence (C) in successive approaches. All three parameters are strikingly different between correct and incorrect responses, with a sharp reversal of average phase angle at 5 cps in the incorrect response.

Here was a very surprising piece of information, that perhaps it was possible for the phase patterns to shift in a predictable way, in terms of whether the response in a T-maze discrimination was correct or not.

Bickford: May I ask how long the sampling for these calculations was?

Adey: This involved the analysis of a period of two seconds of record, using the calculation for a crosscorrelogram, with a truncated series. The validity of the analysis is sufficient to allow one to look at relatively short epochs. It should be mentioned that crosscorrelation is designed to be performed on an infinitely long series. This application to truncated series requires certain relaxations in the rigors of the mathematics.

Before describing the application of cross-spectral analysis, we may digress for a brief discussion of the degree to which phase-locking the hippocampal wave trains to the moment of presentation of the test situation was observed in successive behavioral performances, and at different levels of learning. This problem was studied by a simple averaging technique, with the onset of the averaged epoch time-locked to the moment of presentation of the test situation and a reinforcing tone (12). Observation of the progressive average in the testing of the fully trained animal indicated that the hippocampal electrical activity in the pre-approach epoch behaved as a random phenomenon, and became progressively smaller after 10 to 15 discriminations, whereas the rhythmic averages during the discriminative epoch grew progressively larger.

The subtle nature of the gradual increase in time-locked aspects of these EEG averages in the course of training is shown in Figures 100 and 101. The sample records from the left and right dorsal hippocampi contributed to the computed averages shown at the bottom of each figure. The performance level in Figure 100 was 75 per cent, and the average was essentially devoid of rhythmicity. By contrast, the computed average in Figure 101 shows a highly rhythmic output in an identical test twenty days later, although the performance still remained at about the same level. Visual comparison of the EEG records from the two tests does not indicate significant differences in amplitude or regularity of the 5 cps wave trains. Looking at the individual EEG records, one could not detect this, but apparently in the repetition of the performance certain events are occurring in the brain which tie themselves more precisely to the moment of presentation of the situation.

This phenomenon of the regularity of the average is something which persists in the hippocampal system into overtraining, whereas the regularity of the average in the midbrain and subthalamic record tends to decline once the performance has been substantially overtrained. Figure 102 shows this phenomenon. In this figure we are averaging the records from the midbrain reticular formation over a period of six to eight months. At this stage, the animal was coming to a light cue, and it was at 95 per cent performance. There is a fairly rhythmic average in the reticular formation. Shortly thereafter, the paradigm was changed, and it had to come to a dark cue.

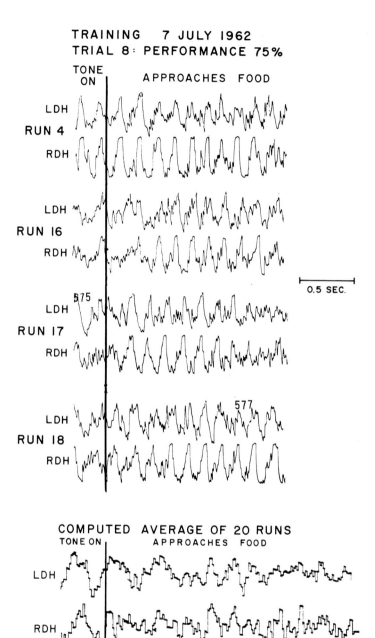

TRAINING 7 JULY 1962
TRIAL 8: PERFORMANCE 75%

Figure 100. Representative hippocampal EEG records with computed averages from 20 of these traces at midtraining in T-maze approach to unlit side of maze. Note irregular character of computed averages. (From Adey & Walter, 12.)

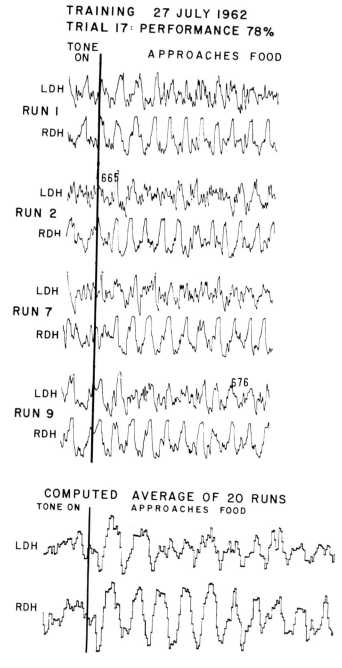

Figure 101. From same animal as in Figure 100, later in training in same paradigm. Note regularity of computed averages. (From Adey & Walter, 12.)

MIDBRAIN RETICULAR ACTIVITY - COMPUTED AVERAGES - T-MAZE TRAINING

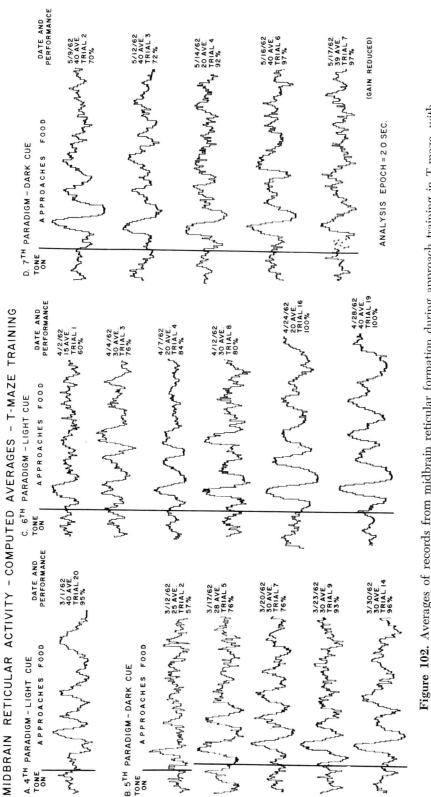

Figure 102. Averages of records from midbrain reticular formation during approach training in T-maze, with successive reversal of training cues over many months, first to light (A), then successively to dark (B), light (C), and dark (D). These averages were prepared on a Mnemotron CAT computer without the advantage of normalization, so that only qualitative comparison can be made between successive records in respect to general rhythmicity, rather than on the separate basis of absolute amplitudes. (From Adey & Walter, 12.)

Within a day of being put into the dark cue situation, the average had
disintegrated into an essentially arhythmic type of configuration. It gradually
came back as the performance improved. We were unkind enough to change
the cue again. Once again the rhythmic average disintegrated, and subsequently reappeared. Then we changed to a dark cue. This was the seventh
paradigm in eight months of the animal's training.

In this last paradigm, the animal's behavior recovered quickly. On the
fourth day it was up to 72 per cent. Although the rhythmic computed average was sustained in hippocampal records at high behavioral performance
levels with repeated retraining to reversed cues, a decline in the rhythmicity
of the computed average was noted in midbrain records after the seventh
reversal in a period of six months (Figure 102). There were indications of
a sophistication in the situation, with a rapid rise in performance to over
90 per cent in the first four trials. The reticular records did not gain a
rhythmicity comparable with that in earlier tests, even at performance
levels over 95 per cent. These findings have been discussed above in relation to phenomena of overtraining.

While we are discussing this problem of phase, I would like to mention
certain other techniques we have used. We have also examined the possibility that the hippocampal wave trains in discriminative performances,
having the general aspect of a single frequency, may actually exhibit some
form of frequency modulation. For this purpose we have used a digital
filtering technique (34), which establishes the digital computer as a narrow-
band filter, and precisely specifies flat-top, shoulder and skirt characteristics
of the filter.

In this way, it has been possible to show that a frequency modulation
is present on these 6 cps wave trains at moments of maximum attention,
and would greatly increase the information-carrying capability of such a
wave train. This analytic technique was first applied to measurements of
variations in the earth's magnetic field appearing as a frequency modulation
in the magnetometer readings from a spinning satellite, and would appear
to offer an extremely powerful tool in the analysis of EEG data.

Here is thus another way in which the amount of information that wave
processes could carry in the cerebral system is greatly increased by the
presence of some form of frequency modulation, or at least it is a potential
increase in the amount of information that could be carried.

Cross-spectral analysis also had its early application in the field of space
science to problems of missile vibration (20). We have described its initial
application to EEG records in learning (13), where it has revealed differences between adjacent zones of the hippocampal system in shared amplitudes, phase relations and coherence functions across a spectrum of frequencies. It has revealed in a most striking way differences in phase patterns between correct and incorrect responses, and provided firm support
for similar findings using simpler crosscorrelation analysis.

For example, one may plot in a correct response the graph of shared amplitudes between two hippocampal channels, across a spectrum from 2 to 20 cycles. In the correct response there is a single peak in the energy shared at about 6 cps. The phase angle between the two channels runs smoothly from, say, 2 to 14 cycles. The coherence factor, which we need not consider in detail, remains high. By contrast, in an incorrect response, the shared amplitude is a rather double-peaked graph, and the phase angle reverses quite sharply at about 5 cps, as would have been predicted from the earlier crosscorrelation analysis shown in Figure 99.

John: Would you tell us how you calculate the cross-spectral analysis?

Adey: The initial step involves an autocorrelation or crosscorrelation function of each record. A form of Fourier analysis is then performed on the correlogram.

Feindel: What does it mean in terms of the EEG pattern? Can you give us a little more of a definition of it?

Adey: In terms of the pattern, it implies that the difference between the correct and the incorrect responses is one in which the shift in relationship occurs principally at the 5 cps region.

In a recent extension of this cross-spectral technique, my colleague Dr. Donald Walter has developed a method to display the phase relations between EEG records from two different regions as a polar plot. This method permits a display of phase relations between two records across a spectrum of frequencies (12). Also, by calculation of complex coherence functions, the probability bounds are established that shared energy levels in any portion of the spectrum will lie within specified phase angles. At the same time the radial dimension of the plot is used to indicate the amplitude transfer function between these records and its probable bounds (Figure 103).

This figure shows that the 6 cps band, already identified as the location of the maximum energy peak in each channel by a separate spectral analysis, is also that in which the transfer vector relating the hippocampal with the entorhinal waves is most narrowly limited, as indicated by the shaded areas. The boundaries of this and other zones are established at the 50 per cent level of probability that the mean transfer vector lies within the zone delineated. It is clear that there is good general agreement between the calculations relating to correct responses on two different days, in the phase relations at and near this best-related frequency. By contrast, the findings in incorrect responses from each of the same two days showed a totally different location for the 6 cps zone (Figure 103A), although there was again good agreement between these incorrect responses in the location of those zones. The incorrect responses also showed a much wider scatter in the distribution of other spectral zones than was seen in the correct responses. A further example from a different animal (Figure 103B) showed a major change in phase relations between entorhinal cortical and hippocampal records in correct and incorrect responses.

Weiskrantz: Are these measures made while the animal approaches?

Adey: It is the analysis of the EEG response epoch between the moment

PROBABILITY BOUNDS ON COMPLEX TRANSFER FUNCTIONS, DORSAL HIPPOCAMPUS TO ENTORHINAL CORTEX

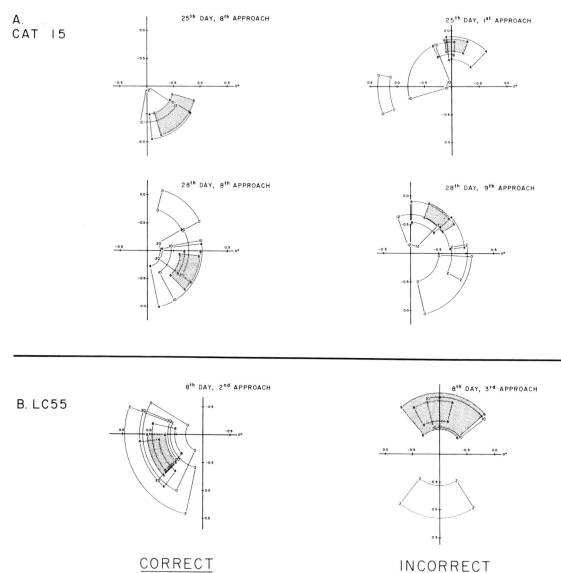

Figure 103. Stochastic models of EEG: examples of polar coordinate plots of probability bounds on complex amplitude transfer functions, dorsal hippocampus to entorhinal cortex. Phase angles are depicted on angular coordinates, and transfer functions are shown on radii. Shaded fans enclose 6 cps portions of spectrum, and are maximum energy zones. Note consistency between correct responses and differences from incorrect responses in one animal (A), and similar wide differences between correct and incorrect responses in another animal (B). (From Adey & Walter, 12.)

the situation is presented and when the animal has put a foot on the pedestal on the incorrect side, which terminates the situation, or, in the other case, when it is responding correctly but prior to its reaching the food.

Bickford: How long a period is that, as a rule?

Adey: It is about 2 seconds, 1.5 to 2 seconds.

John: When you talk about the scatter in the incorrect responses, do you mean that the scatter from trial to trial is like this, or from animal to animal?

Adey: In one trial, the distribution of the sectors phase-wise is around the entire 360 degrees.

John: Have you done anything comparable to this to contrast other structures? For example, have you done similar analyses to contrast dorsal hippocampus with reticular formation?

Adey: We have, but the scatter of phase is too wide. We are going to have to proceed to the Goodman filtering technique (34) to find the answer. There is too much frequency modulation on the diencephalic and other cortical recordings.

The extent to which such findings may reflect a general difference in phase patterns between correct and incorrect decisions in fully trained animals is under continuing investigation. Current studies in a limited series of analyses indicate that such changes do not always occur, and that incorrect responses may be isophasic with the correct ones. This matter is receiving further study, particularly since the complexity of the behavioral response pattern involved in this discriminative task may underlie irregularities noted in some results of these spectral analyses.

These studies with computer analyses have attempted to define, by several techniques not hitherto applied to the examination of electrophysiological data, components in the apparent imprecision of EEG records, which are either phase-locked in leads from circumscribed cortical or subcortical zones in relation to the repeated performance of a learned motor task, or which may have constant phase relations to wave patterns appearing simultaneously in other cortical or subcortical localities, or which may have aspects of phase or frequency modulation on a "carrier" wave train appearing in the course of attentive or discriminative behavior. It is obvious that any one of these three possibilities would provide a frame in which either the nerve cell or the organized cerebral system might adequately "sense" the informational basis of afferent volleys, and the data provide evidence that all three phenomena may have important roles in the various hierarchies from the microcosm of the individual neuron to the macrocosm of complexly organized but profoundly interrelated cortico-cortical and cortico-subcortical systems. More importantly, however, part of the evidence presented would appear to bear significantly on the fundamental nature of essential cerebral processes, viewed as either deterministic or probabilistic phenomena. This will be discussed below.

John: I wonder if you would be willing to spell that out a little. "Probabilistic" is a word that can mean a number of things.

Adey: The thought that we have about it is that the nerve cells, on experiencing a pattern of waves which determines in them some physico-chemical alteration, subsequently become most excitable (and will exhibit the lowest threshold) during the recurrence of an identical pattern of waves. It need not be identical, however, and similarity rather than identity determines the aspect of a probabilistic type of operation. That is as briefly but not as elegantly as I would like to express it.

I would like to proceed finally to the question of cerebral impedance measurements, which we initiated on the basis of the following considerations. First, that the wave process is not the envelope of the firing of nerve cells. Second, that the glial tissue may provide an impedance load to the electrotonic generator in the dendrites. Third, that there could be a tri-compartmental model of the cerebral tissue, with an intraneuronal compartment, an intraglial compartment, and an extracellular compartment. If the concept of Cole (25) were correct, i.e., that the neurons have a very high membrane resistance, so high that the shunt path in extracellular fluid around the neurons would provide the only major pathways for the current through the tissue, then any discernible changes in impedance would very likely relate to changes in non-neural conductance in the tissue.

4. Cerebral Impedance Measurements During Acquisition of a Learned Discriminative Habit

The disclosure of a variety of patterns in slow wave processes in cerebral tissue having highly consistent relations to the performance of a behavioral discriminative task suggested the possible importance of monitoring concurrent changes in functional state in the cerebral tissue from which these wave processes were recorded. The possibility was considered that changes in conductance characteristics, for example, measured in restricted volumes of tissue in hippocampus, septum, amygdala and reticular formation, might provide a series of correlates with states of tissue excitability, and might perhaps show changes related to the acquisition of learned behavior.

It is probable that changes in the state of cerebral tissue relating to the storage of information will not manifest themselves as clearly in aspects of on-going electrophysiological activity presumably involved in transactional mechanisms, as in other more subtle measures capable of revealing long-lasting changes in the functional state of the tissue relating to the storage of information. In particular, it would seem important to pursue the possibility that these storage mechanisms may not lie exclusively within the neuronal compartment of the cerebral system, but that such structures as the glial cells may be importantly concerned by reason of their profound metabolic interrelations with the neuronal compartment which they enclose, and on which they may presumably exercise a modulating influence (8, 9).

We have developed a technique for the recording of impedance at

1000 cps in small volumes of cerebral tissue (less than 1.0 mm³) with chronically implanted coaxial electrodes in freely moving animals. This technique uses microvolt signals producing a current density of the order of 10^{-13} amperes per square micron of electrode surface, considerably below threshold even for cells immediately adjacent to the measuring electrode and, by the use of a differential amplifying system, current changes of the order of 10^{-15} amperes per square micron can be detected. With this technique, we have detected three types of responses, including brief evoked transient changes in hippocampal, septal and reticular impedance, following a variety of peripheral physiological stimuli in visual, auditory, somatic and olfactory modalities, as well as induced rhythmic changes and long-lasting shifts in baseline impedance values in sleep and under the influence of psychotomimetic drugs and in barbiturate anesthesia (9).

There were some questions earlier from Dr. Glaser about the current distribution around the electrodes (see page 105). Most of it flows within a cylinder twice the diameter of the electrode and limited essentially to the distance between the tip of the coaxial barrel and the tip of the central conductor.

In the simplest applications of the technique to a combined measure of hippocampal impedance and the EEG, we find that, as the animal looks out and sees an observer, in each case there is a dip downwards in the impedance record. When a female cat sees a male cat, there is also a fall in impedance measured in the septum. When the animal smells milk, and then a drop of milk is put on its nose, there is also a fall in impedance in the hippocampal system.

During pentobarbital anesthesia there is a long-lasting baseline shift in the upward direction. Painful stimuli produce a momentary decrease, and with the termination of anesthesia there is a return to the baseline level. By contrast, giving one of the cyclohexamine drugs I discussed earlier, the impedance falls for a long period and eventually returns to baseline levels through a period of overshoot.

In these preliminary studies, an indication that the nature of these induced impedance changes might be critically dependent on the previous experience of the particular cerebral system was found in a comparison of the effects of electrically induced seizures in the hippocampal system in two tests ten days apart. Using septal stimulation at some distance from the hippocampus itself, the seizures in the dorsal hippocampus at the first test were followed by trains of rhythmic waves at about 1 cps in the impedance record for 10 to 20 seconds after the abrupt termination of the electrical seizure in the EEG record. These 1 cps waves were discernible in simultaneous EEG records. In repeated seizures over a period of approximately two hours, only a slight upward trend in the baseline impedance occurred. In sharp contrast at a second test ten days later, the same and stronger stimulus parameters produced much shorter electrical seizure episodes, and the 1 cps waves in impedance records were also much reduced. The baseline impedance, however, showed a progressive increase during the test period by about 15 per cent of the pretest value, in a fashion quite different from the initial test, suggesting that the first series of convulsive episodes had established a sensitivity to their repetition. The phenomenon is in many aspects reminiscent of the "anamnestic reaction" well known to the immunologist. It is relevant that the control EEG records preceding each test were essentially identical, so that the mechanisms responsible for the induced impedance change at the second test apparently involve a functional frame in large measure independent of many aspects of on-going electrical activity in the tissue, although probably linked to it, and even dependent on the recurrence of a particular pattern of EEG electrical activity for the evocation of an appropriate impedance change (9).

From these findings, we have extended the impedance recordings to an examination of possible changes in the course of training in a discriminative motor act in the modified T-maze described above (8, 10, 14). It was found that at chance levels of performance separate computed averages of impedance records from the hippocampus during correct and incorrect responses showed only irregular deviations around the baseline (Figure 104). At intermediate performance levels, a transient fall in impedance appeared in the computed average on presentation of the discriminative task, followed by a longer lasting rise (Figure 105). At high performance levels, a deeper transient fall in hippocampal impedance of 2.0 to 6.0 per cent of the baseline value immediately followed presentation of the test situation and

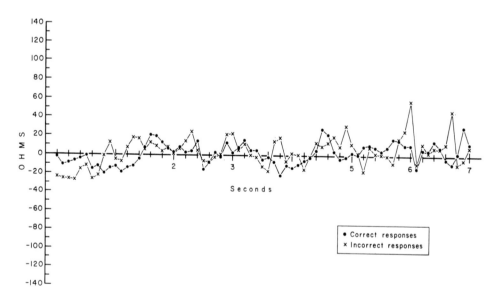

Figure 104. Averaged hippocampal impedance changes during attempted discrimination (approach) for a total of 39 performances on one test day at 57 per cent correct performance level. Discriminative attempts began at 2.0 second mark. Neither correct nor incorrect responses showed consistent deviations from baseline at this performance level. (From Adey, Kado, Didio & Schindler, 10.)

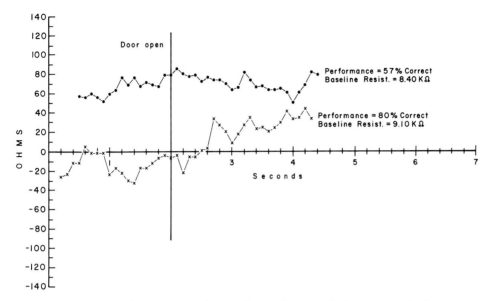

Figure 105. Averaged hippocampal impedance changes during approach, from same leads as in Figure 104 at 80 per cent performance level (graph with crosses). A small fall followed presentation of the situation, and was succeeded by a prolonged rise. (From Adey, Kado, Didio & Schindler, 10.)

persisted beyond the completion of the task (Figure 106). It was followed by a slow rise which exceeded 8.0 per cent of baseline impedance in some cases, with slow return to the pre-approach level after six to eight seconds

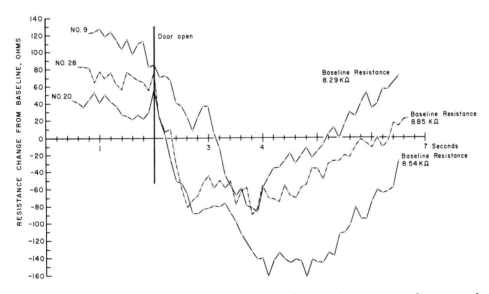

Figure 106. Right mid hippocampus impedance changes during approach: averaged hippocampal impedance records from three different training days at 100 per cent performance level, from same hippocampal leads as in Figures 104 and 105. The deep fall lasted more than three seconds before the onset of the ensuing phase of increased impedance. (From Adey, Kado, Didio & Schindler, 10.)

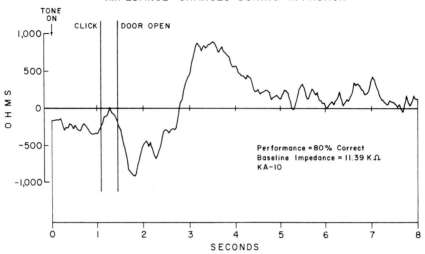

Figure 107. Impedance changes during approach: averaged hippocampal impedance record over eight-second epoch (in a different animal from that in Figures 104, 105 and 106). The time-course of the late epoch of increased impedance is clearly shown. (From Adey, Kado, Didio & Schindler, 10.)

(Figure 107). This "evoked" impedance change persisted undiminished with considerable overtraining. Extinction of the learned habit abolished these impedance changes, which reappeared with retraining. The return to minor random changes in averaged impedance at the beginning of retraining occurred at a time when the approach time was not perceptibly lengthened but performance remained at chance level. The random character of the average thus did not arise from a disordered and irregular motor performance characteristic. No baseline impedance shifts were seen in hippocampal structures during acquisition or extinction of the discriminative habit.

We are recording here in less than a cubic millimeter of hippocampal tissue on one side. If we consider the simultaneous impedance records from both sides, in apparently symmetric placements in left and right hippocampi, there are some fascinating findings at the 80 per cent performance level. Apparently, the impedance changes do not appear simultaneously at the same level of learning and to the same degree in different hippocampal structures. For example, an average computed from five days' data at the 80 per cent level in the left hippocampus shows relatively little change, whereas there is already a very large change in impedance on the right side, which is triggered off by a cue about a third of a second before the door is opened and the animal sees the situation.

Regional differences were noted in the time of impedance changes in the course of training, indicating that, with improvement in behavioral performance, concomitant changes in averaged hippocampal impedance records may occur more slowly on one side than in an essentially symmetrical hippocampal placement in the opposite hemisphere. However, at the 100 per cent performance level the magnitude of the fall in impedance during the discriminative behavior was similar in records from both left and right hippocampi. Although they have so far been examined in detail in only one animal, their very high statistical significance would appear to validate them in support of regional differences in the temporal sequence of brain changes characterizing the learning process.

5. ASPECTS OF A MODEL OF CEREBRAL ORGANIZATION IN LEARNING

The foregoing data have been presented in the frame of a series of possible models of the organization of cerebral systems in the storage of information, based on the structural frame of the cerebral cortex, on the functional aspects of certain cortico-subcortical interrelations, and on a focusing of these considerations at the organizational level of the single cell. We may summarize these hypotheses.

A reasonable model of the impedance shifts might be that they arise in a redistribution of ionic material in the various tissue compartments comprising the cerebral system. Our studies have considered a tricompartmental model, with intraneuronal, intraglial and extracellular divisions. The problem has been discussed elsewhere of reconciling the impedance changes observed here with the concept that the low resistance shunt paths in the extracellular space would effectively mask any such changes attributable to altered resistance in the physiologically active neuronal membrane (9). It would appear that the changes described here may occur at least partly in the intraglial compartment. Hild & Tasaki (40) have indicated that glial cells have a membrane resistance of 3 to 10 ohms per square centimeter, or about one per cent of the usual value assigned to the neuronal membrane. The glial tissue compartment comprises a significant portion of the volume of the dendritic zone of the hippocampal pyramidal cell layer in which most of these measurements were made, and the true extracellular space here appears quite small (36). The glial compartment, essentially enclosing the neurons in many areas, may be regarded as intervening between the neuron and the blood vascular system in metabolic exchanges.

If these impedance changes during functional activity do, in fact, occur in the intraglial compartment, the question arises as to ways in which such impedance changes may relate to electrophysiological activity in neurons. The possibility has been discussed above that information in cerebral systems may be integrated on the basis of rhythmic wave processes arising as electrotonic processes in dendritic structures. The physical proximity of dendritic structures initiating these electrotonic processes to adjacent tissue elements, both dendritic and glial, raises the possibility that those adjacent elements may function as impedance loads to the electronic phenomena.

In particular, the low membrane resistance of glial cells, and the evidence for long-lasting changes in their membrane characteristics after electrical excitation suggest that they may exercise a modulating role on electrotonic dendritic processes, determining aspects of both rate and regularity in their rhythmicity. This impedance loading may have non-linear characteristics, and current computer analysis of such a model by my colleague C. E. Hendrix[*] indicates that such a system of loading on the electrotonic generator may indeed have rhythmic solutions. This model of the interrelations between glial and neural tissue assigns to the glia a modulating role, rather than the conductive role assigned to them by Galambos (32), and is in general agreement with the proposals by Svaetichin and his colleagues (46, 58) from studies in the retina.

We have considered the possibility that electrotonic wave processes arising in dendritic structures may sweep longitudinally from the tips of the dendritic trees toward the cell bodies (37), thus establishing an "intrinsic" rhythm. The extreme proximity of dendro-dendritic contacts in cortical structures (59) may permit electrotonic activity in one neuron to influence adjacent neurons. The individual neuron may thus be viewed as a phase comparator of these extrinsic and intrinsic electrotonic processes sweeping across its surface in complex spatiotemporal patterns. Our computed analyses of these wave processes, described above, have indicated the possibility of a stochastic mode of operation in the sensitivity of cortical neurons to recurrent similar, but not necessarily identical, patterns of waves. This hypothesis of a probabilistic mode of operation would infer that the excitability of the cortical neuron would depend on the relationship of the spatiotemporal pattern of wave phenomena at the cell surface to an "optimal" pattern of waves for which its firing threshold would be lowest. This optimal pattern of waves would be determined by the previous experience of the cell, with the wave phenomena intimately concerned in the physicochemical changes associated with the deposition of the memory trace.

This proposed model of the cerebral system would, therefore, have non-linear and stochastic characteristics. The observation of sizable changes in hippocampal impedance with the performance of a learned habit raises the question as to whether glial tissue may not only be the site of these impedance changes, but also as to whether the interface between glial and dendritic tissues may be a region of special significance in the structural alterations underlying the storage of information. Intimate associations of dendro-dendritic contacts may be similarly involved, but more evidence will be necessary on the frequency of such contacts in a typical cortical volume, and on the changes in membrane conductance in dendritic structures during physiological activation (30, 52, 53) before a relationship could be established between dendritic overlap or contact and the observed impedance changes.

---

[*] Personal communication.

Future developments in impedance-measuring techniques may vastly enhance knowledge of those delicate processes in brain tissue underlying the storage of information, and establish the basis of structural and functional organizations which endow it with a uniqueness not found in "non-learning" neural systems of admittedly great complexity, such as the spinal cord. In particular, the application of techniques for impedance measurements with coherent electromagnetic sources in the spectral absorption range of substances such as the nucleic acids may open exciting opportunities for their monitoring with a speed and accuracy now confined to the transactional mechanisms accessible to current electrophysiological techniques. In this way, we may hope for solutions to such vital questions as the ways in which the electrical events may be responsible for induction of lasting physicochemical changes in neuronal excitability. Perhaps even more challenging are the possible mechanisms by which substances such as the nucleic acids, endowed with the capacity for carrying the vast bulk of genetic information, may in this instance be concerned with the determination of those ionic transport mechanisms directly responsible for establishment of cellular excitability. Such questions remain entirely enigmatic at this time.

Morrell: I would like to ask Dr. Adey whether he feels that the change in impedance, presumably related to a glial shunt, is related to the phase shift away from the hippocampus, or whether he thinks the wave change produces an impedance change.

Adey: We are currently working on a computer model in which the glial tissue is conceived as offering an impedance load to the electrotonic generators in the dendrites. Changing impedance load on the generators would be responsible for whatever alteration in frequency and, hence, in phase occurs in the EEG records.

One of my graduate students from engineering, Mr. C. E. Hendrix, has a very interesting model in which the introduction of minor nonlinearities into such a system produces very rhythmic read-outs in the simulated electrotonic generator.*

Morrell: How would you conceive of the initiation of the impedance change?

Adey: The interface between the neuron and the glia determines some change in ionic content, or quantity of ions in the glial tissue; i.e., that it is at the interface between the neuron and the glia that the trigger mechanism resides to alter these aspects of ionic content in the glial tissue. This is pure hypothesis; we have as yet no data, but theorize on the basis of the observed changes in impedance which appear so likely to arise in the glial compartment.

Feindel: Were all your results in cats or have you confirmed this in the monkey?

---

* Personal communication.

Adey: Only in cats. We have a program now to study it in the monkey.

Feindel: Because, in the cat, although the hippocampus must be very similar in structure, one becomes worried about the amount of extra cortex as compared to a higher animal. Do you think there is much difference anatomically between the organization of the hippocampus and the entorhinal cortex in the cat, as compared to the monkey, in terms of what you are seeking?

Adey: I think the difference would be exemplified by the sort of thing that Sholl (56) described, in which the relative volume of the dendritic tree increases enormously as one goes up the phyletic scale.

In this case, looking at this restricted hippocampal volume, we know by histological check that the electrodes are essentially in the dendritic layer of the hippocampus. Dr. Green and his colleague, Dr. Maxwell, have examined the electron micrographs (36). Would Dr. Green care to comment on the proportions of neuron to glia in the dendritic layer?

Green: I would not like to comment on the relative proportions, as I am unaware of these measurements. There have been some quantitative measurements of relative areas of contact on the neuron made by Blackstad & Dahl (21). I wonder, is there any special reason for picking the glial compartment rather than the intercellular compartment?

Adey: No, only that in discussions with Maxwell I understood that the proportions ran something like 80 per cent neuron, about 16 per cent glia, and about 4 per cent extracellular space. Assuming that these are just round figures, if the conductance of the glia is, say, 100 to 500 times better than that of the neuron, it seems that here is a space which intervenes between the neuron and the true extracellular space in many respects. Therefore, the prime effect of changes in the state of the neuronal tissue will manifest itself in the glial tissue before the occurrence of anything in the intraneuronal space.

Green: I do not quite know where he obtained those figures.

Adey: As a matter of fact, he measured them for us.

Morrell: Do you imply that the change which occurs in the glial, or at least extraneuronal, compartment is the result of ionic shift which ensues as nerve impulses reach synapses?

Adey: Yes. I think it is not necessary to contemplate vast transsynaptic activation of the neurons in order to see the part of the electrotonic phenomenon we call the EEG process. One of the striking features of some of the electron microscopy, as, for example, in the studies of Van der Loos (59), is the extent to which dendritic contacts occur in cortex. My surmise is that, on the basis of the proximity effects that arise, one might see electrotonic effects in organized cortical systems in the absence of the massive transsynaptic activation of neurons. At this stage, however, it is not possible to be categoric. Are you making a play for the transsynaptic activation?

Morrell: No, I just want to pin you to the wall. Are you saying that any kind of electrical activity in the dendrite will produce a current flow that results in ion shift from another dendrite into, for example, glial compartment, and increase thereby the conductivity of the glial compartment?

Adey: Quite probably. Alternatively, there may be some change in the electrotonic status of a neuron which may trigger some process in the glial cell by which ions are released from a bound state within it. It is not necessary to imply that the current flows from the neuron to the glia in a continuous stream of ions at all. I do not think this is very likely.

John: I have two comments. One concerns the possibility that the impedance change originates in the glia. I know only of one measurement of glial electrolyte, but I would appreciate evaluation from someone more qualified than I on its legitimacy. That is the work of Colfer & Essex (26) on the microincineration of brain slices, using the deposition of potassium chloroplatinate crystals. Their conclusion, as I recall, was that there was remarkably little electrolyte in the glia, which caused me a certain amount of perturbation. I do not know if this is a trustworthy finding. If so, it would seem to raise a basic objection to one aspect of Dr. Adey's hypothesis.

I would also like to mention that at the University of Rochester we have been carrying out some mathematical analyses of electrophysiological activity. I will not inflict details on you, but there are certain fundamental similarities, I think, to what Dr. Adey is doing, as I understand it.

We have looked at numerous places in the brain simultaneously. Our findings indicate that, as learning progresses, the relationships between waveforms in numerous regions in the brain lock in, so that where previously there were many diverse and unrelated waveforms, after training there are sets of waveforms which correspond quite closely. There are related clusters of structures, and these organizations decompose during errors, so that the similarity between activity in diverse anatomical structures is not nearly as close as during correct performance.

One implication of our data is that the read-out from memory depends upon a set of relationships between a rather large number of anatomical structures. I would caution against drawing conclusions about the structure of the storage or retrieval mechanism on the basis of an examination which confined its attention primarily to one anatomical structure.

I think that if one examined other brain regions one could find comparable events happening at other places.

Adey: I am quite sure that Dr. John's suggestion that this phase-locking is a manifestation of an approach to the full level of training is quite widely valid throughout the brain. But I am not sure that I see why he feels that the observations in our case, in this one restricted system, may constitute an anomaly.

John: I did not say they are anomalous. I mean there is more to the story than simply this part of it, which is most admirably sketched out for one brain region.

Green: May I say something to this point? I think, in connection with Dr. John's comment, that the particular kind of electrode that is being used to make the read-out should be specified much more precisely than we commonly do.

On the basis of what Lorente de Nó (48) has done, I would say that, in general, the degree to which an electrode can resolve spatially what is going on depends on two quite distinct phenomena. One is the amount of current flowing through the region being sampled, across a particular resistance drop, and the other, and perhaps a much more important one for us, is the relative magnitude of the focal electrode against the magnitude of the reference.

In general terms, for the same kind of generator, we would expect that a very fine electrode would resolve, and in practice it does resolve, much more precisely than a relatively gross one. We see this, for example, with microelectrodes when evoked potentials may attain amplitudes of up to 10 mV or more. So I think this depends very much on the kind of electrode specified. If the electrode is big, it will sample a large area and it will be affected by conflicting signals in the tissue.

Bickford: A couple of points. I am not very familiar with the theta activity in the cat. I have only seen it in your figures, Dr. Adey, just under specific conditions. What happens to it in the everyday activity of the cat? Is it a variable phenomenon? Is it usually there? This relates to a question, really, of the extent to which the presence of the rhythm is secondary to the environmental changes related to the T-maze situation; is it an attention effect? How much do these factors count? I am sure they could not explain everything.

Adey: We have done quite extensive computation on the spectral aspects of hippocampal activity during the period of waiting to perform. In other words, the animal is in the box, sitting quietly for fifteen minutes or half an hour. There is a broad spectrum of slow wave activity. It swings over almost an octave, from 4 to 7 cycles.

This relatively narrow band in the 5.5 cps range appears essentially only during the period of most direct attention; that is, in this paradigm, in the discriminative situation. It does not appear, for example, in relation to the orienting type of movement, where the animal is just looking around in relation to some unrecognized stimulus. This we have distinguished quite clearly on the basis of simultaneous photographs and the EEG record.

Bickford: This is a related point. The system you have investigated in the cat could not, I think, apply to the human, since we do not seem to see any comparable rhythm in the human.

Adey: We have not analyzed our own human data yet in training situations. My colleagues are collecting a great deal of information at the moment. As for the primate, in the auditory discrimination task the monkey shows a drop in the amplitude of its hippocampal activity during the short epoch of the discriminative performance. The type of analysis that we have done so far has been with the filter technique, suggesting that there are components in the theta bands that are not present before the discriminative epoch, but these are small.

Brazier: What is the neocortex doing during these changes in the hippocampus?

Adey: In the visual cortex, in particular, there is no aspect of any thing like alpha desynchronization. It is a high-amplitude type of activity, very often synchronous with the burst in the hippocampus.

Deutsch: It seems to me a great deal of your interpretation rests on the view that you take, or the theory that you have of what happens when an error occurs. I am not quite clear, from what you said, as to what the assumptions are.

Adey: They are not assumption and not theory; it is observation, and we are interpreting observations.

Deutsch: How are you interpreting them?

Adey: The signal systems from the brain are differently organized in the incorrect response.

Deutsch: I think you wanted to assume from this that the region you are observing is in some way acting as a comparator—I believe that was your phrase.

Adey: That the individual neuron is capable of acting as a comparator for slow wave processes.

Deutsch: On the basis of what happens during errors, I take it?

Adey: Whether it is error or incorrect decision, it is not material to the general hypothesis that something other than the normal or, rather, the usual concept of synaptic bombardment of neurons is involved in integration in cerebral tissue.

The fact is that these wave processes are ubiquitous in the cerbral cortex; they are not the envelope of the firing of the neurons. It has been our aim to see if they are sufficiently well specified in their patterns, from one region to another, or in one locus, viewed intrinsically, to enable us to say, "These have the characteristics of information-carrying phenomena." In terms of the amount of information that can be conveyed by spatiotemporal analog processes, it would vastly exceed the amount of information that can be carried by synaptic pulse processes.

Deutsch: It seems to me that an alternative interpretation could be made of your finding, if one were to assume that, instead of an error in the sense of some kind of hitch in the information that the animal is trying to sort, you simply obtained what seems like an error to you, but may not be an error at all to the cat. There may be, for instance, a change in motivation, or something like that.

Adey: In answer to that, we have carefully examined the latency of correct and incorrect responses, and they did not differ. So, at least in the mode of performance, there is no evidence of a change in motivation.

Deutsch: Have you also examined the order in which the errors occur and the times at which they occur?

Adey: Yes; in the fully trained animal this bears no relationship to the particular phase of the test runs. In other words, they do not occur primarily at the beginning or at the end. They do not occur at a time when satiation, for example, might be slowing down the animal's performance, or leading to a lack of interest.

If one considers the cells as occupying a place in which the patterns of waves have different configurations in space and time, the waves will intersect the dendritic tree and the soma from an almost infinitely various series of directions, and in infinitely different patterns. The conceivable number of such patterns to which one cell could be exposed would exceed the number of patterns that would be impinging on it from the synaptic bombardment in a given period of time.

Benzer: You are saying one system would have more information than another.

Adey: A significantly greater number of bits of information would impinge on a cell in the analog mode than in the digital type of operation dependent solely on arriving pulse-coded events.

Benzer: I understand. I thought you were talking about the whole brain.

Morrell: In terms of information handling, how would you place the current doctrine of the synaptic relations of specific areas?

Adey: I do not think it affects that in any way whatever. This is not to be construed as an unlimited application of the field theory to the brain. We are speaking now of the local events occurring on the cell surface. It does not in any way make redundant any classical concept of modes of interconnection, but it does exemplify their great complexity.

Morrell: Would you mind describing exactly how you think propagation of slow waves might occur?

Adey: I know what you are asking about. What you want me to say is this: that the wave phenomenon is the sign of a local process, and that its manifestation at a local level, say in the midbrain of some other region remote from the hippocampus, can occur by reason of axonally propagated phenomena which do not themselves necessarily carry the sign of the wave process; that they will not have a rhythmic discharge imprinted on them; that the pattern of axonal firing which leads to the production of a wave pattern in some remote region does not of itself carry the sign of the rhythmicity.

Morrell: And you agree?

Adey: I agree with that. After all, I think everybody who has recorded activity in the fornix would agree it is virtually impossible to see anything which looks like a theta rhythm or like the firing of axons in a fashion tied to the rhythm pattern in the hippocampus.

Recently, the group in Vienna, Petsche and his colleagues (51), saw cells in the septum firing synchronously with the theta rhythm. But one of the curious things is that the theta rhythm itself is almost impossible to record in the septum. So, there is a multiplicity of evidence suggesting an independence of the neuronal firing and the wave process, both positively and negatively.

Morrell: Concerning the notion that the glia is the only compartment in which impedance change can occur, what about the evidence presented by Schadé & Van Harreveld (55) of a chloride shift into the dendrite? Is not that a rather natural action?

Adey: Yes, but I think the conditions were somewhat, shall we say, pathological. They also observed, as I recall, swellings of the glial tissue under those circumstances. I think that this change in glial volume is one of the contributing factors to the change that they observed in cortical volume as a whole. But I am not aware that this type of massive ionic shift or the change in volume are concomitants of the normal physiological process.

Morrell: Is there any reason to think neuronal impedance changes could not occur? Van Harreveld (55) has measured them in the brain.

Adey: My only contention that it is unlikely is based on the relative membrane resistance of the two compartments under normal circumstances.

Morrell: Has anyone measured the membrane resistance of the dendrite?

Adey: I think there are some suggestions from the Jung School that they have indirectly derived it (27). But it has been measured in glia.

Thompson: I have a question for Dr. Adey. You have shown very clearly a relationship between a change in the hippocampal pattern and a change in behavior by means of your subthalamic lesions. I imagine many of us will go to our respective laboratories and test recent memory in lesioned animals and then evaluate the effect of a critical lesion on hippocampal theta. According to your conclusions, the rhythm of the hippocampus should be altered under these circumstances. But on the basis of the work of Green & Arduini (35), a mammillary body lesion does not affect hippocampal activity and yet, if you take even partly seriously the findings from Korsakoff psychosis and the rat work I presented earlier, such a lesion does produce a recent memory disturbance.

Would you then indicate what is going on. Might the mammillary bodies be contributing to recent memory because it comes under the influence of the hippocampus, and not the reverse?

Adey: I think that the correction of the concept of reciprocity of connections is such a broad one that it would not be appropiate to spend a lot of time on it now. For example, if one looks at the distribution of the fornix fibers as they degenerate following section of the fornix or septal lesion, a great many of them do not go to the mammillary body (28). They terminate in more dorsal regions, in the thalamus, in the rostral hypothalamus, and so forth, and the proportion of them that terminate in this fashion increases the higher one goes in the phyletic scale. I am not sure of the exact figures, but I think that something like 40 per cent of the fornix in man terminates in the mammillary body. The rest of it is lost before it even gets there.

As to the question of the converse series of connections going up into the hippocampus from the anterior diencephalon, at this stage we know very little specifically about them. They may go through to the septum; in fact, many of them probably do. The histology, or attempts to examine the connections histologically, have not been highly successful. There is little doubt, though, that a stream of activity goes from rostral thalamic area through the septal areas, and in some way enters the hippocampus.

Weiskrantz: First of all, just for the record, Dr. Adey, if your implication was that I was saying the hippocampus is the site, I just wish to say I was saying something quite different.

Adey: I was perhaps tilting at windmills. I was not trying to suggest it to you.

Weiskrantz: I did not want that inference to be drawn. There is one thing that comes up as a question here, and is related to a general issue. It concerns correlations between electrical phenomena and behavior, and whether or not the phenomena are simply epiphenomena.

One of the questions is this: we know that memories established in the sorts of learning situations in which you put your animals are not very much interfered with by anesthesia, electroshock, freezing, and so forth. Would you expect these very same events to affect impedance changes or phase shifts in your animals?

Adey: Certainly; the barbiturate anesthetic state produces very profound changes. What is your question?

Weiskrantz: The question is, if such fairly drastic procedures *do* produce relatively permanent changes, or at least changes which outlast the agent, such as anesthesia, what would be the significance of the electrical changes you have seen, bearing in mind that these drastic procedures do not affect the animal's retention?

Adey: I think there is a misapprehension here. Those impedance changes that we saw with anesthesia did not outlast the anesthesia. The same way with the impedance changes in learning. These were evoked, and appeared in relation to the required task, which implies that, within the tissue, there is some trigger mechanism sensitive to previous experience associated with the release of ions, or some other phenomenon which we measure as a conductive change in an evoked fashion. The baseline impedance is not shifted in the course of the learning procedure.

Weiskrantz: Would you expect that this evoked impedance change would be altered by hitting hard the system with, say, electro-convulsive shock?

Adey: We have not tried electro-convulsive shock. The only phenomena relevant to this I imagine are the observations that, if you habituate or extinguish the behavior response, the impedance change disappears, and then reappears with relearning.

Henry: Have you now a very clear picture as to why these impedance shifts are not associated with vascular changes?

Adey: Yes. The evidence that this is *not* a vascular change is fairly categorical. First of all, many of the phenomena establish themselves extremely rapidly. For example, a single loud click, under the influence of cyclohexamine, produces a step in the impedance record which is fully established in about 100 msec. So you have a step and then another baseline. It takes all of 15 minutes for this to decline, although it was established so rapidly.*

REFERENCES

1. ADEY, W. R., Organization of the rhinencephalon. In: *The Reticular Formation of the Brain* (H. H. Jasper et al., Eds.). Little, Brown, Boston, 1958: 621-644.

2. ———, Recent studies of the rhinencephalon in relation to temporal lobe epilepsy and behavior disorders. *Int. Rev. Neurobiol.*, 1959, 1: 1-46.

3. ———, Studies on learning: discussion. In: *Brain Function, Vol. I. Cortical Excitability and Steady Potentials; Relations of Basic Research to Space Biology* (M.A.B. Brazier, Ed.). UCLA Forum No. 1, Univ. of California Press, Los Angeles, 1963: 148-158.

4. ADEY, W. R., BELL, F. R., and DENNIS, B. J., Effects of LSD-25, psilocybin and psilocin on temporal lobe EEG patterns and learned behavior in the cat. *Neurology*, 1962, 12: 591-602.

5. ADEY, W. R., and DUNLOP, C. W., The action of certain cyclohexamines on hippocampal system during approach performance in the cat. *J. Pharmacol. Exp. Therap.*, 1960, 130: 418-426.

6. ADEY, W. R., DUNLOP, C. W., and HENDRIX, C. E., Hippocampal slow waves; distribution and phase relationships in the course of approach learning. *Arch. Neurol.*, 1960, 3: 74-90.

7. ADEY, W. R., DUNLOP, C. W., and SUNDERLAND, S., A survey of rhinencephalic interconnections with the brain stem. *J. Comp. Neurol.*, 1958, 110: 173-203.

8. ADEY, W. R., and KADO, R. T., Changes in impedance in hippocampal structures during discriminative performance in cat. *Fed. Proc.*, 1962, 21: 359.

9. ADEY, W. R., KADO, R. T., and DIDIO, J., Impedance measurements in brain tissue of animals using microvolt signals. *Exp. Neurol.*, 1962, 5: 47-66.

10. ADEY, W. R., KADO, R. T., DIDIO, J., and SCHINDLER, W. J., Impedance changes

---

* *Added by Dr. Adey after the Conference:* We have recently completed studies of interrelations between impedance and blood pressure changes in hypothermia and hypercapnia, and made some observations on carotid blood flow and cerebral impedance. Briefly, the changes in blood pressure and blood flow show no primary relationship to the impedance changes, and there are basic qualitative differences in impedance changes in different cerebral structures by identical stimuli.

in cerebral tissue accompanying a learned discriminative performance in the cat. *Exp. Neurol.*, 1963, **7**: 259-281.

11. ADEY, W. R., and LINDSLEY, D. F., On the role of subthalamic areas in the maintenance of brain-stem reticular excitability. *Exp. Neurol.*, 1959, **1**: 407-426.

12. ADEY, W. R., and WALTER, D. O., Application of phase detection and averaging techniques in computer analysis of EEG records in the cat. *Exp. Neurol.*, 1963, **7**: 186-209.

13. ADEY, W. R., WALTER, D. O., and HENDRIX, C. E., Computer techniques in correlation and spectral analyses of cerebral slow waves during discriminative behavior. *Exp. Neurol.*, 1961, **3**: 501-524.

14. ADEY, W. R., WALTER, D. O., and KADO, R. T., Examination of integrative processes in cerebral systems by computer analysis of electroencephalographic and impedance records. In: *XXII International Congress of Physiological Sciences*, Vol. II, Abstracts of Communications (J. W. Duyff et al., Eds.). Excerpta Medica, Amsterdam, 1962: No. 1063.

15. ADEY, W. R., WALTER, D. O., and LINDSLEY, D. F., Subthalamic lesions. Effects on learned behavior and correlated hippocampal and subcortical slow-wave activity. *Arch. Neurol.*, 1962, **6**: 194-207.

16. ALAJOUANINE, T. (Ed.), *Les Grandes Activités du Rhinencéphale. Vol. II. Physiologie et Pathologie du Rhinencéphale*. Masson, Paris, 1961.

17. ANDY, O. J., and AKERT, K., Seizure patterns induced by electrical stimulation of hippocampal formation in cat. *J. Neuropath. Exp. Neurol.*, 1955, **14**: 198-213.

18. ANDY, O. J., CHINN, R. M., ALLEN, M. B., and SHAWVER, E. F., Influence of mesencephalic and diencephalic stimulation on limbic system seizures. *Neurology*, 1958, **8**: 939-952.

19. BALDWIN, M., and BAILEY, P. (Eds.), *Temporal Lobe Epilepsy*. Thomas, Springfield, 1958.

20. BLACKMAN, R. B., and TUKEY, J W., *The Measurement of Power Spectra*. Dover, New York, 1959.

21. BLACKSTAD, T. W., and DAHL, H. A., Quantitative evaluation of structures in contact with neuronal somata. An electron microscopic study of the fascia dentata of the rat. *Acta Morph. Neerl.-Scand.*, 1962, **4**: 329-343.

22. BRAZIER, M. A. B., and BARLOW, J. S., Some applications of correlation analysis to clinical problems of electroencephalography. *EEG Clin. Neurophysiol.*, 1956, **8**: 325-331.

23. CHAPMAN, L. F., WALTER, R. D., ADEY, W. R., CRANDALL, P. H., RAND, R. W., BRAZIER, M. A. B., and MARKHAM, C. H., Altered electrical activity of human hippocampus and amygdala induced by LSD-25. *Physiologist*, 1962, **5**: 118.

24. CHOW, K. L., and SURVIS, J., Retention of overlearned visual habit after temporal cortical ablation in monkey. *A.M.A. Arch. Neurol. Psychiat.*, 1958, **79**: 640-646.

25. COLE, K. S., Permeability and impermeability of cell membranes for ions. *Cold Spring Harbor Symp. Quart. Biol.*, 1940, **8**: 110-122.

26. COLFER, H. F., and ESSEX, H. E., The distribution of total electrolyte, potas-

sium and sodium in the cerebral cortex in relation to experimental convulsions. *Am. J. Physiol.*, 1947, **150**: 27-36.

27. CREUTZFELDT, O., and STRUCK, G., Neurophysiologie und Morphologie der chronisch isolierten Cortexinsel der Katze: Hirnpotentiale und Neuronentätigkeit einer isolierten Nervenzellpopulation ohne afferent Fasern. *Arch. Psychiat. Nervenkr.*, 1962, **203**: 708-731.

28. DAITZ, H. M., and POWELL, T. P. S., Studies of the connexions of the fornix system. *J. Neurol. Neurosurg. Psychiat.*, 1954, **17**: 75-82.

29. DOTY, R. W., BECK, E. C., and KOOI, K. A., Effect of brain-stem lesions on conditioned responses of cats. *Exp. Neurol.*, 1959, **1**: 360-385.

30. ECCLES, J. C., Membrane time constants of cat motoneurons and time courses of synaptic action. *Exp. Neurol.*, 1961, **4**: 1-22.

31. EDINGER, L., *Vorlesungen über den Bau der nervösen Zentralorgane des Menschen und der Tiere*. Vogel, Leipzig, 1904.

32. GALAMBOS, R., A glia-neural theory of brain function. *Proc. Nat. Acad. Sci. USA*, 1961, **47**: 129-136.

33. GASTAUT, H., and LAMMERS, H. J., *Anatomie du Rhinencéphale*. Vol. I in: *Les Grandes Activitiés du Rhinencéphale* (T. Alajouanine, Ed.). Masson, Paris, 1961.

34. GOODMAN, N. R., Measuring amplitude and phase. *J. Franklin Inst.*, 1960, **270**: 437-450.

35. GREEN, J. D., and ARDUINI, A., Hippocampal electrical activity in arousal. *J. Neurophysiol.*, 1954, **17**: 533-557.

36. GREEN, J. D., and MAXWELL, D. S., Hippocampal electrical activity. I. Morphological aspects. *EEG Clin. Neurophysiol.*, 1961, **13**: 837-846.

37. GREEN, J. D., MAXWELL, D. S., SCHINDLER, W. J., and STUMPF, C., Rabbit EEG "theta" rhythm: its anatomical source and relation to activity in single neurons. *J. Neurophysiol.*, 1960, **23**: 403-420.

38. HERRICK, C. J., The functions of the olfactory parts of the cerebral cortex. *Proc. Nat. Acad. Sci. USA*, 1933, **19**: 7-14.

39. HESS, E. H., Imprinting. An effect of early experience, imprinting determines later social behavior in animals. *Science*, 1959, **130**: 133-141.

40. HILD, W., and TASAKI, I., Morphological and physiological properties of neurons and glial cells in tissue culture. *J. Neurophysiol.*, 1962, **25**: 277-304.

41. HOLMES, J. E., and ADEY, W. R., Electrical activity of the entorhinal cortex during conditioned behavior. *Am. J. Physiol.*, 1960, **199**: 741-744.

42. HUNT, H. F., and DIAMOND, I. T., Some effects of hippocampal lesions on conditioned avoidance behavior in the cat. *Acta Physiol.*, 1959, **15**: 203-204.

43. KAADA, B. R., RASMUSSEN, E. W., and KVEIM, O., Effects of hippocampal lesions on maze learning and retention in rats. *Exp. Neurol.*, 1961, **3**: 333-355.

44. KLÜVER, H., and BUCY, P. C., Preliminary analysis of functions of temporal lobes in monkeys. *Arch. Neurol. Psychiat.*, 1939, **42**: 979-1000.

45. LASHLEY, K. S., Studies of cerebral function in learning. VII. The relation between cerebral mass, learning, and retention. *J. Comp. Neurol.*, 1926, **41**: 1-58.

46. LAUFER, M., FATEHCHAND, R., SVAETICHIN, G., and VALLECALLE, E., On the control of nervous function by glial networks. In: *XXII International Congress of Physiological Sciences*, Vol. II, Abstracts of Communications (J. W. Duyff et al., Eds.). Excerpta Medica, Amsterdam, 1962: No. 963.

47. LINDSLEY, D. F., and ADEY, W. R., Availability of peripheral input to the midbrain reticular formation. *Exp. Neurol.*, 1961, 4: 358-376.

48. LORENTE DE NÓ, R., Analysis of the distribution of the action currents of nerve in volume conductors. Concluding notes. *Stud. Rockefeller Inst. Med. Res.*, 1947, 132: 384-482.

49. ORBACH, J., MILNER, B., and RASMUSSEN, T., Learning and retention in monkeys after amygdala-hippocampus resection. *Arch. Neurol.*, 1960, 3: 230-251.

50. PENFIELD, W., Functional localization in temporal and deep Sylvian areas. *Res. Publ. Ass. Nerv. Ment. Dis.*, 1958, 36: 210-226.

51. PETSCHE, H., STUMPF, C., and GOGOLAK, G., The significance of the rabbit's septum as a relay station between the midbrain and the hippocampus. I. The control of hippocampus arousal activity by the septum cells. *EEG Clin. Neurophysiol.*, 1962, 14: 202-211.

52. RALL, W., Branching dendritic trees and motoneuron membrane resistivity. *Exp. Neurol.*, 1959, 1: 491-527.

53. ———, Electrophysiology of a dendritic neuron model. *Biophysical J.*, 1962, 2 (Supp.): 145-167.

54. ROSVOLD, H. E., and MISHKIN, M., Non-sensory effects of frontal lesions on discrimination learning and performance. In: *Brain Mechanisms and Learning* (J. F. Delafresnaye et al., Eds.). Blackwell, Oxford, 1961: 555-576.

55. SCHADÉ, J. P., and VAN HARREVELD, A., Ion movements in cerebral cortex. *EEG Clin. Neurophysiol.*, 1959, 11: 613.

56. SHOLL, D. A., A comparative study of the neuronal packing density in the cerebral cortex. *J. Anat.*, 1959, 93: 143-158.

57. SMITH, G. E., Some problems relating to the evolution of the brain. *Lancet*, 1910 (1): 1-6; 147-153; 221-227.

58. SVAETICHIN, G., LAUFER, M., MITARAI, G., FATEHCHAND, R., VALLECALLE, E., and VILLEGAS, J., Glial control of neuronal networks and receptors. In: *Neurophysiologie und Psychophysik des visuellen Systems* (R. Jung and H. Kornhuber, Eds.). Springer, Berlin, 1961: 445-456.

59. VAN DER LOOS, H., A substrate for ephaptic interaction of neurons in the cerebral cortex? In: *XXII International Congress of Physiological Sciences*, Vol. II, Abstracts of Communications (J. W. Duyff et al., Eds.). Excerpta Medica, Amsterdam, 1962: No. 1067.

MEMORY AND SPEECH FUNCTION
IN THE TEMPORAL LOBE IN MAN

WILLIAM FEINDEL
Montreal Neurological Institute
Canada

Perhaps our arrival at this stage should be tempered by James Thurber's version of Alexander Pope's famous saying, "The proper study of mankind is man,—says man!"

No doubt most of us now realize, from the many studies already presented, that memory is a rather complex function. It can be broken down into many compartments, some of which are manifested at the clinical level, and others derived by the technical approaches which have been used for the study of memory in lower animal forms. Perhaps you will agree that one of our problems is to define what in fact our tests for memory are supposed to be testing.

I would like to present for your consideration a few main points. First, a review of the anatomical structures in the temporal lobe which we now consider to be concerned with memory; second, a presentation of three case reports to illustrate the method of the study of memory and speech in clinical material; and finally, an indication of some of the gaps which still remain in the problem of correlating the anatomy and functional aspects of memory.

It is quite evident from the material already presented that the bulk of our information on responses to brain stimulation continues to be derived from carefully controlled animal experiments. By comparison, the gleanings of the neurosurgeon from observation of the human brain during essential surgical treatment must seem scanty and incomplete to the anatomist, physiologist, psychologist and biochemist. As experimental scientists they are able to plan their experimental strategy, but the neurosurgeon and neurologist must be content with those experiments that nature has contrived. Clinical findings can only be obtained when the opportunity presents itself and, because of these varied circumstances, these data are open to considerable latitude in interpretation. Nevertheless, however imperfect they may appear to those working under more strict experimental criteria, the findings give us unique insight into such functions as sensation, emotion, speech, and memory, which are difficult or indeed sometimes inaccessible to study by experiments on lower animals (21, 28, 31). Combined with careful assessment before and after operation of the patient's behavior and intellectual capacity (15) and correlated with the pathological identity of the diseased structures (29), these clinical studies continue to extend our understanding of the human brain and in particular of that complex region which we label anatomically the temporal lobe.

The results which I wish to report here have all been obtained on patients who have epileptic seizures which preferentially involve structures in the temporal lobe. The lesion, that is to say, the area of damage, has been placed there by a disease process. It sets off abnormal discharge of nerve cells, manifested by changes in the electrical activity of the brain and in the patient's behavior.

The lesion, most commonly a scar, small tumor, or vascular anomaly, may be relatively local and amenable to surgical excision. During operation, when the brain is exposed, its electrical activity can be recorded and the cortex and certain deeper structures in the temporal lobe can be stimulated electrically. Since the patient is necessarily conscious during these operations in order to make it possible to identify areas of the cortex such as, for example, those concerned with speech, he can report his reactions, and his behavior can be observed and tested. Since the operation is lengthy, the range and complexities of these tests must clearly be kept within modest limits and directed always toward the immediate problem of defining the abnormal area of brain and controlling and guiding the site and extent of surgical removal.

The methods of study and the surgical techniques illustrated in these case reports have been evolved by Dr. Penfield and his associates at Montreal over a period of some thirty years (2, 4, 6, 19, 20, 21, 24, 25). The operation protocols on more than 1400 patients continue to provide a wealth of material for retrospective study. The surgical team is supported by an invaluable group of investigators who have taken on special fields of interest such as neurophysiology, neurology, radiology, neurochemistry, and psychology, and without whom these studies would not be possible (8, 9, 10, 13, 15, 16, 21).

For the sake of historical perspective we may remind ourselves that three centuries ago, at the University of Oxford, another type of brain conference was going on from day to day involving a small group which consisted of two medical practitioners, three medical students and a professor of astronomy. They were meeting much as we are today to examine the brain and to discuss its function. But their approach was simple and much less pretentious. The senior member of this group, whose portrait is the frontispiece to this volume, was Dr. Thomas Willis; he was the head of what we might today well call a medical research team (3). He had evidently become discontented with the concept inherited from the ancient physicians that the mind was located in the ventricles of the brain (1).

Willis and his colleagues decided to look at the brain and nerves for themselves. To this end he and his friends dissected and sketched the nervous system in a great variety of animals including the earthworm, the oyster, the lobster, the sheep and man. Although you will note slight variations in the species, I think you will agree that the pattern of approach was not dissimilar to that of this present Conference.

The professor of astronomy was Christopher Wren who, as is well known, was the architect of St. Paul's Cathedral. It was he who manufactured the copper etchings of the brain dissections for Willis' book, *Cerebri Anatome*

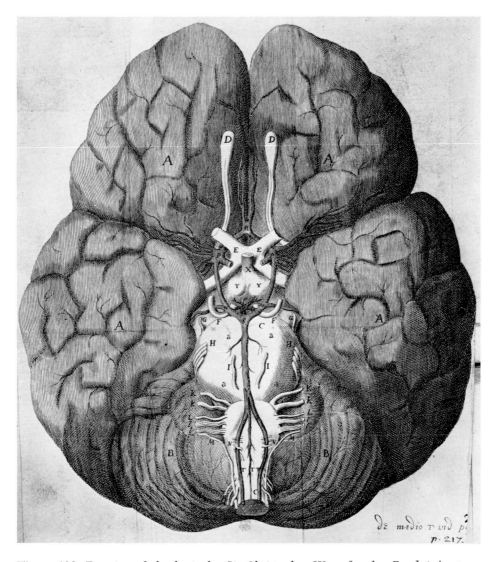

Figure 108. Drawing of the brain by Sir Christopher Wren for the *Cerebri Anatome* by Thomas Willis, 1664 (32). This is the first accurate representation of the temporal lobes of the human brain.

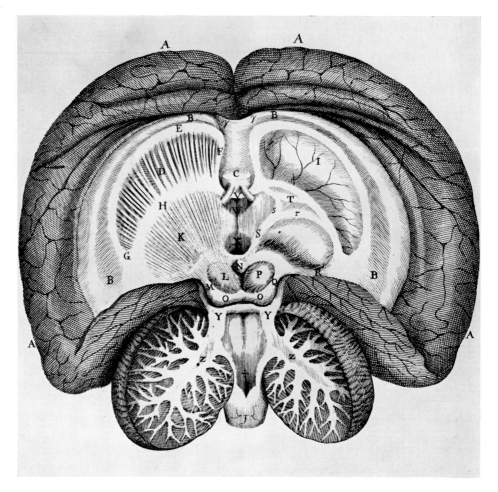

Figure 109. The interior of the brain, from *De Anima Brutorum* by Thomas Willis, 1672 (33). The columns of the fornix are seen crossing downward behind the anterior commissure (V).

(32). These beautiful illustrations, published in the middle of the seventeenth century, surpassed in detail anything that had appeared up to that time on the anatomy of the brain—far more elegant than the efforts of Leonardo or of Calcar and Vesalius or of Casserius.

The first accurate drawing of the temporal lobe, particularly of its medial portion, is illustrated in Willis' *Cerebri Anatome* (Figure 108). This region had suffered badly in the illustrations of previous anatomists. The cranial nerves, the uncus, the hippocampal gyrus and mammillary bodies are clearly indicated; Willis also depicted a number of internal structures of the brain which until then had been represented only in crude fashion. By a skillful method of dissection he contrived to see the inside of the brain by lifting up the occipital lobes and splitting the corpus callosum and the columns of the fornix. An illustration in Willis' *De Anima Brutorum* (33) shows the columns of the fornix and the anterior commissure just in front (Figure 109). The

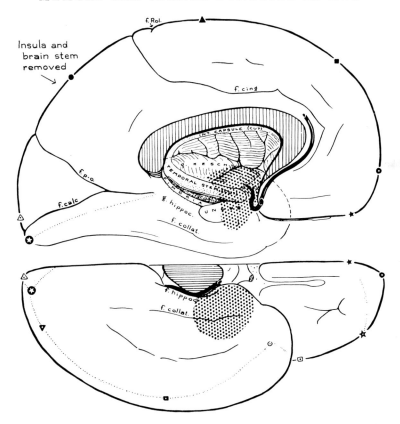

Figure 110. Drawing showing mesial structures of the temporal lobe and insula. The shaded area indicates where stimulation produced automatism with blocking of memory recording.

cerebellar cortex, so beautifully illustrated in Dr. Palay's electron micrographs, can also be seen. These drawings, three centuries old, put in a succinct way the anatomical structures related to memory function with which we are still vitally concerned.

In his preface to *Cerebri Anatome* (32), published in 1664, Willis wrote, "Wherefore to explicate the uses of the Brain, seems as difficult a task as to paint the Soul, of which it is commonly said, That it understands all things but it self . . ."* One of the purposes of this Conference, it seems clear, is to "explicate", particularly in reference to memory function, the role of some of these cerebral structures depicted so well by Willis and his circle of friends so long ago.

Turning now to the anatomy of our own day, Figure 110 is a general view of the brain with the temporal lobe dissected and turned aside from the temporal stem. It shows the mesial deep surface with the hippocampal gyrus, the tip of the ventricle with the hippocampus in the floor of the ventricle and the uncus immediately beneath with the amygdala below it. We should

---

* From the translation by Samuel Pordage, published in London in 1681 (34).

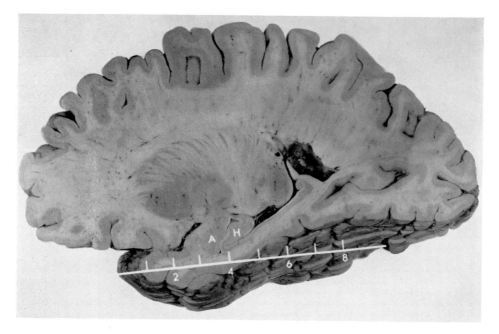

Figure 111. Sagittal section of brain to show deep structures of the temporal lobe, amygdala (A) and pes hippocampi (H), and one-centimeter intervals from the temporal pole.

note that the cortex of the insula and the orbito-frontal region are not far removed.

In another view (Figure 111) the temporal lobe is shown on a sagittal section with the amygdala (A) and the pes hippocampus (H). The marks are placed at 1 cm intervals from the tip of the temporal lobe. You will note that the amygdala lies between 3 and 4 cm from the tip while the hippocampus extends from 3.5 cm to about 7 cm from the tip.

As can be seen in the drawing from Willis' *Cerebri Anatome*, the optic tract, the mammillary body and the globus pallidus lie just medial to the mesial structures of the temporal lobe. In a previous review (5) of the anatomy of this region we emphasized the close interrelationship of the gray islands of the claustrum and those of the amygdala. These gray islands are separated by bundles of the uncinate fasciculus.

I would like now to present some illustrative case records. The first case is H. H., age 29. This patient had several seizures with chewing movements and salivation. On one occasion post-ictal speech difficulty was noted. Neurological examination was normal. The patient was right-handed. The EEG showed a left temporal abnormality with slow and sharp waves. Pneumogram and angiogram indicated a space-occupying lesion in the left anterior temporal region.

At operation a cholesteatoma, 4 cm in diameter, covered by a thin layer of brain tissue, occupied more than half of the temporal fossa (Figure 112).

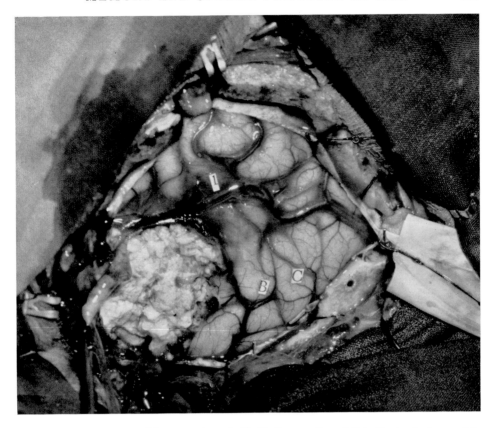

Figure 112. The exposed brain in Case 1, H. H. Letters B and C indicate electrographic abnormality. Stimulation at point 1 gave difficulty with speech as indicated in the text.

The cortex of the temporal pole had been displaced backward and medially by the tumor. Stimulation at point 1, in the lower part of the sensory cortex, produced difficulty in speaking. Stimulation caused the patient to be interrupted and to produce a long-drawn sound. When asked why, he answered that he had a sensation in the back of his mouth that seemed to interfere with his ability to speak.

On the drawing of the operative findings (Figure 113), the large-dotted area represents the cholesteatoma. The open circles indicate areas where stimulation, well above the threshold for the motor responses, caused no speech interference. The letters B and C represent electrographic abnormality. The area of excision is represented by the dense shading. The cholesteatoma was removed, as well as a region of temporal cortex immediately behind it which showed high voltage sharp waves.

Following excision, while still on the operating table, H. H. was shown drawings of objects on cards. He had difficulty naming "shoe" and called a hand "five fingers". He named other objects correctly. On the evening of the day of operation he named "ball-point pen" correctly but then called a flashlight "ball-point". From then on during the post-operative period he had no demonstrable speech difficulty. His visual fields remained full.

The patient reported that many facts which he had forgotten in recent months were beginning to return spontaneously after the operation. There was also improvement in his attention and concentration. Psychological test values obtained by Dr. Brenda Milner and her associates (15) exhibited improvement in all spheres of speech and memory function. Eight months after operation the patient reported only occasional difficulty remembering names of persons. Testing at that time showed no speech or memory difficulty and an I.Q. rating somewhat higher than before operation (Table 19).

In this instance, interruption of speech by stimulation of the post-central cortex appeared to be related to a sensation felt by the patient in the back of his mouth. Counting was interrupted by long-drawn vocalization. The interference with naming toward the end of the cortical excision as well as immediately after operation indicated that the left temporal lobe in this patient was dominant for speech. There was mild impairment of memory function noted by the patient and confirmed by psychological testing. This was

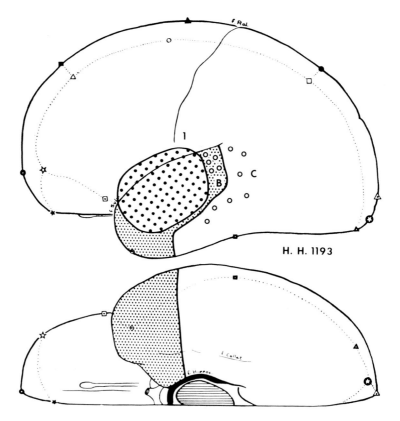

Figure 113. Diagram to show the site of the cholesteatoma (coarse-dotted area) and excision fine-dotted area) in Case 1, H. H. Circles indicate stimulation with no impairment of speech.

TABLE 19

	Preoperative	14 days postoperative	8 months follow-up
Full-scale I.Q.	116	120	124
Verbal I.Q.	120	130	126
Performance I.Q.	109	106	120
Memory quotient	103	103	115

not present eight months after operation. It is worth noting that improvement in the psychological test values occurred despite the fact that this patient had a large lesion which no doubt had been compressing the anterior and medial parts of the temporal lobe for many years.

The second case which I would like to describe is that of J. Wa., age 29, who had had seizures since the age of four years. He described that these attacks would leave him with a loss of memory for some things which had happened just before the attack came on. Even the minor attacks would wipe out for about twenty-four hours the memory of things which he had learned, for example, for examinations.

His attacks began with a feeling in the abdomen, an empty or strange feeling which came up over his body and "blanketed" his head. This seemed to take over from anything he was doing at the time so that he usually stopped any activity. He described one attack when he was thinking about taking a trip to Atlantic City. He also had the feeling that he was looking for something and could not find it. He recalled going downstairs and saying repeatedly to his mother, "I can't find it, I can't find it." He could not seem to stop saying this. He cannot recall now what it was that he seemed to be looking for. In some attacks he had a hot peppery taste in his mouth which stayed for fifteen to twenty minutes. He knew that he had trouble naming things after an attack. He reported that he knew clearly what the objects were but found it impossible to get out the word. He was ambidextrous, playing golf right-handed and writing with his right hand but playing tennis and throwing a ball with his left hand.

The important features of his attacks were elaborate automatic behavior, amnesia for what occurred during the attack and sometimes oblivion for what had happened before the attack. The electroencephalogram showed a left temporal abnormality and carotid amytal tests (30) showed speech interference from injection on the left side.

At operation the left temporal lobe was exposed; the small tickets in Figure 114 show the sites where stimulation responses were obtained by electrical stimulation. Some of these having to do with speech and memory may be briefly mentioned. Interference with speech was produced at points 1, 2, 3, 8 and 10. At point 3, the patient said, "Something that stops me from talking just for a moment." Stimulation at point 12 produced arrest of counting. When asked if it were the same as the stammering produced before by

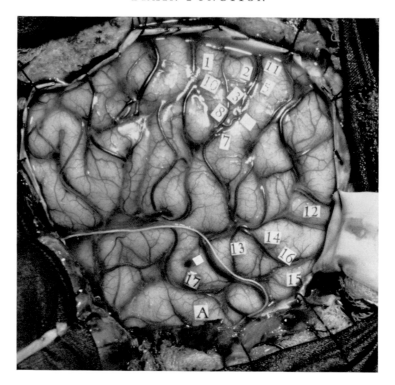

Figure 114. Operative photograph from Case 2, J. Wa. The white thread indicates the line of excision. Numbered stimulation tickets as described in the text.

stimulation of the motor cortex, he answered, "Completely different." He said that he knew what he wanted to say but could not get the words out. On repeat of the stimulation he was shown the picture of a flag and said "clag".

Stimulation by a depth electrode in contact with the periamygdaloid region at point 17 in the temporal cortex (Figure 115) caused the patient to appear confused. His speech was unclear and he said, "A guy in white— a female white." He then explained that he actually saw something that seemed crazy, which was a woman sitting on a deck of cards. The patient further described that he seemed actually to see this woman and then, as he continued looking at Dr. Brindle, the (male) anesthetist, she seemed to take his place. Deep stimulation when repeated caused the patient to say that he had a funny feeling in his stomach which he had noted before his attacks. At another point, 16 in Figure 115, the patient stated that there was a feeling of falling away, being far away, and when the surgeon was counting he noted a change in the surgeon's voice which seemed to correspond with the period of stimulation. After excision of the lateral cortex of the temporal lobe, stimulation in the region of the amygdaloid under direct vision produced again "that feeling" in his head. He had difficulty in talking and appeared confused. He said to the anesthetist, "A very slight attack; a funny feeling," and further said, "boys and girls are here," pointing to his mouth, "and the man is up here," pointing to his head.

Before further excision an attempt was made to test his memory function. This was repeated again after the final removal, which included excision of the uncus and the first centimeter of the hippocampus, and again no memory change was detected. There was some evidence of speech impairment after the final excision.

Up until the second post-operative day he was able to name most things correctly, but from then until the end of the first two weeks after operation he developed great difficulty in naming which gradually cleared.

Detailed psychological testing was carried out again by Dr. Milner. In summary, the patient's full-scale I.Q. before operation was 104, two weeks after operation, 95, and seven months later, 110. His verbal I.Q. at the same intervals measured 98, 95 and 114. His memory quotient, which was rather low before operation, was tested at 74, 85 and 88. Again, despite an epileptic lesion which had been present for a period of twenty-five years, there was significant improvement in the test values for memory function

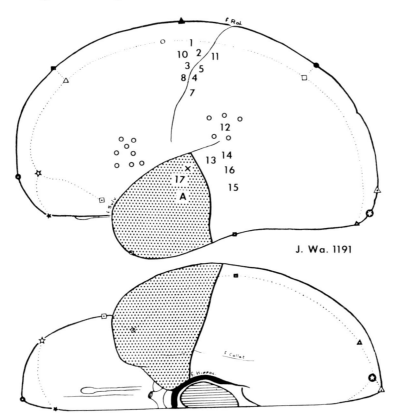

Figure 115. Diagram of stimulation points and extent of excision (dotted area) in Case 2, J. Wa. Circles indicate sites of stimulation with no impairment of speech. At 17 X, deep stimulation electrode was inserted.

seven months after temporal lobectomy. It is something of a paradox, previously emphasized by Penfield (21), that epileptogenic tissue produces impairment of function, and the removal of that abnormal tissue with arrest of seizures results in improvement.

The third case I wish to report is B. Br., age 54, who had had seizures for twenty years. These began with a feeling of generalized weakness, lack of contact, automatic movements, and were followed by speech impairment and disorientation. The patient reported that he did not remember things he did during these spells.

This patient was ambidextrous. With this right hand he wrote, brushed his teeth, shaved, used a hammer, and combed his hair, but threw a ball with his left hand and kicked with his left foot. He had been taught to use his right hand at school for writing. He had a brother and sister who were both left-handed.

Injection of amytal into the carotid artery was carried out by Dr. Charles Branch, who reported that there was definite impairment of speech on the right side and what was interpreted as a mild disturbance of speech

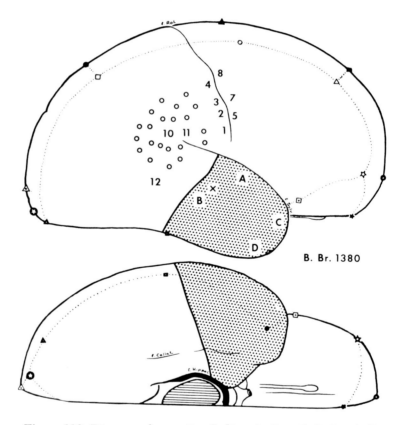

Figure 116. Diagram of operative findings in Case 3, B. Br. A, B, C and D indicate sites of electrographic abnormality; X indicates site of depth electrode insertion. Stimulation numbers as described in text.

on the left side. Electrographic records showed a clear abnormality in the right mesial temporal region.

At operation the right temporal and central regions were exposed (Figures 116 and 117). At point 7, there was interference with motor control of speech, and at points 10 and 11 there was interference with naming. At point 12 there was further difficulty with naming. For example, when shown scissors he said "shirt" and "cuts" and made scissor-like motions with his hand. When asked to spell the word, he began "s-c-" but was unable to finish. During another stimulation at point 12 he was asked to explain his favorite geometry proposition which was that of the cyclic quadrilateral. He had great difficulty in doing this, mispronouncing the words, and hesitating. When asked afterwards, he said he had trouble in "getting words and putting thoughts into words." Despite this, in discussion after the operation, he said that the idea of the theorem and its proof had remained quite clear in his mind in spite of this inability to speak properly.

Depth stimulation, 5 cm from the temporal tip and at a depth of 3 cm at point X, produced a brief period when the patient did not respond. The electrical activity from the cortex at that time showed a dramatic change

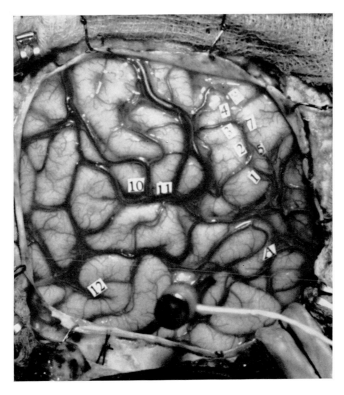

Figure 117. Operative photograph in Case 3, B. Br., showing depth electrode inserted in the second temporal convolution. Stimulation and recording were carried out with this electrode.

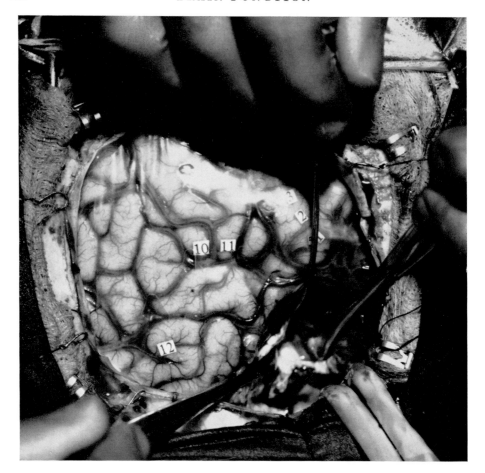

Figure 118. Operative photograph following first stage of excision, Case 3, B. Br., showing identification of the site of the depth of the electrode in the amygdaloid.

with wiping out of the background activity and replacement of the spike and slow wave abnormality by fast low voltage activity. At another depth stimulation he appeared to be out of contact for a while, with interruption of counting and the same low voltage activity. When asked what had happened he said, "I forgot what came next." During excision the tip of the electrode, which had been marked by blue dye, was identified as being in the mesial part of the amygdala (Figure 118).

Following operation the patient developed difficulty in naming which persisted for many weeks but gradually cleared. When examined four months after operation he had slow speech but named objects correctly and commented that his memory had improved. Follow-up psychological test values are not yet available.

This patient was remarkable in that he had had seizures for a period of twenty years but had carried on effectively as a schoolteacher in mathematics and showed a full-scale I.Q. of 125, with a verbal I.Q. of 133, and a memory quotient of 143. His case is also of extraordinary interest because, although he was ambidextrous, both his long-standing epileptic abnormality and his speech function were related to the right hemisphere. This is one of the clearest examples of this paradoxical relationship that we have studied.

As regards the temporal lobe and memory, there are three different sets of evidence from clinical studies which indicate that the temporal lobe is crucially involved in memory function:

a) Memory flashbacks by stimulation. From the study of seizure patterns and responses to stimulation, Penfield (20) indicated that the lateral cortex of the temporal lobe should be called interpretive cortex, much as other areas of cortex are called sensory or motor or visual. Responses from this temporal cortex have been grouped under the term of memory recall but can be divided into *illusions*, such as the change in the sound of a voice and of things appearing farther away, and into *experimental hallucinations* or flashbacks, which are a sudden recall of some past experience to the patient in a vivid and immediate way. This material has been reviewed recently by Mullan & Penfield (17) and by Penfield & Perot (23). The experimental responses and the illusions can be produced from the lateral part of the temporal lobe on either side. There is a trend toward the distribution on the non-dominant side which may be related to the fact that the corresponding area on the dominant side of the brain is concerned with speech.

b) A second line of evidence (5, 6) indicating that the temporal lobe is involved in memory function is the fact that deep stimulation in the peri-amygdaloid region produces episodes during which the patient has attacks of behavioral automatism when he is confused, has irrelevant speech and later is oblivious of any activity that he may have carried out himself or which may have been carried out around him at the time. This is so in spite of the fact that these may be what one could term minor attacks. On this basis one can conclude that there is a region in the mesial temporal area where electrical stimulation seems to interfere with memory recording.

We can then contrast these two main regions of the temporal lobe by saying that from the lateral cortex the stimulation produces a change in the patient's view of things or produces a memory flashback, whereas from the mesial temporal region and implicating the amygdala, stimulation produces interference with memory recording (2).

c) Memory impairment with bitemporal lesions. Although many hundreds of cases have been operated upon with temporal lobectomy on one side with insignificant changes in memory function, two cases which have been studied in detail by Penfield & Milner (22) showed a dramatic and overt impairment of recent memory. These patients characteristically could not remember information after they had been subjected to even the most minor distractions.

Finally, we have to consider briefly the complementary role of hippo-campus, hippocampal gyrus, amygdaloid, claustrum and certain other areas in regard to this role of recent memory. It seems that the evidence at the moment does not allow us to resolve this question. There has been much emphasis upon the role of the hippocampus which has perhaps come about unwittingly.

First of all, in the series reported by Scoville and Milner (16, 26, 27) it should be noted that, with the exception of one patient who had a severe epileptic problem, these patients had serious psychotic disorders. A number of these patients had had electroshock and a number, as Milner care-fully pointed out, were unable to be tested psychologically in the full for-mal sense following operation. None of them had pre-operative psycho-logical testing comparable to that to which they were subjected following operation. Three of these cases were judged to have a severe recent mem-ory impairment and, in two of those, the surgical removal was estimated at 8 cm along the mesial part of the temporal lobe, approaching it under the frontal lobe, splitting the tip of the temporal lobe and then going pos-teriorly. This was carried out on both sides.

This 8 cm removal would carry the surgeon behind the brain stem. Of the three cases, however, who had the most severe memory loss, one patient had a removal of only 5 cm in extent. On the other hand, there were sev-eral other patients who had removals of 5-6 cm and had moderate impair-ment of memory, and one patient with a removal estimated at 4 cm who had no demonstrable memory difficulty.

If one groups them, of course, it is apparent that the most severe loss seems to be in the group which had the largest removal, but there are very important discrepancies which I think should not be brushed aside. We can perhaps leave it at that for the moment.

In the two Montreal cases (22), there is certainly no question that there was a distinction between the lateral temporal cortex and the mesial tem-poral region in one patient, because the operations were carried out in two stages and the memory defect appeared only after the second procedure. The second removal included a portion of the amygdala as well as the hippocampus and hippocampal gyrus. The removal in these two cases, it should be stressed again, was unilateral, with the memory defect being related to the fact that there was also electrographic abnormality on the opposite temporal region, producing in fact a functional bitemporal abla-tion.

I believe from a review of these clinical cases that it is still impossible to say whether the hippocampus or the amygdala alone or some other sur-rounding area is concerned separately with this memory loss. For the time being they have to be grouped together in this relationship.

It is probably fair to say that the enormous amount of material in the literature on animal experimental work in this field still leaves the question to be more precisely studied (9, 11, 12, 18). From a practical point of view it is important to find out if a patient with electrographic abnormality in both temporal lobes can eventually be subjected to a bitemporal operation. At the present time we seem to have no reason to believe that this patient would not be converted into an individual with no means of recording experience. In terms of the extent of the removal, one should point out that at 4 cm from the tip of the temporal lobe the amygdaloid is partly but not completely removed, and at 5 cm the pes hippocampus and a portion of the hippocampus are removed. It is quite clear that the removals at 5 cm from the tip do take out a considerable portion of the hippocampus (see Figure 111). Another difficulty is the very close apposition of the hippocampus to the uncus and amygdaloid. It is difficult for the surgeon to remove the amygdala without damaging a portion of the anterior part of the hippocampus.

No doubt a good deal of useful information will be derived from the carotid amytal tests in relation to testing of memory during the transient phase, when the patient is under the influence of this drug injected into a portion of one half of his brain. These studies are being pursued by Dr. Brenda Milner and Dr. Charles Branch.

In summary, this has been a review of some of the aspects of speech and memory function in the temporal lobe of man. Impairment of speech can be produced not only by disturbance in the primary cortical areas subserving speech but also by disturbance of the sensory and motor cortex.

Three main lines of evidence can now be marshalled to confirm the role of the temporal lobe in memory mechanisms. The lateral cortex and the gray matter extending from the first temporal gyrus into the Sylvian fissure appear to be concerned with memory recall, as based on stimulation responses. The periamygdaloid region on stimulation evokes a blocking of memory recording probably by virtue of afterdischarge which fires into central regions and which can affect widespread cortical activity. Bilateral disturbance or excision of the mesial temporal region has been shown to be associated with profound disturbance of recent memory, so that learning and recall of recent information is severely reduced. The precise anatomical structures associated with this profound defect have not yet been clearly segregated but the periamygdaloid region, the hippocampal gyri and the hippocampus itself appear to be most crucially involved.

As an epilogue, Figure 119 shows what we might call the first Brain Research Institute, which I thought would be of particular interest to Dr. Magoun and Dr. French. It is the house in Oxford where Dr. Thomas Willis lived during the seventeenth century. It is here that Willis and his friends congregated surely to discuss the function of the brain, and if you walk along one of the few remaining quiet streets in that traffic-ridden city today you will come across it. While we can no doubt be inspired by the contrail overhead, we should note the horse-drawn wagon below, which is perhaps

Figure 119. Beam Hall, the house in Oxford where Dr. Thomas Willis lived in the seventeenth century.

a more realistic symbol of our present understanding of the mind and the use of the potentialities of our brains.

Adey: I would like to discuss, first, Dr. Feindel's very elegantly drawn picture of the differences between the lateral and ventral temporal lesions. I think there can be no doubt that the concept of the lateral cortex of the temporal lobe as being an interpretive area of cortex will find much support in future research.

However, turning to the results of the stimulation and ablation in the region of the uncus, I think that the clinical experiment, by the very nature of the difficulties involved, cannot of itself draw the essential differences that one would like to see between the amygdaloid and hippocampal components. In fact, some of the animal experiments have already indicated there are fine differences that can be drawn in this regard.

In particular, the studies of Lesse (14) and Freeman (7) have shown that the electrographic activity that characterizes the cat's amygdala in the 38 to 40 cps bursting is something which is associated with long-term sets of attention, as, for example, in the states of hunger, rage, and sexual excitement, and that this tends to subside and disappear as the states or these drives are satisfied. In essence, one might suppose that the focusing of attention to the environmental situation is something in which the amygdala is vitally concerned.

By contrast, I think one might draw the image of the hippocampus as being an organ which has its prime function in the interpretive aspects of the immediate past, as it may occur in the vital few seconds that precede the present, and perhaps in establishing the set by which we continue to focus attention on the immediate future. This latter is, perhaps, a little speculative in relation to the more specific evidence that Lesse and others have provided for the amygdaloid functions.

However, turning to the specifics of the human situation, the stimulation in the region of the uncus is something which is very difficult to accomplish with an isolated stimulation of hippocampal tissue or amygdaloid tissue in this region of overlap.

We ourselves have been much concerned with this possibility, that perhaps the electrical stimulus may lack the requisite localization. Be that as it may, I think that the question of the role of the hippocampus and the amygdala, the respective assignment that one can give to their function, is something in which a little more detail can be imparted from the animal experiments than one might conclude from Dr. Feindel's experiments or observations.

French: Dr. Feindel, do you think that the lateral surface of the temporal lobe has some connection with information storage also?

Feindel: Yes, just in those terms.

French: Do you think it significant that such phenomena occur only after excitation of injured temporal lobes? Have you stimulated these areas without evoking memory-related responses?

Feindel: Yes, many times. This is the whole question again, of parameters, percentage of responses, and so on, which I think could be pursued also in regard to the motor-sensory cortex and many other areas of cortex. The fact that one gets or does not get a response is, as you know yourself, dependent upon a great many variables. The fact that one does evoke a response is, I think, quite acceptable positive evidence that this area must have something to do, as you say, with memory recall. I think it is important, however, as Dr. Adey mentioned, that because something is produced from a minute area of nerve tissue one must not assume this is a center, for example, of memory. Penfield has emphasized many times (19, 20) that one can evoke a memory flashback, such as the one I quoted before, from a patient, and that part of the temporal lobe can then be removed. Afterward this can be discussed with the patient and he is still quite aware of what was produced. This is rather clear evidence that the cortex at the site of stimulation is not itself the "storehouse" of memory.

The same is true of the hippocampus. We have many cases of unilateral hippocampal removals where there has not been this dramatic disorder of memory recording, such as the two patients showed who were presumed to have bilateral temporal disturbance. The areas of temporal cortex and the periamygdaloid region give responses on stimulation which are not obtained from the extensive regions of cortex available to the surgeon in many other operations, and I think that one can be confident in considering these specifically related to memory function.

Bickford: I would like to put in a plea, based on our experience with depth stimulation, for consideration of other regions of the temporal lobe, apart from the uncus-hippocampus region and its circuits which, of course, are well known anatomically and rather apt to be unduly emphasized, perhaps because they are targets for stereotaxis.

We find, as Dr. Penfield has in the past, a tremendous variety of interesting effects resulting from stimulation of the surface of the lateral part and infolded cortex of the temporal lobe. I am talking now of the cortex, subcortex, going down to, but not including, the hippocampal region, probably including a lot of white matter. We find not only epileptic discharges in this area but a large variety of effects quite as dramatic as any that are being described here for the uncus-hippocampus-amygdala region.

I wonder if our concentration on this latter region is not due to the fact that it is an anatomic entity, and the other regions are unnamed anatomically and difficult to describe. I would think a great deal more research effort, both in animal work and in man, ought to be given to that region of the temporal lobe. I am talking of the three temporal gyri, the superior, middle and inferior, and their subcortical parts, really the outer shell of the temporal lobe. Largely, you are concerned with the inner and medial shell.

Feindel: I gave you a capsular summary. As you know, there are many case reports in which the area about which you speak has been stimulated, yet these responses have not been produced.

Bickford: We find responses constantly when we stimulate there. Maybe this is a difference of acute human material tested at operation, and human subjects with chronically implanted electrodes.

Feindel: It may be. I think the concentration that seems presented here is the result of reviewing a great many cases and picking up positive responses. For example, the 16 or so cases we had with behavioral automatism and some of the features from periamygdala stimulation represent a review of several hundred stimulation case reports. I would not like to give the idea that these are consistent findings that we get in every case and that we are ignoring other parts of the temporal lobe.

Bickford: Neither would I like to belittle that work, which is fundamental, of course. All I am saying is that not much attention is paid to the temporal lobe in volume. The lateral part we find to be constantly active in memory mechanisms, whether it is illusions of various kinds or suppression of the kind I shall show later.

REFERENCES

1. CLARK, E., The early history of the cerebral ventricles. *Trans. Coll. Phycns. Philadelphia,* 1962, **30**: 85-89.

2. FEINDEL, W., Response patterns elicited from the amygdala and deep temporoinsular cortex. In: *Electrical Stimulation of the Brain* (D. E. Sheer, Ed.). Univ. of Texas Press, Austin, 1961: 519-532.

3. ——, Thomas Willis (1621-1675)—The founder of neurology. *Canad. Med. Assoc. J.*, 1962, **87**: 289-296.

4. FEINDEL, W., and GLOOR, P., Comparison of electrographic effects of stimulation of the amygdala and brain stem reticular formation in cats. *EEG Clin. Neurophysiol.*, 1954, **6**: 389-402.

5. FEINDEL, W., and PENFIELD, W., Localization of discharge in temporal lobe automatism. *A.M.A. Arch. Neurol. Psychiat.*, 1954, **72**:605-630.

6. FEINDEL, W., PENFIELD, W., and JASPER, H., Localization of epileptic discharge in temporal lobe automatism. *Trans. Am. Neurol. Soc.* 1952, **77**: 14-17.

7. FREEMAN, W. J., Correlation of electrical activity of prepyriform cortex and behavior in cat. *J. Neurophysiol.*, 1960, **23**: 111-131.

8. GLOOR, P., The pattern of conduction of amygdaloid seizure discharge. *Arch. Neurol. Psychiat.*, 1957, **77**: 247-258.

9. ——, Amygdala. In: *Handbook of Physiology; Neurophysiology II* (J. Field, H. W. Magoun and V. E. Hall, Eds.). American Physiological Society, Washington, D.C., 1960: 1395-1420.

10. GLOOR, P., and FEINDEL, W., Affective behaviour and temporal lobe. In: *Physiologie und Pathophysiologie des vegetativen Nervensystems. II. Band. Pathophysiologie* (M. Monnier, Ed). Hippokrates-Verlag, Stuttgart, 1963: 685-716.

11. GOL, A., KELLAWAY, P., and SHAPIRO, M., Behavioral changes in the monkey and the cat after extensive hippocampal removal. *Neurology*, 1962, **12**: 303.

12. GUÉNAULT, A. M., and MACDONALD, D. K. C., Memory and language. *Nature*, 1962, **193**: 523-525.

13. KLINGER, J., and GLOOR, P., The connections of the amygdala and of the anterior temporal cortex in the human brain. *J. Comp. Neurol.*, 1960, **115**: 333-369.

14. LESSE, H., Amygdaloid electrical activity during a conditioned response. *EEG Clin. Neurophysiol.*, 1959, Supp. **7**: 177-180.

15. MILNER, B., Psychological defects produced by temporal lobe excision. *Res. Publ. Ass. Nerv. Ment. Dis.*, 1958, **36**: 244-257.

16. ——, The memory defect in bilateral hippocampal lesions. *Psychiat. Res. Rep.*, 1959, **11**: 43-52.

17. MULLAN, S., and PENFIELD, W., Illusions of comparative interpretation and emotion. *A.M.A. Arch. Neurol. Psychiat.*, 1959, **81**: 269-284.

18. ORBACH, J., MILNER, B., and RASMUSSEN, T., Learning and retention in monkeys after amygdala-hippocampus resection. *Arch. Neurol.*, 1960, **3**: 230-251.

19. PENFIELD, W., The cerebral cortex in man. I. The cerebral cortex and consciousness. *Arch. Neurol. Psychiat.*, 1938, **40**: 417-442.

20. ——, The rôle of the temporal cortex in recall of past experience and interpretation of the present. In: *Neurological Basis of Behaviour*

(G. E. W. Wolstenholme and C. M. O'Connor, Eds.). Churchill, London, 1958: 149-174.

21. PENFIELD, W., and JASPER, H. H., *Epilepsy and the Functional Anatomy of the Human Brain*. Little, Brown, Boston, 1954.

22. PENFIELD, W., and MILNER, B., Memory deficit produced by bilateral lesions in the hippocampal zone. *A.M.A. Arch. Neurol. Psychiat.*, 1958, **79**: 475-497.

23. PENFIELD, W., and PEROT, P., The brain's record of auditory and visual experience. A final summary and discussion. *Brain*, 1963, **86**: 595-696.

24. PENFIELD, W., and RASMUSSEN, T., *The Cerebral Cortex of Man. A Clinical Study of Localization of Function*. Macmillan, New York, 1950.

25. PENFIELD, W., and ROBERTS, L., *Speech and Brain-Mechanisms*. Princeton Univ. Press, Princeton, 1959.

26. SCOVILLE, W. B., The limbic lobe in man. *J. Neurosurg.*, 1954, **11**: 64-66.

27. SCOVILLE, W. B., and MILNER, B., Loss of recent memory after bilateral hippocampal lesions. *J. Neurol. Neurosurg. Psychiat.*, 1957, **20**: 11-21.

28. SERAFETINIDES, E. A., and FALCONER, M. A., Some observations on memory impairment after temporal lobectomy for epilepsy. *J. Neurol. Neurosurg. Psychiat.*, 1962, **25**: 251-255.

29. VICTOR, M., ANGEVINE, J. B., MANCALL, E. L., and FISHER, C. M., Memory loss with lesions of hippocampal formation. *Arch. Neurol.*, 1961, **5**: 244-263.

30. WADA, J., and RASMUSSEN, T., Intracarotid injection of sodium amytal for the lateralization of cerebral speech dominance. Experimental and clinical observations. *J. Neurosurg.*, 1960, **17**: 266-282.

31. WALKER, A. E., Recent memory impairment in unilateral temporal lesions. *A.M.A. Arch. Neurol. Psychiat.*, 1957, **78**: 543-552.

32. WILLIS, T., *Cerebri Anatome*. Martyn & Allestry, London, 1664.

33. ———, *De Anima Brutorum*. Davis, London, 1672.

34. ———, The anatomy of the brain. In: *The Remaining Medical Works of that Famous and Renowned Physician, Dr. Thomas Willis* (S. Pordage, Transl.). Dring, Harper, Leigh and Martyn, London, 1681: 50-192.

STIMULATION OF THE HIPPOCAMPUS IN MAN USING IMPLANTED ELECTRODES

MARY A. B. BRAZIER[*]
Brain Research Institute
University of California
Los Angeles

The group at UCLA with which I am associated in studies in man has been greatly interested in the problem of disturbance or distortion of memory by electrical stimulation of the hippocampus. In this work my collaborators have been Dr. Robert Rand and Dr. Paul Crandall from Neurosurgery, Dr. Charles Markham and Dr. Richard Walter from Neurology, Dr. Ross Adey from Anatomy, and Dr. Loring Chapman as psychologist to the group.[†]

Such observations as we have been able to make are severely limited by the following conditions under which they are made:

(a) the subjects do not have normal brains, since they are all cases of severe temporal lobe epilepsy, resistant to control by medication;

(b) only those electrode placements necessitated by the diagnostic goals are used;

(c) at all times the welfare of the patient has had to come first, and no test can be unduly prolonged.

In the patients in this series, bipolar electrodes are implanted under surgical anesthesia by stereotaxic techniques developed by Dr. Rand on the basis of the Talairach Atlas (1). The actual electrodes used have been modified and improved from time to time; after insertion, they are left in place for 14 to 20 days to permit study of the patient in the unanesthetized and near-normal state. In most of the patients examined so far in this series, eight bipolar electrodes were implanted in deep structures of each temporal lobe, the targets being the amygdala, the pes hippocampus (or hippocampus proper) and three sites within the hippocampal gyrus. In some, electrodes were placed also in the uncus and in the tip of the temporal lobe.

In a search for loci of low threshold for electrical seizure and for trigger zones, each deep point in turn is stimulated, starting initially with currents of low intensity and raising the amperage if no result is obtained. The range

[*] The work of this investigator is supported by Career Research Award #5-K6-NB-18, 608 from the National Institutes of Health, Grant #NB 04773 USPHS, and Contract NR 233(69) from the U.S. Office of Naval Research.
[†] The clinical investigations of this group are supported by Grant #NB 02808 USPHS.

299

of current strength used has varied from 0.9 ma to 4 ma, and the frequency of stimulation from 1/sec. to 100/sec. A biphasic form of current pulse is used in these studies and the current is monitored on a cathode ray oscilloscope for each test run.

In reference to findings pertinent to the subject under discussion at this conference, namely memory changes, only in one patient in our small series of seven have we found any disturbance of memory in the *absence* of electrical seizure or afterdischarge. More common were those who showed some evidence of hallucinatory experience during the afterdischarge evoked by hippocampal stimulation. Two or three of the patients, when questioned by Dr. Chapman during these episodes, would mumble disjointed sentences of a very few words only, but apparently indicative of some hallucinatory experience. Except for one of these cases, there was no unequivocal evidence to indicate that "remembered" experiences lay behind the broken sentences.

It is the feeling of our group that disturbances of this kind, when they accompany electrical seizures or afterdischarges, cannot be differentiated as specific memory effects, neither as evocations nor as distortions. The condition of the patient during these electrical discharges may so closely resemble the picture of a temporal lobe seizure that the resultant state of confusion and temporary obfuscation does not make it justifiable, in our view, to define this as a specific effect on memory.

In one of the cases where fragmented sentences suggested some such hallucinatory experiences, the patient verbalized them one minute after the end of a stimulus train applied to the left pes hippocampus which had evoked an electrical seizure (though not a clinical one). When the afterdischarge died out, there were striking runs of 6/sec. theta waves in the hippocampal gyrus ipsilateral to the stimulation (Figure 120). There was no change in the irregular activity of rather faster frequency, present in the contralateral hippocampus. It was during this theta activity, ipsilateral to the stimulus, that the patient mumbled that he "heard a song". He did not, however, sing the song nor could questioning bring out any further details of his subjective experience.

In only one of the seven cases we have so far was a really structured sentence or formalized experience verbalized. This was after a mild clinical seizure, triggered by hippocampal stimulation, had just ceased. The clinical purpose of this test was search for a locus of low threshold which would evoke signs analogous to those of the patient's spontaneous seizures. The patient spoke with some distress of a previous automobile accident in which a child who was riding with him was severely maimed. There was nothing bizarre or hallucinatory about his report; it was clearly a subject that he thought about frequently and had, in fact, discussed previously with members of the group. There would seem to be no grounds for particularly associating this recall with the stimulation.

One needs to remember that, in any test situation in which a patient is

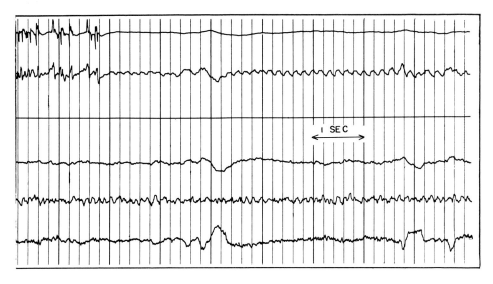

Figure 120. Appearance of the EEG one minute after stimulation of the left hippocampus and during the period when the phrase "I heard a song" was being verbalized
by the patient. Electrodes in a mid site in the left hippocampal gyrus show a 6/sec.
rhythm, those in the contralateral pes hippocampus a more rapid and more irregular
rhythm. Bipolar recordings. Channels: 1st, left amygdala; 2nd, left hippocampal gyrus;
4th, right hippocampal gyrus; 5th, right hippocampus (pes); 6th, right amygdala.

continuously being questioned by the psychologist and being pressed by him
to verbalize his subjective experiences, any reports that may be elicited can
scarcely be regarded as spontaneous effects of the stimulation; they are
responses evoked by questioning. One further dilemma is met if one attempts
to correlate the exact incidence of the subjective event with its counterpart
in time in the EEG tracing, for any verbal report is necessarily of a past
experience and not of the specious present.

More interesting is the one case in which, on bilateral stimulation of the
hippocampus, the patient, although responding accurately to immediate
conversation, suddenly and spontaneously reported loss of recent memory;
this occurred, not at the time of the afterdischarge, but after it had ceased.
The figures which follow illustrate the EEG of this patient, taken during
stimulation and during immediate recall tests being given to the patient at
the same time.

In earlier tests the same day, it had been found that the right hippocampus in this epileptic patient had a lower threshold for seizure discharge
than the left, and that this discharge could be triggered by bilateral stimulation of the amygdalae. During this stimulation and the electrical seizure
caused by it, the patient had no clinical signs but reported a vague subjective aura which she described as a "warning". Her performance on recall
tests was perfect though her answers were delayed. Figure 121 shows that
seizure discharge was evoked in the right hippocampus whereas the left,

with its higher threshold for seizure, gave only an evoked response to each stimulus pulse.

Half-an-hour later, the test was repeated with the same electrographic result, but this time there was no subjective aura (Figure 122). Her recall was accurate and there were no clinical signs. Stimulation was, therefore, not interrupted and it is interesting that the electrical seizure and its after-discharge died out in spite of this continued stimulation. Again the left hippocampus gave only evoked responses, the right hippocampus with its lower threshold going into electrical seizure.

Bilateral stimulation of the hippocampus was then tested at low current strengths. This immediately evoked an electrical seizure on the right (Figure 123). The patient reported an aura, but her responses to the recall tests were still accurate though delayed and her voice was faint. Again the electrical seizure died out although stimulation was continued (Figure 124). Her re-

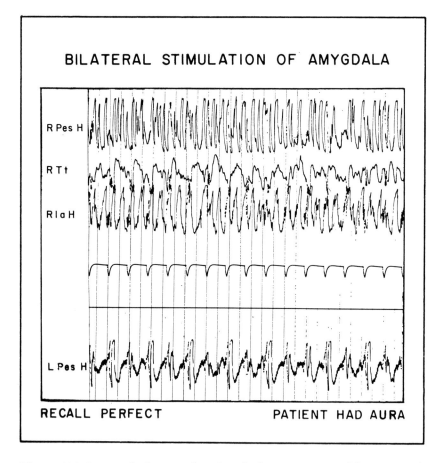

Figure 121. Seizure discharge induced in the hippocampus and hippocampal gyrus by 3/sec. stimulation of the amygdalae bilaterally. The left hippocampus shows only a single evoked response to each stimulus pulse. RPes H: right pes hippocampus; RTt: right temporal tip; RlaH: right anterior hippocampal gyrus; LPesH: left pes hippocampus. Bipolar recordings.

call was unimpaired. The handwritten notes on the tracing are Dr. Adey's notes on the pairs of words being given to the patient as tests of immediate recall. In later studies a voice tape synchronized with the EEG was incorporated in the experimental design.

In this same patient, half-a-minute after the end of this stimulation period and after the discharge had died out, the EEG became very disturbed with runs of 8 cycle waves appearing in the hippocampal gyrus (Figure 125). Whether or not a rhythm of this frequency should be described as theta may be questioned. The patient continued to respond well to recall tests.

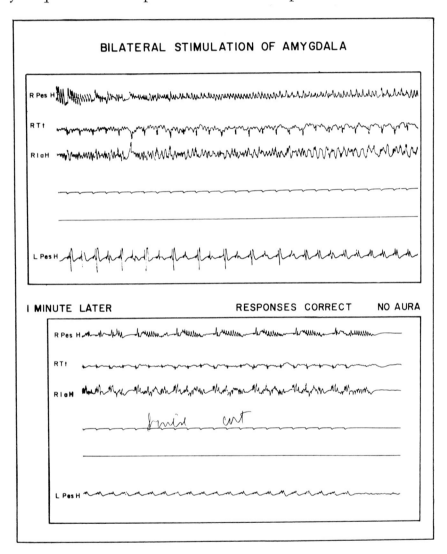

Figure 122. Electrical seizure evoked in the right hippocampus and hippocampal gyrus by 3/sec. pulses applied simultaneously to both amygdalae. Note that the discharges begin to die out in spite of continued stimulation (4th channel). Only discrete evoked responses appear in the left hippocampus. Labeling as in Figure 121. Bipolar recordings.

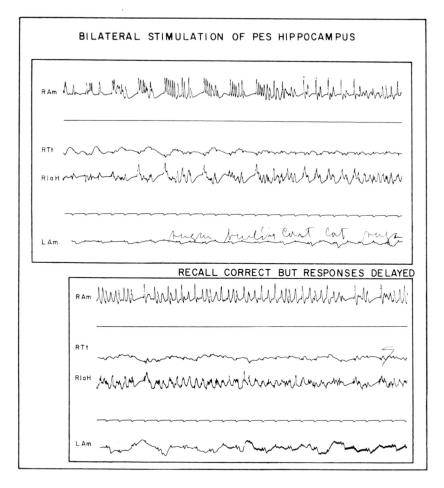

Figure 123. Right-sided electrical seizure evoked by bilateral stimulation of the pes hippocampus by 3/sec. pulses. RAm: right amygdala; RTt: right temporal tip; RlaH: right anterior hippocampal gyrus; LAm: left amygdala. Bipolar recordings.

One minute after the end of the afterdischarge and one half-minute after the EEG shown in the last figure, the patient suddenly felt a warning. She broke into the conversation with the psychologist and spontaneously reported, "I can't remember where I am or when I came." The EEG showed spiking in the right amygdala and hippocampal gyrus followed by long trains of 8 cycle waves in the right hippocampal gyrus just before she spoke (Figure 126). As the electrodes in the pes hippocampus of each hemisphere were being used for stimulating, recordings from these sites were not available.

The patient was disoriented as to time, date and month, but thought she must be in the UCLA Medical Center where she had been under treatment for several months, since she remembered being admitted. She knew who she was and why she was in the hospital but could not remember the events of the morning. She did not remember Dr. Chapman by voice although he had been giving her the recall tests all morning. On questioning, it was found that she did not remember having a visitor on the previous Sunday (i.e., three days before). When asked if she remembered Christmas (two days before) she said, "Was I here for Christmas?" She did, however, remember coming into the hospital and all the details of an automobile accident in which she had been involved 16 months previously. She did not remember Christmas festivities on the ward or having had a visitor on Christmas Eve. She had no memory of receiving a recent letter from her children or of events during approximately the previous ten days, but remembered every-

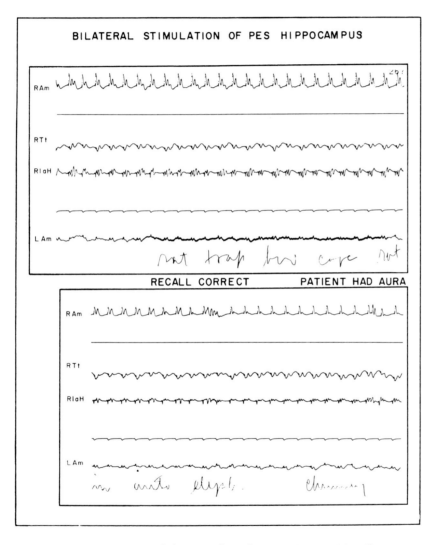

Figure 124. Continuation of the recording shown in Figure 123, illustrating the dying out of the electrical seizure in spite of continued stimulation with 3/sec. pulses (5th channel).

thing before that. This memory defect cleared for the most part in 10 to 12
minutes from the end of the stimulation. The EEG remained very disturbed
but did not spike.

The runs of 8 cycle waves in the hippocampal gyrus did not correlate
with memory disturbances for they could be evoked by unilateral hippocampal stimulation without impairment of recall; they were, however,
usually accompanied by an aura.

One more finding in this patient is perhaps of interest. A circuit was
arranged by Dr. Adey so that the patient could herself control the flow of
current pulses to her brain, though not their parameters. The circuit was
designed so that no pulse train could last longer than 15 seconds. This procedure was only attempted for the self-stimulation of the less sensitive side,

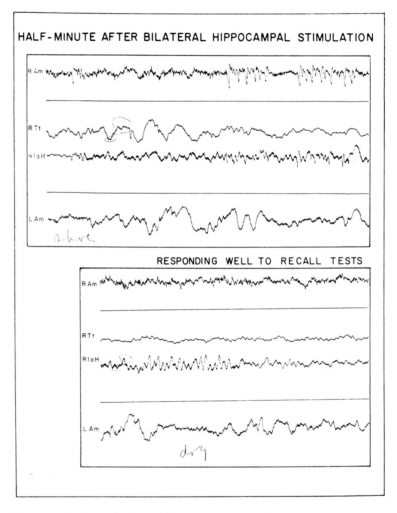

Figure 125. Samples from the continuation of recordings shown in
Figures 123 and 124. Note trains of 8/sec. waves in the right anterior hippocampal gyrus.

namely the left pes hippocampus. The resultant electrical discharge was
limited to the ipsilateral amygdala, but the patient continued to self-stimu-
late and apparently had no subjective sensation, for she reported no aura
and continued to count correctly. In fact, when a control test was run in
which, unknown to her, the current had been disconnected, she was unaware
of any change. No evidence could be gathered that this was either a pleas-
ant or an unpleasant experience for the patient since her reaction was a
neutral one.

In our small series of patients, only seven so far (1962), this is as far as we
can go in contributing to the question under discussion at this conference,
that of memory disturbance. That is, in one case we have evoked a hallucin-

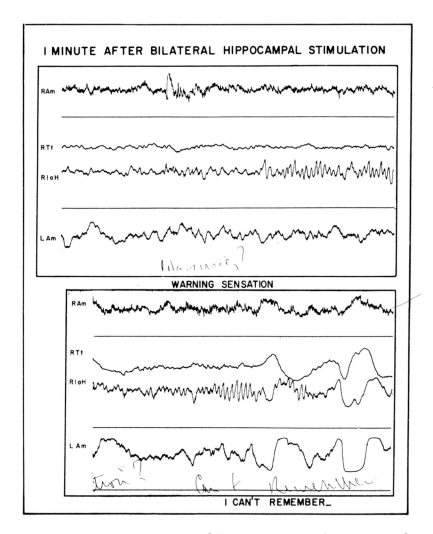

I MINUTE AFTER BILATERAL HIPPOCAMPAL STIMULATION

RAm

RTt

RIaH

LAm

WARNING SENSATION

RAm

RTt

RIaH

LAm

I CAN'T REMEMBER_

Figure 126. Further continuation of Figures 123, 124 and 125. Abnormal
spiking appearing in the right amygdala and anterior hippocampal gyrus,
followed by trains of 8/sec. waves in the latter electrode site.

atory experience (the hearing of a song), and in one we have produced a temporary and completely reversible block of recent memory only.

The striking feature of this temporary memory loss was its restriction to the period of recent experience, long-term memory and the ability for immediate recall being unimpaired. Since this effect proved to be completely reversible, it would seem clear that the stimulating current had not broken up the mechanism responsible for storage of the memory of this period but had temporarily blocked its retrieval. The unimpaired ability of the patient in the tests of immediate recall during this period would indicate that the mechanism for inserting material into immediate memory was also unimpaired.

Before ending I would like to repeat my indebtedness to the collaborators I named at the beginning of my talk, and especially to emphasize how much the electroencephalographic studies owe to the collaboration of my colleague, Dr. Richard Walter, and the observations of the patient's behavior to Dr. Loring Chapman. My colleagues should not, however, be held responsible for the interpretations of the phenomena as proposed here.

Bickford: I would like to present rather quickly, perhaps, a situation we have studied with a film, in which there is a paralysis of retrieval of information from the memory system, very much like what Dr. Brazier has presented, but I think a little different. We have three instances somewhat different in that the memory suppression has been achieved at a less intense level of stimulation than I gather was used in the case Dr. Brazier presented, insofar as seizures (electrographic or clinical) did not occur. The only phenomenon that could be detected was failure of information retrieval.

I should say that these are epileptic patients. They have implanted leads. I will not go into any detail except to show in Figure 127 the location of the leads from which this phenomenon was obtained. Stimulation was through bipolar electrodes at 20/sec. (1 msec. pulse) and 3 volts. The suppression of recall, which I will show by means of a film,* has been obtained in two patients. In one of these, R. H., it was obtained independently from the two temporal lobes (A and B). In another case, H. M., we only tested this on the left because we only had left-sided leads. We had bilateral leads in the first case.

Notice that the depth at which this paralysis of recall is obtained ranges from 1.5 to 2 cm from the surface. These cases have been superimposed by X-rays, with some overlay. We think there is really a rather good correspondence. For the case in which it was obtained bilaterally, A and B have been superimposed on the left in this diagram. In general, we think this is about the middle of the lobe, a depth of 2 cm, which puts it superficial to the hippocampus, probably in the white fiber system.

We do at times find afterdischarge, but I should emphasize we can pro-

---

* The editor regrets that the reader is unable to share in the material presented in this medium.

duce this paralysis of recall, on occasion, without any afterdischarge occurring at the point we stimulate. These are all unilateral stimulations. As a matter of fact, we have never attempted bilateral stimulation of the temporal lobe.

The case I shall be describing is the one that was stimulated at C (Figure 127). I should explain that, first of all, we make a control stimulation of an adjacent contact which is just one centimeter from the one which produces the effect. I should say we found this effect has a very specific location. We have had a great deal of experience in stimulating through depth leads in almost all parts of the brain but we have never found this effect from any region other than the one indicated. We do not see it in the control from adjacent stimulation.

The tests we use include one which does not require verbal communication by the patient; this is important. We taught the patient to make a little motor maneuver which consisted of his going up and down his fingers when we touched the hand. Our purpose was to avoid any complication from induced aphasia. We tested to see whether the patient could repeat the maneuver he had been instructed to make.

We think this is a rather ordinary, simple situation, quite comparable to the one Dr. Brazier has indicated, a model in which there is a simple sequential rolling back of recall. The longer recent recorded memory can be titrated, its possibility of recall can be suppressed sequentially into the past. The longer you stimulate, the more you press back the amnesia, as it were. It may be a few moments for short stimulation, or an hour, two hours, weeks, and so forth, leaving intact the older memories laid down, which can be perfectly adequately recalled. It is important to note that all our patients

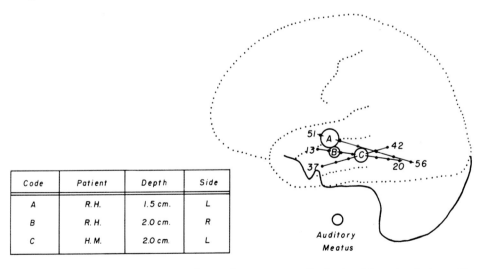

Code	Patient	Depth	Side
A	R. H.	1.5 cm.	L
B	R. H.	2.0 cm.	R
C	H. M.	2.0 cm.	L

Figure 127. Regions showing paralysis of memory recall obtained by stimulation with bipolar electrodes; X-ray superimposition. See text.

eventually were able to recall suppressed material, indicating that the retrieval rather than the recording mechanisms are involved.

Perhaps I should just emphasize the differences we have here. I think you might agree that, since the patient was able to speak throughout the stimulation, he did not have an automatism; he was able to respond directly in spite of failure in the test for recall. We have seen this effect without any seizure discharge occurring in the stimulated area, or on the other side. We think this impairment of recall can be produced unilaterally. It is not necessarily associated with a seizure; it is a non-specific, chronologically sequential paralysis of information recall affecting all modalities. We believe that storage is not affected, insofar as we can see, except possibly for a short time during the stimulation.

The effects are highly localized, we have not found this in other regions of the brain, and there seem to be no aphasic elements involved.

Benzer: I would hope to be clear on at least the question of whether unilateral or bilateral interference is or is not effective. In human cases, there must be a very limited number of instances, but surely in the case of rats one should be able to get a clear-cut decision on whether you need one active structure or both.

Thompson: With respect to learning and memory, rat work indicates bilateral lesions are necessary.

Mishkin: May I qualify that? A unilateral frontal lesion in monkey *is* sufficient to produce significant impairment.

REFERENCE

1. TALAIRACH, J., DAVID, M., and TOURNOUX, P., *L'Exploration Chirurgicale Stéréotaxique du Lobe Temporal dans l'Epilepsie Temporale.* Masson, Paris, 1958.

OBSERVATIONS ON THE AMNESTIC SYNDROME IN MAN AND ITS ANATOMICAL BASIS

MAURICE VICTOR
Cleveland Metropolitan General Hospital
Cleveland

My remarks will deal with the functions of memory and learning and will be based on observations made in man—a fact which provides a special reason for including them in this symposium. It is in man that the functions of memory and learning and, for that matter, all those functions which we term intellectual, have attained their greatest degree of subtlety and complexity, and it follows that man is the ideal subject in which to study derangements of these functions. Certain instances of human disease, which will be described presently, provide the clinician with opportunities to study memory function that can hardly be duplicated by the study of animals or individual organs or tissues.

Clinicians have for many years been impressed with a unique and relatively common affection, in which retentive memory is impaired out of all proportion to other cognitive functions. The terms amnestic, amnestic-confabulatory, or Korsakoff's psychosis are used interchangeably to designate this syndrome. It possesses two salient features, which are always conjoined: (*a*) an impaired ability, varying in degree, to reproduce information that had been acquired before the onset of the illness, i.e., a retrograde amnesia, and (*b*) an inability to acquire new information and skills, i.e., an anterograde amnesia. Confabulation, an ill-defined symptom which has through common usage come to be regarded as a specific feature of Korsakoff's psychosis, is neither consistently present in this syndrome nor essential for the diagnosis. Although the anterograde and retrograde amnesia are the dominant features of Korsakoff's psychosis, other cognitive and perceptual functions, which depend little or not at all on memory, are impaired to a relatively minor degree. As a rule, patients with this disorder have only limited insight into their disability, and they tend to be apathetic, inert, and indifferent to everything that is going on around them. All of these features will be elaborated presently.

In addition to these positive features, the definition of Korsakoff's psychosis requires that certain aspects of mental function be intact. The patient must be alert and responsive, aware of his surroundings and the meaning of what is said to him; he should show no serious defect in social behavior; he should be capable of making proper deductions from given premises and of solving such problems as can be concluded within his forward memory span. These negative features are of particular importance, for they help to set apart Korsakoff's psychosis from many other disorders in which the basic defect is not in retentive memory but in some other psychological mechanism. For example, the stuporous or delirious patient fails to remember day-to-day events during the acute phase of his illness, and later has an amnesia for this period. In these situations the defects are fundamentally in the sphere of attention, concentration and perception, so that there is a failure to record information properly in the first place; in other words, the disorder is essentially a perceptual one or one of "registration". In a similar vein, the severely depressed patient may fail to register much of what is going on around him because of profound disinterest or inattention. On the other hand, the process of registration and retention may be intact, and the process of recall may appear to be affected; this state pertains in the hysterical patient, whose lost memories may be recaptured under hypnosis or by other means. If the clinical use of the term amnestic syndrome is to have any precision, then it must be limited to the disease states which manifest themselves by a relatively pure defect in retentive memory —and this is the sense in which the term will be employed here.

The amnestic syndrome, as defined above, has been observed in a wide variety of disease states—in cerebrovascular disease, nutritional and degenerative diseases of the brain, encephalitis, and certain types of brain tumor. In this presentation only two disease states will be discussed in detail: the alcoholic form of Korsakoff's psychosis, in which the amnestic syndrome is related to lesions in the diencephalon, and an unusual instance of cerebral infarction, exemplifying the memory disorder which results from bilateral hippocampal lesions. In both of these clinical circumstances the lesions were discrete and stable and therefore eminently suited to the delineation of clinical-anatomical relationships. We have also observed relatively pure disorders of memory in certain cases of brain tumor, encephalitis and senile dementia, but these will be referred to only briefly, since their pathological changes were diffuse and poorly defined and therefore yielded less useful information concerning the anatomy of the amnestic disorder. Throughout the discussion the emphasis will be on our own observations, particularly in relation to the Wernicke-Korsakoff syndrome, with which we have had an extensive experience. Such a discussion will of necessity be less complete, but probably of greater interest than a recitation of data obtained by others.

Korsakoff's Psychosis in the Alcoholic Patient

Our studies of Korsakoff's psychosis have been made on a large number of patients (more than 300 in all), and neuropathological examinations have been made in 54 of them. In this section only certain aspects of these studies will be considered—the relation of Korsakoff's psychosis to Wernicke's disease, the nature of the amnestic symptoms and confabulation, the results of psychological testing and the pathological changes. Some of the subject matter to be discussed here, particularly the clinical features of the Wernicke-Korsakoff syndrome, has appeared in previous reports, to which the reader is referred for a more detailed account than is possible at this time (51, 54).

1. THE RELATION OF KORSAKOFF'S PSYCHOSIS TO WERNICKE'S DISEASE

The amnestic disorder always occurs on a background of serious and prolonged inebriation, but alcohol plays only a secondary role, i.e., it displaces food in the diet, and the damaging effects on the nervous system are due to nutritional depletion. At a certain stage of depletion the patient develops, over a period of several hours or days, oculomotor signs (horizontal and vertical nystagmus, paralysis of the external recti and of conjugate gaze), an ataxia of stance and gait, and a global confusion. This clinical triad was first clearly described by Wernicke and now is designated universally by his name. In about 60 per cent of these patients a neuropathy of varying severity is present and, in a small proportion, the optic nerves are also involved. Initially, most patients with Wernicke's disease show a derangement of all psychic function. The patient is apathetic, indifferent to his surroundings and at times drowsy, though he can be readily roused and is rarely unconscious. Spontaneous speech is minimal. He is inattentive and cannot concentrate on the simplest tasks. Many questions go unanswered, or the responses may be slow and labored. The questions which the patient does answer betray disorientation, misidentification of those around him, and an inability to grasp the meaning of his illness or immediate situation. Many remarks are not to the point, nor do they show any consistency from one moment to another. Under these circumstances it is difficult to assess memory function, but when the patient's interest and attention can be maintained long enough to ensure adequate testing, one finds that an impairment of retentive memory constitutes part of the general mental disorganization.

Under the influence of a balanced diet, and specifically of thiamine, the ocular palsies and vertical nystagmus improve quickly and completely; the horizontal nystagmus and ataxia recede more slowly and often persist as permanent neurological stigmata. Also, with the administration of thiamine, the patient becomes more alert, attentive and responsive, and the confusional state, which seems to be compounded of apathy, a perceptual disorder and faulty memory, gradually subsides over a period of several days or weeks. Then it is clearly recognized that the patient is afflicted with the typical amnestic-confabulatory syndrome of Korsakoff. Once the latter is established, the result is usually one of severe disability. Nevertheless, a rare patient recovers completely or almost so, and a significant portion shows a partial recovery of memory function over a period of several months or years. Almost all the patients who confabulate in the early stages of the illness lose this symptom in the chronic phase.

It is evident, from these clinical observations, that Wernicke's disease and Korsakoff's psychosis are not separate diseases, but that changing ocular signs, the transformation of the global confusional state into the amnestic-confabulatory syndrome and this in turn into a non-confabulatory amnestic state, are simply successive stages in the recovery from one disease process. We have also determined, from an examination of many alcoholic patients in a psychiatric hospital, that over 80 per cent of patients with chronic Korsakoff's psychosis either had ocular and ataxic signs at the onset of their illness or still showed the residual manifestations of these signs many years later. On the basis of these observations, and also on the basis of nutritional and pathological evidence, it is our belief that *in the alcoholic, nutritionally depleted patient,* Korsakoff's psychosis is but the mental component of Wernicke's disease, and that the two may suitably be designated as the Wernicke-Korsakoff syndrome.

2. The Nature of the Anterograde and Retrograde Amnesia in Korsakoff's Psychosis

As has been stated, the distinctive attributes of Korsakoff's psychosis are the retrograde and anterograde amnesia and the fact that these two defects are always conjoined. The patient invariably shows a permanent and complete gap in his memory for the acute phase of the illness. The totality of the amnesia for this portion of the illness is due no doubt to the impairment of registration and the general confusion which are so prominent during this period. Following the acute part of the illness the patient is left with a distinctive disorder of learning (memorizing) which is usually severe but nevertheless incomplete in degree. This defect applies to all aspects of new learning, whether it be the memorization of names, objects, nonsense syllables, a line of poetry, a card game or motor skill. Since the adaptation to every new situation requires the formation of new memories and their integration with past experience, it is the defect in these functions that renders the patient helpless in society and capable of performing only the most habitual and routine tasks.

The importance of the defect in memorization was originally emphasized by Wechsler (57), who demonstrated the striking inability of the Korsakoff patient to learn difficult word associations. He regarded this disorder, rather than the obliteration of old associations, as the most significant psychological abnormality in Korsakoff's psychosis, and attempted to explain the various abnormalities in behavior and mental function on this basis. Recently, a similar hypothesis has been propounded by Barbizet (4). Admittedly, certain aspects of confabulation or fabrication could be a consequence of such a difficulty, in that the patient, unable to make appropriate associations, responds with the readiest one, derived from his stock of old memories. However, a defect in memorization alone would not account for the retrograde amnesia, i.e., the ablation of personal experiences and other information which the patient had been able to recall efficiently during a period of months or years which preceded the onset of the illness.

The retrograde amnesia is quite variable in extent and in its degree of completeness. One patient, for example, who developed Korsakoff's psychosis at age 40, thought she was still in Ireland. Actually she had emigrated at age 19, but she had virtually no memory for events or experiences since that age, including her marriage and having raised four children to adulthood. Rarely is the retrograde amnesia so extensive or sharply defined. Usually the severe impairment of memory extends over a period of several years before the onset of the illness and the point at which it ends cannot be sharply defined. Furthermore, the retrograde amnesia is rarely complete. As a rule, the patient retains isolated bits of information with varying degrees of accuracy and he relates these to one another without regard to the gaps which separate them or to their proper temporal sequence. This defect becomes prominent after the acute stage of the illness has passed and some improvement in function has occurred, and remains a dominant feature in all but the few patients who make a complete recovery. This inability to correlate experiences in terms of time relationships accounts for certain instances of confabulation and for the characteristic manner in which patients retell stories (see below) and is a consistent, and, in this sense, a fundamental defect in Korsakoff's psychosis.

It is a truism that in alcoholic Korsakoff's psychosis, as in all amnestic syndromes, remote memories are better preserved than recent ones, but this statement requires qualification. The line which divides past memories into "recent" and "remote" is hardly distinct and only in the rare patient can one define it with precision. It is our impression that memories of the distant past are impaired to some extent in practically all patients with Korsakoff's psychosis, and seriously impaired in many. The patients' vocabulary and general facility with language, long-standing motor skills and social habits are well preserved.

We have been quite unable to discern the factors which govern what is forgotten and what is remembered. This aspect of the memory disorder seems to follow no distinctive or consistent pattern. Patients may show gaps in their memory for seemingly important and emotionally charged events, and at the same time be able to recall casual items or ones in which they were not personally involved. A similar paradox may pertain in regard to new memories. For example, we have on several occasions confronted a patient with the news that his closest relative, on whom he was completely dependent, had died. Such a patient would appear shocked and distressed, indicating that he had grasped the significance of our statement, but within a minute or two, if this represented his forward memory span, he would

lose his distressed facial expression, and a few minutes later he would remember neither the examiner nor what he had been told. Yet the same
patient may have learned, and then persistently recalled, some fact of no
particular importance.

3. CONFABULATION

This symptom merits brief consideration since it is generally regarded
as a specific feature of Korsakoff's psychosis and a requisite for the diagnosis. The acceptance of this view depends to a large extent on how one
defines the term, but on this matter, unfortunately, there is no uniformity of
opinion. Even if one accepts a very broad definition of the term, it has been
our experience that some patients simply do not confabulate, particularly in
the chronic, stable phase of the illness. In the early stages, confabulation
may be a prominent symptom, but not in every patient, and even when
present it is not consistently elicitable.

In most instances of Korsakoff's psychosis, the presence of confabulation
is associated with one of two particular aspects of the illness. In the earliest
stage, confabulation appears to be related to the state of confusion. Under
these circumstances the confabulation is comparable with that which occurs
in the course of any acute confusional or delirious state, and in all of them
the symptom probably has its origin in a disorder of perception. At a later
stage in the illness, the confabulation seems to depend on that aspect of the
memory defect in which events are related without regard for their proper
temporal sequence. If one is not fully aware of the patient's past experiences, the gross temporal dislocations may give them an implausible or fic-
tional aspect. Whether one defines this as a memory defect or confabulation
is pedantic.

The statement that the Korsakoff patient "fills in" gaps in memory with
fabrications, implying a conscious effort to hide the memory defect, out
of embarrassment or for other reasons, has not been borne out by our observations. In fact, the opposite seems to pertain, i.e., as the patient improves, he tends more and more to admit that he does not know the
answers to questions and one is less able to provoke confabulation.

4. RESULTS OF FORMAL PSYCHOLOGICAL TESTING IN KORSAKOFF'S PSYCHOSIS

Our original psychological studies (53, 55) were designed to determine
whether or not there were any abnormalities other than amnesia and confabulation. The tests employed were the Wechsler-Bellevue Intelligence
Scale (58) and the Wechsler Memory Scale (59), and the patients were
tested during the period in which they were improving and also during
the stable chronic stage of their illness. The tests emphasized the changing
character of the mental abnormality and provided support for the view that
the central features of this psychosis are an affection of retentive memory,

an inability to learn and to retain new information, and a derangement in the ordered time relations of long established memories.

The capacity to retell stories that were read to the patient was character-istically and severely impaired. Occasionally the patients introduced new material, usually having some logical relation to the story but more com-monly there were gross errors of omission, incorrect juxtaposition, condensa-tions or combinations of isolated facts, so that the meaning of the whole was distorted. Their performance on this test was analogous to the distorted manner in which they related their personal experiences, and constituted a characteristic abnormality in the convalescent and chronic phases of the illness. The relation of this particular abnormality to confabulation has been mentioned.

The basic psychological tests also disclosed a characteristic, though not specific, impairment of certain cognitive functions which seemed to de-pend little or not at all on memory. The most consistent failure was with the Digit Symbol task and, to a less marked degree, with Arithmetic and Block Design. Applying the interpretations generally given to these sub-tests, the defects were in learning ability in a new situation, concentration, spatial organization and in verbal and visual abstraction. In other words, there was an impairment of the capacity to think clearly and to reason with data immediately before the patient, i.e., in circumstances where memory function is not a major factor. The consistency of these findings, even in the stable phase of the illness, suggested that the Korsakoff syndrome could not be explained in terms of memory loss alone.

These observations stimulated Dr. George Talland to undertake an in-tensive investigation of the cognitive damage in Korsakoff's psychosis. Using a wide range of psychological tests, he studied a group of 24 of our chronic cases, and compared their performance to that of a control group of chronic alcoholics who had been abstinent for several months and who had no nutritional or other medical disease, and to that of a group of neurological patients who had been hospitalized for long periods but who showed no signs of brain disease. The results of these studies have been reported in a number of publications and will only be summarized here in their briefest form (40, 41, 42, 43, 44).

A battery of psychological tests, designed to explore various perceptual processes, showed a number of consistent defects which could not be at-tributed to a primary abnormality in learning or memorizing. Whereas the Korsakoff patient showed no deficit in tasks which depend on immediate apprehension, he was handicapped if the task was changed and a new mental "set" required, especially while the first task was continued. It seemed that the patient was excessively dependent upon the immediate sensory input, in the sense of being unable to detach himself from it by imagery or change his orientation towards it, and this in itself prevented the patient from assimilating a diversity of newly presented material. In

addition to to the perceptual defects, the Korsakoff patient evidenced in-
adequacy of function in concept formation. Only the simplest concepts
could be constructed, and the criteria for the classification of a series of
newly presented material were much more vague than those of the control
subjects. Usually the Korsakoff patient was incapable of discovering the
unfamiliar criteria necessary for categorization, and the concepts once acquired were not effectively applied in the formation of sequential concepts.
Talland has suggested that the inability to adopt new attitudes of orientation to a situation may be the basic abnormality in both the perceptual
and conceptual deficits.

Many of the shortcomings of the Korsakoff patient, which were so conspicuous on clinical observation, were confirmed when subjected to quantitative analysis. The patients were found to be inactive and lacking in initiative and spontaneity. They showed an obviously greater difficulty than
the control sample in memorizing newly presented material and the rate
of forgetting what had been learned was more rapid. All forms of learned
material were affected, i.e., tasks involving word symbols or numbers or
even motor skills, and the emotional content of this material seemed to
have little influence on what was forgotten or remembered. There was no
evidence of repression or of symbolic distortion in the recalled material. Attempts at relearning were almost totally ineffectual, information being
repeatedly recalled in much the same distorted form, sometimes after intervals which exceeded the length of memory span. Preliminary observations on the establishment of conditional reflexes suggested that they could
be formed as readily as in the normal subject but were more quickly extinguished.

5. The Neuropathological Changes in the Wernicke-Korsakoff Syndrome

The pathological changes to be described are based on a study of 54
cases (11). In 46 of these, the clinical signs of Wernicke's disease had been
observed during life, and in 23 of the 46 the symptoms of Korsakoff's psychosis had also been recognized. In 18 of the remaining 23 the diagnosis of
Korsakoff's psychosis could not be made with certainty during life, since
many of them had died in the acute stage of the illness; in five of the 23,
however, mental function had been assessed, and the symptoms of Korsakoff's
psychosis had not been found. There were three patients who did not have
any ocular or ataxic signs during life, but only an amnestic syndrome. A final
group of five patients had died of delirium tremens or hepatic coma, and
post-mortem examination showed pathological changes identical with those
found in the cases known to have had Wernicke's disease and Korsakoff's
psychosis.

The topography of the lesions was remarkably constant. Aside from circumscribed lesions in the medulla, pons, periaqueductal region of the midbrain and anterior lobe of the cerebellum (doubtless the basis of the ocular

and gaze palsies, nystagmus and cerebellar ataxia), which are not our concern at the moment, the principal changes were located in the medial parts of the medial dorsal, pulvinar and anteroventral nuclei, and in the mammillary bodies and most terminal portions of the fornices. The general distribution and extent of the lesions are illustrated in Figures 128, 129 and 130. Minor and inconstant microscopic changes were found in other thalamic nuclei (paracentral, medial ventral, lateral dorsal, parafascicular and ventral anterior nuclei, the centrum medianum and midline nuclei) and in the hypothalamus dorsomedial, ventromedial, paraventricular, lateral and preoptic nuclei). In serial sections of many of these cases the following structures were found to be intact: cerebral cortex, lenticular and caudate nuclei, all other nuclei of the thalamus and hypothalamus (except those enumerated above), the nuclei and fibers of the H fields of Forel, subthalamus, nuclei of Luys, red nuclei, substantia nigra, reticular formation, subthalamus, hippocampi and major parts of the rhinencephalon, the fornices (except the intramammillary or supramammillary parts), septal nuclei, cingulate gyri and cingulum, and nuclei of the diagonal band of Broca.

The lesions consisted of a loss of medullated fibers and nerve cells, large numbers of adventitial histiocytes and microgliacytes, increased cellularity of capillaries and small blood vessels, and an increase in fibrous astrocytes, their proportions depending on the age of the lesions. Evidence of hemorrhage (extravasated red blood cells or hemosiderin-filled macrophages) was noted in approximately 20 per cent of cases, but seldom was this conspicuous and, in some instances, it may have represented an agonal change.

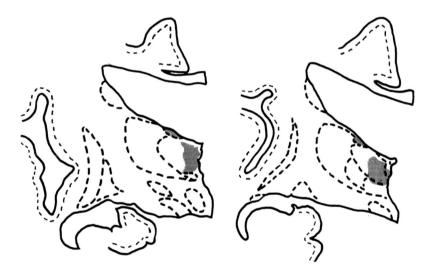

Figure 128. Diagram of the thalamic lesions in the Wernicke-Korsakoff syndrome; the shaded areas show the pattern of involvement of the medial-dorsal and anteroventral nuclei in coronal sections. (From Adams, Collins & Victor, 1.)

The nature of the pathological changes and their distribution were strikingly similar in the cases with Wernicke's disease and those with Korsakoff's psychosis. There were, at the same time, several small differences, the most important of which pertained to the involvement or lack of involvement of the medial dorsal nucleus of the thalamus. As noted above, our series of post-mortem cases included five patients in whom the signs of Wernicke's disease had been present during life without evidence of memory defect. In each of these five cases the medial dorsal nucleus was carefully studied and found to be free of disease; furthermore, these were the only cases in which this portion of the thalamus was not affected. On the other hand, there were severe and chronic lesions of the mammillary bodies in all five. There were five additional cases in which memory defect had been recognized during life, and in these the medial dorsal nucleus was virtually the only thalamic nucleus affected; unfortunately, the pulvinar, which usually is involved together with the medial dorsal nucleus, was not available for study in these cases. Nevertheless, these observations indicate that the mammil-

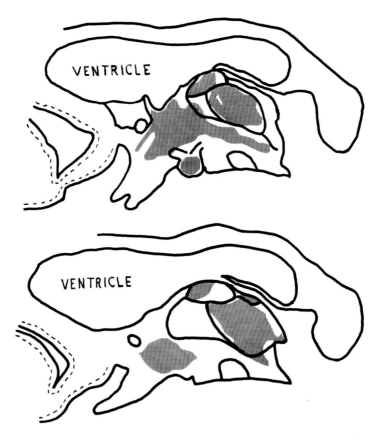

Figure 129. Lesions in the wall and floor of the third ventricle. Shaded areas show the pattern of involvement of the thalamus and hypothalamus, including the mammillary body. *Above:* paramedian section; *below:* sagittal section 3 mm lateral to the section above. (From Adams, Collins & Victor, 1.)

lary bodies may be severely affected in the absence of a memory defect and that the thalamic lesions, rather than the mammillary ones, are critical in memory function.

The latter idea finds support in several experimental studies. Spiegel and his co-workers (37) placed stereotaxic lesions in the medial dorsal nucleus of human subjects, and found that for several weeks after the operation these patients showed temporal disorientation, lack of spontaneity, decreased responsiveness to sensory stimuli and a memory defect for recent and past events. Ingram (21) has shown that cats subjected to destructive lesions in the medial dorsal nuclei seemed to forget their previous training and to learn more slowly than before the operation. The recent experimental findings of Thompson & Hawkins (46) are of particular interest in this regard: they taught rats an avoidance response and a kinesthetic and visual discrimination habit and then destroyed the mammillary nuclei, premammillary area, supramammillary area, and the posterior hypothalamic nucleus; these lesions had no appreciable effect on retention of either habit.

The symptoms of apathy, drowsiness, disinterest and so forth, which are so prominent initially and so readily reversible, are probably attributable to a functional derangement of structures in parts of the thalamus, hypothalamus and upper midbrain which lie adjacent to the observable lesions.

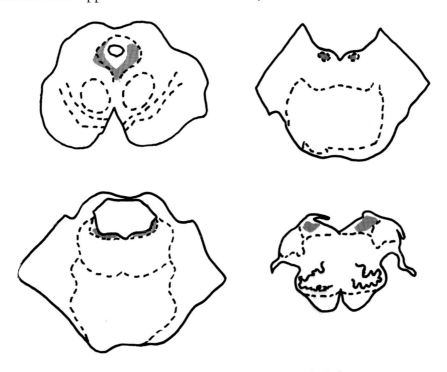

Figure 130. Horizontal sections of the brain stem. Shaded areas represent the common loci of the Wernicke lesions: periaqueductal gray matter, floor of the fourth ventricle, abducens, and vestibular nuclei. (From Adams, Collins & Victor, 1.)

6. Korsakoff's Psychosis Due to Diencephalic Tumors

An amnestic syndrome of the Korsakoff type has been observed frequently with certain tumors, particularly with craniopharyngiomas, pituitary adenomas with extrasellar extension, and occasionally with other tumors at the base of the brain. The medical literature contains a large number of reports of such cases, which have been reviewed by Williams & Pennybacker (61) and by White & Cobb (60) among many others, and there is no need to pursue this subject here. Doubtless, the disorder of memory in these instances is attributable to the involvement of the floor and walls of the third ventricle, and in this general sense these cases reinforce the notion that the lesions in the diencephalic region are important in memory function. However, because of the indistinctness of their boundaries and the indefinable effects of edema, compression, and so forth, the lesions created by tumors are of little value in delineating precise clinical-anatomical relationships.

Memory Loss with Lesions of the Hippocampal Formations

It is generally acknowledged that, in addition to the diencephalon, certain portions of the temporal lobes, specifically the hippocampal formations, are of particular importance in regard to memory and learning. The most convincing evidence for this idea has been derived from patients subjected to surgical resections of these regions (32, 35, 36). The oft-quoted case of Glees & Griffith (18) may have been due to a vascular lesion or to an inclusion-body encephalitis. Lesions of the hippocampal formations may be caused by many disease states, but the example chosen for discussion here is one of temporal lobe infarction. The patient to be described had shown a severe and disproportionate disorder of memory function, which was stable and carefully documented over a period of several years. The brain was studied in serial sections, so that a fairly complete anatomical evaluation was possible. The lesions proved to be old and discrete, and this allowed some conclusions to be drawn regarding the anatomical basis of memory. This case has been the subject of a previous report, to which the reader is referred for details of the clinical and pathological findings (52).

A 54-year old right-handed man (BP 170/108) suffered the abrupt onset of a right homonymous hemianopia in November, 1951. Except for this abnormality he remained well until two years later, when a similar accident occurred. This time the left visual field of each eye was involved and the patient was left with grossly restricted vision, only the macular portions of the visual fields being spared. Immediately after the second stroke, and for a period of three years thereafter, while he was under close observation, he was noted to have a pronounced impairment of retentive memory and an inability to learn and to retain new facts and skills. He would ask the same question over and over again. He spent hours watching baseball on television but, as soon as the set was off, he was unable to remember the score or any other detail of the game. However, he was able to recall correctly the highlights of games that had been played many years before. He could not remember whether he had smoked a cigarette or simply put it away. He would forget simple instructions given by his wife and would neglect to read notes which had been left to reinforce his memory. During this period he was still able to play bridge adequately and actually taught his nephew the game of solitaire (he had known these games many years) but he was unable to learn new card games of lesser complexity.

The patient also showed a fairly well-defined retrograde amnesia that extended back about two and one-half years before the second stroke. Events which had occurred prior to 1951 could be recalled with accuracy. Although his performance on the Wechsler-Bellevue Intelligence Scale was rated as "bright normal", the tests designed to measure concentration, shifting from one mental set to another, and abstract thinking were somewhat below his own verbal mean. Along with these deficits the patient exhibited a mild but definite behavioral change, consisting of a persistent inactivity, indifference and loss of incentive. The gravity of the memory defect was appreciated very little, if at all, by the patient.

It should be stressed that despite the amnestic and behavioral disorder, a number of functions, some of which were dependent upon past memory, were intact. The patient was alert and responsive. There was no apraxia, agnosia, or aphasia. Habitual motor acts, such as those involved in dressing and eating, had not been forgotten. Recognition (so-called "involuntary recall" or "gnostic memory") was unimpaired. There were no misidentifications or misinterpretations and no indications of spatial disorientation. Comprehension of visually and verbally presented instructions was intact; he could read and write fluently and express himself adequately. The psychic derangement shown by this patient was indistinguishable from instances of Korsakoff's psychosis which complicate alcoholism and malnutrition.

Death occurred in December, 1956, a few days after a basilar artery occlusion. The post-mortem examination disclosed a massive brain stem infarct, which was very recent and obviously related to an atherosclerotic basilar artery thrombosis. Coronal sections of the formalin-fixed brain demonstrated a cavitated, trabeculated, yellow brown softening along the inferomedial aspect of the left temporal and occipital lobes; a similar though much more restricted lesion was present on the right. These lesions extended posteriorly into the medial and inferior portions of the occipital lobes. Of particular importance were softenings in the splenium of the corpus callosum and commissure of the fornix. On the left, the body of the fornix was approximately one-third the size of that on the right, and the left mammillary body was shrunken.

Microscopically, the most significant pathological alterations were found bilaterally in the hippocampal formation, fornix and related structures.

These lesions, as well as the secondary degenerations in the fornices, are illustrated in Figure 131. On the left, there was a severe cell loss and gliosis in the hippocampus, subiculum and cortex of the medial aspect of the lateral occipito-temporal gyrus. The alveus and fimbria hippocampi, substantia reticularis alba of the hippocampus, and medullary lamina of the gyrus dentatus were pale and shrunken. On the right, there was a patchy loss of pyramidal cells in Sommer's sector of the hippocampus and a small gliotic lesion in the parahippocampal gyrus, and the fimbria hippocampi was shrunken and pallid. The left fornix was shrunken throughout its extent, while the right contained a discrete softening in the anterior portion of its crus, interrupting the fibers of the fimbria hippocampi. There was a loss of nerve cells and gliosis in both mammillary bodies, affecting particularly the lateral portions of the medial nuclei, the left more than the right. On both sides the uncus, the amygdaloid body and terminal digitations of the hippocampus were unaffected.

This case supplements the growing body of evidence that the medial parts of the temporal lobes, particularly the hippocampal formations and their connections via the fornix, constitute a mechanism of fundamental importance for learning and memory. It also reinforces the belief that a loss of memory occurs only if the lesions of the hippocampal formations are bilateral. In this case there was, in addition to a large hippocampal lesion in the left, a small lesion in the crus of the right fornix, which interrupted the efferent hippocampal fibers on that side. There are isolated reports of memory loss following resection of one temporal lobe (32, 56), but in none of the cases has the absence of contralateral disease been confirmed by post-mortem examination.

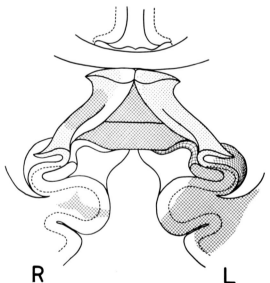

R   L

Figure 131. Diagram (modified from Villiger) of the hippocampal formations, fornices and splenium of the corpus callosum. Cross-hatched areas represent infarct necrosis in the parahippocampal gyrus, subiculum, hippocampus, and dentate gyrus on the left; in the parahippocampal gyrus and the crus of the fornix on the right; in the splenium of the corpus callosum (below) and in the commissure of the fornix (above) in the midline. Stippled areas represent secondary degeneration in the fornix on the left and in the fimbrial portion of the fornix on the right. (From Victor, Angevine et al., 52.)

Some Additional Observations on the Relations of Hippocampal Lesions
to Disorders of Memory

Certain examples of senile dementia and inclusion body encephalitis have contributed to our knowledge of the anatomy of memory, as have a number of experimental studies. These data will now be briefly reviewed. The disorder of mental function in senile dementia is a complex one and usually embraces many facets of mental function, not simply those pertaining to memory. Nevertheless, in a certain number of patients with Alzheimer's disease, memory function is affected initially and more or less exclusively, and confabulation is prominent, a syndrome to which the term presbyophrenia has been applied. In cases such as these, it has been reported that the "Alzheimer" changes are most prominent in the hippocampal region (12, 49). This has been our impression also, based on a limited experience with this type of senile dementia.

As a general rule, the memory disorder of Alzheimer's disease is insidious in onset and gradual in its evolution. Occasionally, however, the onset of the memory disorder is abrupt, suggestive of vascular disease. We have observed a remarkable instance of this sort in an 84-year old man. While on a train, in apparent good health, he suddenly became confused, and from that moment on he lost his memory for his wife, friends, home or whereabouts. In the four years that followed this episode he showed a consistent inability to remember day-to-day events or to commit to memory the simplest information. In addition, there was a retrograde amnesia of more than fifty years duration; he could recall his early years on a farm in Minnesota and his education at West Point, but he had no memory of his participation in the Spanish-American war or of his home, in which he had lived for almost forty years. Post-mortem examination disclosed no evidence of cerebral infarction but a marked atrophy of both temporal lobes, particularly of the hippocampus and hippocampal gyrus. Microscopically, there was a loss of nerve cells, and the characteristic senile plaques and neurofibrillary tangles of Alzheimer's disease, again most prominent in the hippocampus and hippocampal gyrus. These changes were bilateral.

In recent years attention has been drawn to a unique form of encephalitis and to the fact that patients who survive this illness may be left with an amnestic syndrome of the Korsakoff type. In the beginning, confusion, delirium and auditory or visual hallucinations may be prominent in addition to the non-specific symptoms of encephalitis. The pathological changes take the form of a necrotizing hemorrhagic lesion involving primarily the medial portions of the temporal lobes and hippocampi, the posterior parts of the orbito-frontal convolutions, and to a lesser degree the contiguous portions of the cerebral cortex. The singular aspect of the microscopic picture is the presence of intranuclear inclusion bodies in glial cells and, less often, in neurons. The virus of herpes simplex has been isolated from a number of these cases, and rising titers of antibodies to this virus have been demonstrated in many others. The clinical and pathological features of this disease have been recently described by Drachman & Adams (14) and by Haymaker et al. (20), and good clinical accounts have been given by Rose & Symonds (34) and by Brierley and co-workers (6).

The Anatomical Basis of Memory

One might pause at this point and attempt to derive some general notions about the anatomical substratum of memory. The data which have been presented clearly indicate that bilateral lesions in the medial portions of the diencephalon or the inferomedial portions of the temporal lobes derange memory and learning out of all proportion to other cognitive and behavioral functions. The diencephalic structures of particular importance in memory function appear to be the medial dorsal nuclei of the thalamus and not the mammillary bodies. At least this is our conclusion, based on a study of the alcoholic form of Korsakoff's psychosis. In regard to the temporal lobes, the hippocampal formations (gyrus dentatus, hippocampus and parahippocampal gyrus) appear to be crucial for memory function, judging from the case we studied. Since the uncus, amygdaloid body and anterior portion of the hippocampus of both sides were spared in this particular instance, we concluded that the amnestic symptoms did not depend on lesions in these structures. These observations are in accord with those of Scoville & Milner (36), who pointed out that a loss of memory did not follow resections of the most anterior parts of the temporal lobes, but that a permanent loss of retentive memory occurred if the resections included the hippocampal formations.

However, even a brief examination of the literature on this subject discloses a wide divergence of opinion as to which portions of the diencephalic-temporal structures are specifically involved in memory function. The discrepancies relating to the mammillary bodies and medial dorsal nuclei have been discussed. In relation to the temporal lobe, one of the points made by Dr. Feindel is particularly pertinent. He and Penfield (15) have noted that in patients with paroxysmal automatic behavior, the initial pattern of the seizure may consist of an awareness of confusion or a difficulty with memory, and, furthermore, that the period of amnesia may long outlast the period of automatic behavior. These attacks may be reproduced by stimulation of the periamygdaloid area, but not by stimulation of the tip of the temporal lobe or other portions of the temporal lobe cortex. The authors proposed, on the basis of these observations, that the periamygdaloid area forms a portion of the memory-recording mechanism.

Animal experiments allow somewhat different interpretations. Mishkin (26) has found that bilateral ablation of the "ventral temporal cortex" in monkeys caused impairment of remembering and learning visual discrimination problems. A similar abnormality in monkeys has been demonstrated by Orbach and associates (31) to follow the bilateral removal of the amygdala and major portions of the hippocampus and hippocampal gyrus. Stepién et al. (38) subjected two monkeys to a similar operative procedure, and found that the animals had lost their ability to learn certain discrimination tests which depend on the retention of compound auditory and visual stimuli. In the rat, impairment of avoidance learning followed lesions placed in this general vicinity (45). The data of Kaada and co-workers (22) indicate that lesions of the hippocampus, fornix, and mammillary bodies seem to interfere with maze learning and retention, provided the rats are incompletely trained preoperatively.

Despite the fact that the fornix contains many of the efferent fibers from the hippocampal formation, there is little evidence that interruption of this projection system is in itself associated with a loss of memory. The case reported by Sweet and co-workers (39) is unusual in this regard. In their patient, the free portions of both columns of the fornix were sectioned to facilitate removal of a tumor of the third ventricle. After the operation, the patient showed a severe and lasting defect in memory and learning, a patchy retrograde amnesia, and a mild impairment of other cognitive functions, as well as a general apathy and lack of spontaneity—i.e., the characteristic features of Korsakoff's psychosis. The findings in this case are at variance with the observations reported by others. García-Bengochea et al. (16) could discern no abnormalities in the behavior of monkeys following section of both fornices. Nor has any permanent defect in memory been reported following the operative section of the fornices in man (2, 3, 13, 17).

It is evident from the foregoing remarks that the anatomy of memory is an extremely complicated matter, and to think of it simply in terms of an interruption of a pathway which involves the hippocampus, fornix and mammillary bodies is an oversimplification, to say the least. To begin with, the hippocampus projects, via the fornix, to many parts other than the mammillary bodies (27, 28). The uncertainties and discrepancies regarding the role of the hippocampal formations and other parts of the temporal lobes and the fornix have just been summarized. Whether the mammillary bodies have anything to do with memory function may be questioned. If indeed the medial dorsal nucleus of the thalamus is critical in memory function, then it should be noted that no direct connections between this structure and the hippocampal formation have yet been demonstrated. Obviously, the precise anatomical arrangements subserving memory function in the temporal lobes and diencephalon remain to be delineated.

Finally, one must consider the roles of the neocortex and the brain stem reticular formation in memory function. It is known both from human cases (10, 25) and animal experiments (23) that very large lesions of the neocortex cause an impairment of retentive memory and learning function, and that this effect is related to the size of the lesion rather than to its locus. More important are the circumscribed areas of cortex related to special forms of learning and memory. Thus, a lesion of the dominant temporal lobe impairs the patient's ability to remember words and to relearn them. In a similar sense the dominant parietal lobe is related to geometric figures and numbers, the non-dominant parietal lobe to visual-spatial relations, and so forth. The reticular formation is of obvious importance, since a state of alertness and attentiveness is a requisite for any learning.

Any hypothesis concerning the anatomical substratum of learning and retentive memory must include, therefore, not only the diencephalic-rhinencephalic structures, but also the whole of the neocortex and the midbrain reticular formation. Such a hypothesis has recently been suggested by Adams, Collins & Victor (1). The diencephalic-hippocampal structures are involved in all the active phases of learning and integration of newly formed memories regardless of the sense avenue through which the new information reaches the organism in order to be assimilated, or of the final pathway of its expression; and it seems to make little difference whether the acquired experience involves functions that are classed as purely cognitive or emotional. This does not imply that memory is localized in these structures, or that these parts of the brain form a "memory center", but means only that these are the sites where the smallest lesions have the most devastating effects on memory and learning, and that they form a tenuous but vital link between the reticular formation and neocortex. The more general aspect of psychic activity, which extends to every form of learned behavior, might be designated as the universal or "U" factor of memory. Restricted regions of the temporal, parietal and occipital cortex, while contributing to this "U" factor, also have particular relationships to the several forms of special memories. The latter might be designated as the "S" factors of memory. The precise manner in which these factors relate to one another is an interesting but unsolved problem.

Some Tentative Conclusions Regarding the Psychological Derangement in Korsakoff's Psychosis

The amnestic syndrome in man comprises the following abnormalities: (a) a major impairment of the patient's ability to recall memories that had been formed before the onset of the illness and to acquire new skills and information after the onset, (b) a relatively minor but definite impairment of perceptual and conceptual functions, and (c) a diminution of the patient's initiative and spontaneity. These abnormalities form the core of the amnestic syndrome. Confabulation is not considered to be a fundamental or primary symptom, for reasons that have been discussed. The profound confusion and apathy which characterize the onset of Wernicke's disease may also be regarded as epiphenomena, insofar as they are evanescent and probably depend on the functional derangement of diencephalic structures contiguous to those responsible for the amnestic syndrome *per se*. In a similar sense, the hallucinations and bizarre behavior which occur in herpes simplex encephalitis reflect the involvement of portions of the temporal lobes other than the hippocampal formations.

An immediate problem in regard to the amnestic syndrome is to decide how the various abnormalities relate to one another and which one of them, if any, is primary. Insofar as the disorder of memory and learning is the most prominent feature of the syndrome, one's first inclination is to regard it as fundamental and the other symptoms as derivative. One may postulate that the memory disorder is responsible for the patient's passivity and lack of incentive. According to this view, the inability to form new memories and to integrate new information with old, and hence to plan for the future, may deprive the patient of any stimulus to action. However, our studies (55) and those of Talland (40, 41) indicate that the disorder of memory does not wholly account for the defects in perception and certain other cognitive functions.

Conversely, the perceptual disorder is probably not responsible for the memory disorder, since the former is always comparatively mild and usually clinically inapparent, requiring special tests for its demonstration. The lack of causal relationship between the perceptual and memory disorders has been emphasized by a recent case which showed, despite the most detailed and careful testing, a severe and persistent memory defect following an attack of encephalitis, but no perceptual disorder.*

Similarly, the lack of initiative and spontaneity which characterizes the Korsakoff psychotic can hardly be held responsible for the memory defect. These abnormalities, as well as the perceptual and conceptual ones, could conceivably contribute to the learning difficulty, and one might even speculate that past memories are not lost, but that the patient simply lacks the incentive to search for and to retrieve them. However, such a theory would not explain why the Korsakoff patient can retrieve some past memories and not others, or why he should find it easier to recall memories of the far past than of the recent past. The fact of the matter is that the patient cannot recall certain past experiences no matter how hard he tries, or by any means.

To summarize—amnestic, perceptual and affective symptoms are consistently found in Korsakoff's psychosis, although they are of unequal prominence. Nevertheless, each of these abnormalities is basic and independent, i.e., they are not entirely dependent upon or derived from one another.

Numerous theories have been proposed to explain the psychic derangement of Korsakoff's syndrome, either in terms of memory alone (Lidz, 24), or of certain aspects of memory function, such as a failure of memorization (Barbizet, 4), an inability to form new associations (Wechsler, 57) or a disordered time sense (Van der Horst, 50). Other authors have selected a certain aspect of the perceptual or conceptual disorder (Buerger-Prinz &

---

* R. D. Adams, personal communication.

Kaila, 8) or the lack of incentive (Grünthal, 19; Pick, 33) as the primary one. These hypotheses, and others not mentioned here, have added to our understanding of individual symptoms of Korsakoff's psychosis but have failed to provide the explanation for all of them.

An hypothesis designed to explain the psychological derangement in Korsakoff's psychosis should embrace all the abnormalities in this syndrome or at least suggest a common psychological disorder from which the others are derived. This hypothesis will also have to explain how a single pathological process, acting over a circumscribed period of time, not only impairs all future learning, but the memory of experiences that had occurred before the illness struck, and why the most recent memories are the most vulnerable. This singular feature suggests that memories are not formed in an instant but take days or weeks or even years for their formation. A satisfactory hypothesis will have to account not only for these psychological factors but for the anatomical ones as well. Perhaps some of the modern theories of memory, such as the one which forms the theme of this conference, will find their place in a comprehensive theory of memory. It is possible, just as genetic and immunological specificities have been found to depend on macromolecular codes, that memory and learning also may involve a chemical writing of experience in macromolecular code in the cells of the brain. At the moment, however, a wide gap exists between a number of fundamental biological observations, provocative as they are, and the observed clinical and anatomical facts concerning memory and learning in man. The attempt to bridge this gap is one of the most challenging problems facing both the clinician and the basic scientist.

Adey: The very interesting evidence from Dr. Victor's studies calls for little amplification on my part. The image he has drawn of the interrelations between the hippocampus and the diencephalon as being crucially involved in the recent memory function is something that I think also has gained important ground in such studies as those of Bucy & Klüver (7), where some 117 pages of the *Journal of Comparative Neurology* have been devoted to the study of the brain of one of the original monkeys (the brain of Aurora), some twenty years after the animal was sacrificed in the original studies of what is now called the Bucy-Klüver syndrome. This study has disclosed very extensive and complex interrelations between almost all aspects of the diencephalon and rostral midbrain. It is extremely difficult, from Klüver's account, to come away with any concise picture of the more important connections, if one dared to call one type of connections more important than another.

The advantage of the long-term study displayed there was that, by the use of retrograde cell degeneration, probably many transsynaptic connections were revealed. In other words, it was not something confined to the immediate aspect of the first synapse of the neurons entering into the hippocampal system or, conversely, those connections which come out of the hippocampal system.

Turning to the question of what zones in the diencephalon may have primary importance, I think studies presented here by Dr. Thompson, as well as our own, have indicated that the region coursing between hypothalamus and thalamus close to the midline appears to provide one of the main pathways extending caudally, at least as far as the rostral midbrain, for connections between rhinencephalic structures and the central core of the reticular formation. In comparative anatomy, the studies by Bodian (5) in 1940 on the brain of the Virginia opossum exemplified a whole series of midline connections coursing up and down from rhinencephalic structures as far caudally as the midbrain.

More recent work from the Palma school by Carreras and his colleagues (9) has exemplified this in the cat. We have as yet relatively little data in the primate in this regard. I think that is something which studies such as those of Dr. Victor will help to elucidate.

Weiskrantz: I feel that we really are getting to the point where we can start very intensively putting some labels on those rather crude boxes of mine.

First of all, referring back to my first figure (No. 80), with respect to the number of D's: I think this is a point that perhaps is apparent from what has been said subsequently. Instead of having a number of separate boxes, we have, in fact, a continuous series, going backwards in time. You can imagine that, as material enters into the "D" system, it somehow, and I think Dr. Victor stressed the necessity of this, becomes stronger, or at least more resistant to interference.

Another point: I think perhaps the work on the amygdala in animals has not been put in its complete perspective. If one imagines transfer from A via C to some system like D, and if one also imagines everything that comes into A cannot possibly enter D because there is too much of it, then two questions have to be asked: *whether* material is going to get through from A to D, and *what* it is that one has just decided to let through the filter, since all cannot be transferred.

It seems to me that a great deal of the work on lesions in the amygdala in animals is related to the question of whether the material gets through, because such animals are very confused about what is, in crude terms, good and bad in their environment.

I would suggest that the question of what gets through, how one identifies this, how one puts it together, is related to the hippocampal gyrus and the system of which it is part. The kind of function Dr. Adey is supposing, which correlates the two separate sorts of information and pushes them down into some other system, seems to me extremely promising. It fits in very well with that type of idea.

I wanted to ask for one specific point of information, Dr. Victor. In your general description of the Wernicke-Korsakoff syndrome, you spoke of anterograde and retrograde amnesia. You mentioned that, in the early stage, the retrograde amnesia can be very severe, going back over a period of some years. In the final or third state, where there is just the amnesia, which you call the "U" factor, you said the retrograde amnesia was variable. Can you give any indication of the range of variability?

Victor: There is always a complete and lasting defect in memory for the acute illness, and for events covering several months before the acute illness. In addition, there is usually a severe though incomplete impairment of memory extending over several years before the illness.

I have also been able to convince myself that there are always gaps in the memories of the far past, although this aspect of memory function is generally better preserved than memory of the recent past. If one has an opportunity to check the patient's testimony against known facts, one finds that memories of events occurring during early life are quite incomplete.

We have been unable to recognize the factors which determine what is forgotten or what is remembered. Events of high emotional content seem to be forgotten as readily as the most casual items. Furthermore, in presenting the patient with new ideas, he appears to have equal difficulty in retaining the emotionally charged and the casual item.

Morrell: Dr. Victor, when you treat the patients with thiamine, is there a pattern of memory recovery?

Victor: That is a difficult question, and I can answer it only in a general way. First of all, as you may know, the ophthalmoplegia of Wernicke's disease recovers quickly, over several days; the ataxia improves less quickly, but very definitely under the influence of thiamine alone. Concomitant with the improvement in eye function, i.e., over a few days, the patient becomes more alert and more responsive, less sleepy, more attentive, and able to concentrate, and I believe he loses some degree of his general confusion, that is, he is less given to misinterpretations and misidentifications. Of this we are quite certain.

However, memory function returns very slowly and we are still not entirely certain that thiamine deficiency alone is the critical factor. It should also be emphasized that memory is not lost completely up to a certain point in time beyond which it is completely intact. There are large gaps in memory, greater in the immediate than in the far past. When memory function returns, it does so all along the line, so to speak. At least, this is my clinical impression. I do not know if this answers your question. Are you interested in the role of thiamine *per se* in improving memory function or in the pattern of memory improvement?

Morrell: I wondered if you could say these traces are lost, or whether the difficulty is in their retrieval.

Victor: I think they are lost; at least not under hypnosis or by any other method of which I am aware can one get the patient to recall events which he is unable to recall spontaneously at that time. But over a period of nine months to a year or a year and one-half, sometimes even longer than that, there can be a considerable restoration of memory function, i.e., of the ability to recall events of the immediate and remote past. In very general terms, after a year and one-half or two years there is no further recovery.

Morrell: And the memory deficit goes back how long?

Victor: Again, it is variable from one patient to another but, in the way I indicated to Dr. Weiskrantz, it extends back many years. In severely affected patients, memories of earliest childhood are also impaired. But it is very important to remember there are isolated islands of intact memory, even within the most severe period of memory loss.

Thompson: I do not want to give the impression that what has been found with rats ought to be extrapolated completely to man but, at the same time, I also do not necessarily want to dismiss the discrepancies between the work on humans and on rats, simply on the basis of a phylogenetic difference.

I believe, first of all, it might be premature to conclude, as I think you did, Dr. Victor, that lesions of midbrain structures will not affect recent memory. For example, the lesions that Dr. Adey and I described are at the junction between the midbrain and the diencephalon. In the rat, at least, substantia nigra damage interferes with so-called recent memory.

Then I want to comment on the retrograde amnesia found in the early stages of Wernicke's syndrome. Some years ago we found that lesions of the interpeduncular nucleus, which is quite close topographically to the mammillary region, produced what might be called retrograde amnesia in rats (47). It is interesting to note, however, that this effect is transitory and disappears about three weeks postoperatively (48). This finding, I believe, is especially noteworthy since, in our survey of the brain stem, no other lesion gave us this transitory effect.

I might suggest that possibly lesions in the region of the third ventricle in man might encroach upon the area corresponding to the interpeduncular nucleus in lower mammals, namely the posterior perforated substance, and this damage could possibly account for the retrograde amnesia that you do find, with eventual recovery.

In the third place, the medial dorsal nucleus lesions that you described are very interesting, of course, and would suggest a re-evaluation of the data on Korsakoff psychosis. Yet this nuclear mass is so close to the anterior thalamus that it would be difficult to ascribe the accompanying amnestic syndrome solely to medial dorsal nucleus damage.

Victor: How about Spiegel's cases (37)? Did they not show a five- or six-week period of memory defect following medial-dorsal lesions?

Thompson: Yes. But Spiegel also said he seemed to have obtained greater effects when his lesions were placed more anteriorly.

Then I want to mention another factor concerning recent memory losses following lesions of the brain. With respect to the structures which I have found to be critical for recent memory in the rat, namely the mammillary bodies, hippocampus, anterior thalamus, precallosal limbic area, lateral preoptic area, septum, and lateral hypothalamus, all gave more serious effects with larger lesions. It is possible, therefore, that those cases you described in which there was involvement of the medial dorsal nucleus, are the cases in which there exists extensive damage to the mammillary bodies. Lack of involvement of this thalamic nucleus may be correlated with slight lesions of the mammillary bodies.

Finally, I want to mention the difficulty I have in concluding that certain specialized memories are localized in the cerebral cortex.

Victor: I did not mean to limit the effects of cortical ablation to the ribbon of gray matter over the cerebral hemispheres. Obviously, an undercutting of the fibers derived from cortical cells will produce the same effects.

Mishkin: I would like to comment on a possible circuit which is directly related to the structures that Dr. Victor has told us are involved in the Korsakoff syndrome. This is based on evidence arising out of investigations in the monkey.

First I want to talk about the similarity between the results in monkey and in man, and then possibly an important difference, to see if there might be some way of resolving the difference.

In monkey, we know of approximately five structures in the forebrain, injury to which will produce an impairment in delayed alternation, delayed response, or both. One is the prefrontal cortex, another is the hippocampus, and another is the anterior portion of the cingulate gyrus. Recently, Dr. Sidney Schulman, at the University of Chicago, has provided evidence that complete lesions of the dorsomedial nucleus in the thalamus will also produce this effect.* A fifth one is the head of the caudate nucleus.

Lesions in any one of these five regions will produce the impairment. Lesions elsewhere in the forebrain do not seem to.

The interesting thing about this, in terms of the anatomy, is that very recently Nauta (30) has shown with his silver technique that the frontal cortex projects through the subcallosal fasciculus to the caudate, and through the cingulum, with offshoots to the anterior cingulate, to the hippocampus directly. This seems to be a rather strong bundle of connections. Then, of course, there is the reciprocal connection between the dorsomedial nucleus and the frontal cortex. So here we have, for the first time, direct anatomical support for a circuit that Dr. Victor has implicated in his work in man, and that we have implicated in the monkey.

The one important difference, and this is what really bothers us in all of our investigations, is that we are not convinced yet that these deficits in delayed alternation and delayed response are in fact deficits of recent memory. At least, there is still a good deal of controversy about this in the literature on animal work.

---

* Personal communication.

The differences, it seems to me, between the kinds of lesions that we are talking about in monkey and the kinds of lesions that you are talking about in man are not differences in locus—the locus seems to fit nicely. But the type of pathology in monkey is generally a clean-cut surgical removal. In man, this is only rarely so.

I am wondering if the kind of defect that we find in monkey, which we are still hesitant to call a defect in recent memory, would not turn out to be a defect in recent memory if, in fact, the structures were involved pathologically in the same way they are involved in man.

Feindel: I would like to add to Dr. Mishkin's remarks about Nauta's findings. A fascinating report has appeared recently (29), in which Nauta describes a sort of triangular circuit, connecting the dorso-medial nucleus of the thalamus to the orbital cortex of the frontal lobe and the amygdala. There are to-and-fro connections. The strongest anatomical path appears to be from the amygdala to the thalamus and from the dorso-medial nucleus to the orbital cortex. The orbital cortex connects backward to the temporal cortex and claustrum. There would be opportunity for these connections to feed into the amygdala.

I share with Dr. Adey and his group the same concern about the difficulty of segregating or combining the functional roles of hippocampus and periamygdaloid regions. It is quite possible they cannot be segregated. I think, on the other hand, there has been a tendency to push aside the periamygdaloid region, perhaps on the basis of inadequate evidence.

The triangular circuit provides a means for the temporal cortex and amygdala to have, as it were, an anterior circuit which does not need to feed into the hippocampo-fornix system. This is interesting in relation to the patients where the fornix has been destroyed and overt memory deficit does not seem to be present. Although one can argue that the fornix is not the only outflow from the hippocampus, it is a significant one, and the fact that it can be cut bilaterally without producing the type of temporal lobe memory defect is something of a paradox. The relation of the hippocampal outflow through the fornix to the mammillary body to this type of memory defect has also been put aside by Dr. Victor's material.

Adey: This question of the hippocampal input-output mechanisms cannot be disposed of merely by section of fornix, since there is such a wealth of evidence showing how the hippocampus projects into its own overlying gyrus and, from there, there can undoubtedly be a vast variety of subcortical connections.

Feindel: I am not questioning those at all. I was just meaning to imply that the fornix has been considered rather important and the fact is, it does not seem to be.

One further difficulty is exactly the point that you mention, that is, the mesial temporal region has multisynaptic pathways which feed into complex structures. My own feeling would be that the periamygdaloid region and the hippocampus as well as the surrounding cortical zones are all very much concerned with this aspect of memory function.

I would also like to make a plea to those in the group who are making lesions and carrying out depth recording to study the claustrum. One of the most significant features of Nauta's studies is the connection of the orbital cortex of the frontal lobe, apparently by way of the uncinate fasciculus, to the claustrum. In an early study of automatism with Dr. Penfield (15), we mentioned the significance of the claustrum in the human because of its rather large size. It seems to have been ignored, possibly because it has a slab-like structure which is difficult to reach. It may be an important mechanism to allow the mesial temporal or the lateral temporal cortex to feed into a horizontal layer of cells and thus bring about a wide distribution.

Mishkin: I would like to comment on the second circuit about which Nauta (30) has recently given us information, and which Dr. Feindel has just referred to. There is reason to believe that this second circuit is quite different from the one I mentioned first, and may serve quite a different function.

For example, lesions in the orbital frontal cortex, which is part of the second or ventral system, produce defects which are qualitatively different from the defects produced by lesions in the dorsal lateral cortex, belonging to the dorsal system. We know the projections to and from the medialis dorsalis are also different. The lateral frontal cortex projects to the lateral portion and receives projections from it, whereas the orbital frontal cortex sends and receives projections from the medial magnocellular portion. Not only can we make that distinction but, as Dr. Weiskrantz and others have shown, damage to the amygdala and damage to the hippocampus, one related to the ventral and the other to the dorsal system, also produce different behavioral effects.

Phylogenetically, there is a vast development of the parvicellular portion of the medialis dorsalis. In cat this nucleus is mainly magnocellular in nature. In monkey, I believe it is divided more or less equally. In man, I suspect the parvicellular portion is relatively larger still. In terms of Dr. Victor's findings of memory defect in cases with medialis dorsalis pathology, it is not unreasonable to suppose that that portion of it related to the dorsal system, rather than that portion of it related to the ventral (orbital-amygdala-magnocellular) system, is responsible for the defect in memory.

Feindel: I am not sure that one is justified in concluding that. The fact that the small cell portion becomes more prominent may be possibly a reflection of the enormous enlargement of frontal cortex and may not have any specific relationship to memory function *per se.*

Mishkin: The evidence is not really based on the medialis dorsalis. It is evidence based on the other parts of the ventral circuit which, when damaged, do not produce the defect related to impairment in recent memory.

Morrell: I would like to know whether anyone considers that these lesions (made in various places and disrupting various aspects of memory mechanism) have in any case conclusively interfered with storage mechanisms, rather than with what one might call the more dynamic aspects of memory recording or retrieval of information from storage.

Feindel: If you include lesions in man, one of the two cases studied in detail by Milner in Penfield's series (15, 32) did have retrograde amnesia for about four years before operation, with certain retained patches.

Deutsch: Dr. Victor testified that some of the cases do recover some of the lost memory.

Weiskrantz: I was going to raise a similar question. I think, from the logic of the lesion material, it is impossible to make this distinction. You can only make the distinction between affecting the storage or affecting the retrieval, provided you can subsequently return the system to normal. I think this is the very great relevance of Dr. Bickford's observations. There was, for a period of time, what would look like a recording difficulty but this was reversible. We cannot tell from the lesion material, unless the lesion can be "reversed", whether the lost memories would become available once again. I think this difficulty is built into the logic.

REFERENCES

1. ADAMS, R. D., COLLINS, G. H., and VICTOR, M., Troubles de la mémoire et de l'apprentissage chez l'homme; leurs relations avec des lésions des lobes temporaux et du diencéphale (observations anatomo-cliniques). In: *Physiologie de l'Hippocampe.* Centre National de la Recherche Scientifique, Paris, 1962: 273-295.
2. AKELAITIS, A. J. E., Psychobiological studies following section of the corpus callosum. *Am. J. Psychiat.,* 1941, **97**: 1147-1157.
3. ———, Studies on corpus callosum. VII. Study of language functions (tactile and visual lexia and graphia) unilaterally following section of the corpus callosum. *J. Neuropath. Exp. Neurol.,* 1943, **2**: 226-262.
4. BARBIZET, J., Defect of memorizing of hippocampal-mammillary origin: a review. *J. Neurol. Neurosurg. Psychiat.,* 1963, **26**: 127-135.
5. BODIAN, D., Studies on the diencephalon of the Virginia opossum. II. The fiber connections in normal and experimental material. *J. Comp. Neurol.,* 1940, **72**: 207-297.
6. BRIERLEY, J. B., CORSELLIS, J. A. N., HIERONS, R., and NEVIN, S., Subacute encephalitis of later adult life. Mainly affecting the limbic areas. *Brain,* 1960, **83**: 357-368.
7. BUCY, P. C., and KLÜVER, H., An anatomical investigation of the temporal lobe in the monkey (Macaca mulatta). *J. Comp. Neurol.,* 1955, **103**: 151-252.
8. BUERGER-PRINZ, H., and KAILA, M., On the structure in the amnesic syndrome. In: *Organization and Pathology of Thought* (D. Rapaport, Ed.). Columbia Univ. Press, New York, 1951: 650-686.

9. CARRERAS, M., MACCHI, G., ANGELERI, F., and URBANI, M., Sull'attività elettrica della formazione ammonica. Effetti determinati dall'ablazione della corteccia entorinale. *Boll. Soc. Ital. Biol. Sperim.*, 1955, **31**: 182-184.

10. CHAPMAN, L. F., and WOLFF, H. G., The cerebral hemispheres and the highest integrative functions of man. *Arch. Neurol.*, 1959, **1**: 357-424.

11. COLLINS, G. H., VICTOR, M., and ADAMS, R. D., A neuropathological study of Wernicke's disease and Korsakoff's psychosis. *J. Neuropath. Exp. Neurol.*, 1961, **20**: 289-291.

12. DIVRY, P., Des lésions de l'infundibulum dans la démence sénile. *J. Belge Neurol. Psychiat.*, 1935, **35**: 591-599.

13. DOTT, N. M., Surgical aspects of the hypothalamus. In: *The Hypothalamus* (J. C. Brash, Ed.). Oliver & Boyd, London, 1938: 131-185.

14. DRACHMAN, D. A., and ADAMS, R. D., Herpes simplex and acute inclusion-body encephalitis. *Arch. Neurol.*, 1962, **7**: 45-63.

15. FEINDEL, W., and PENFIELD, W., Localization of discharge in temporal lobe automatism. *A.M.A. Arch. Neurol. Psychiat.*, 1954, **72**: 605-630.

16. GARCÍA-BENGOCHEA, F., CORRIGAN, R., MORGANE, P., RUSSELL, JR., D., and HEATH, R. G., Studies on the function of the temporal lobes. I. The section of the fornix. *Trans. Am. Neurol. Ass.*, 1951, **76**: 238-239.

17. GARCÍA-BENGOCHEA, F., DE LA TORRE, O., ESQUIVEL, O., VIETA, R., and FERNÁNDEZ, C., The section of the fornix in the surgical treatment of certain epilepsies. *Trans. Am. Neurol. Ass.*, 1954, **79**: 176-178.

18. GLEES, P., and GRIFFITH, H. B., Bilateral destruction of the hippocampus (Cornu Ammonis) in a case of dementia. *Mschr. Psychiat. Neurol.*, 1952, **123**: 193-204.

19. GRÜNTHAL, E., Zur Kenntnis der Psychopathologie der Korsakowschen Symptomenkomplexes. *Mschr. Psychiat. Neurol.*, 1923, **53**: 89-132.

20. HAYMAKER, W., SMITH, M. G., VAN BOGAERT, L., and DE CHENAR, C., Pathology of viral disease in man characterized by nuclear inclusions. In: *Viral Encephalitis* (W. S. Fields and R. J. Blattner, Eds.). Thomas, Springfield, 1958: 95-204.

21. INGRAM, W. R., Modification of learning by lesions and stimulation in the diencephalon and related structures. In: *Reticular Formation of the Brain* (H. H. Jasper et al., Eds.). Little, Brown, Boston, 1958: 535-544.

22. KAADA, B. R., RASMUSSEN, E. W., and KVEIM, O., Effects of hippocampal lesions on maze learning and retention in rats. *Exp. Neurol.*, 1961, **3**: 333-355.

23. LASHLEY, K. S., In search of the engram. *Symp. Soc. Exp. Biol.*, 1950, **4**: 454-482.

24. LIDZ, T., The amnesic syndrome. *Arch. Neurol. Psychiat.*, 1942, **47**: 588-605.

25. McFIE, J., and PIERCY, M. F., Intellectual impairment with localized cerebral lesions. *Brain*, 1952, **75**: 292-311.

26. MISHKIN, M., Visual discrimination performance following partial ablations of the temporal lobe. II. Ventral surface vs. hippocampus. *J. Comp. Physiol. Psychol.*, 1954, **47**: 187-193.

27. NAUTA, W. J. H., An experimental study of the fornix system in the rat. *J. Comp. Neurol.*, 1956, **104**: 247-271.

28. NAUTA, W. J. H., Hippocampal projections and related neural pathways to the midbrain in the cat. *Brain*, 1958, **81**: 319-340.

29. ———, Neural associations of the amygdaloid complex in the monkey. *Brain*, 1962, **85**: 505-520.

30. ———, Some efferent connections of the prefrontal cortex in the monkey. In: *The Frontal Granular Cortex and Behavior* (J. M. Warren and K. Akert, Eds.). McGraw-Hill, New York, 1964: 397-409.

31. ORBACH, J., MILNER, B., and RASMUSSEN, T., Learning and retention in monkeys after amygdala-hippocampus resection. *Arch. Neurol.*, 1960, **3**: 230-251.

32. PENFIELD, W., and MILNER, B., Memory deficit produced by bilateral lesions in the hippocampal zone. *A.M.A. Arch. Neurol. Psychiat.*, 1958, **79**: 475-497.

33. PICK, A., Beitrag zur Pathologie des Denkverlaufes beim Korsakow. *Z. ges. Neurol. Psychiat.*, 1915, **28**: 344-383.

34. ROSE, F. C., and SYMONDS, C. P., Persistent memory defect following encephalitis. *Brain*, 1960, **83**: 195-212.

35. SCOVILLE, W. B., The limbic lobe in man. *J. Neurosurg.*, 1954, **11**: 64-66.

36. SCOVILLE, W. B., and MILNER, B., Loss of recent memory after bilateral hippocampal lesions. *J. Neurol. Neurosurg. Psychiat.*, 1957, **20**: 11-21.

37. SPIEGEL, E. A., WYCIS, H. T., ORCHINIK, C. W., and FREED, H., The thalamus and temporal orientation. *Science*, 1955, **121**: 771-772.

38. STEPIÉN, L. S., CORDEAU, J. P., and RASMUSSEN, T., The effect of temporal lobe and hippocampal lesions on auditory and visual recent memory in monkeys. *Brain*, 1960, **83**: 470-489.

39. SWEET, W. H., TALLAND, G. A., and ERVIN, F. R., Loss of recent memory following section of fornix. *Trans. Am. Neurol. Ass.*, 1959, **84**: 76-82.

40. TALLAND, G. A., Psychological studies of Korsakoff's psychosis: II. Perceptual functions. *J. Nerv. Ment. Dis.*, 1958, **127**: 197-219.

41. ———, Psychological studies of Korsakoff's psychosis: III. Concept formation. *J. Nerv. Ment. Dis.*, 1959, **128**: 214-226.

42. ———, Psychological studies of Korsakoff's psychosis: V. Spontaneity and activity rate. *J. Nerv. Ment. Dis.*, 1960, **130**: 16-25.

43. ———, Psychological studies of Korsakoff's psychosis: VI. Memory and learning. *J. Nerv. Ment. Dis.*, 1960, **130**: 366-385.

44. TALLAND, G. A., and EKDAHL, M., Psychological studies of Korsakoff's psychosis: IV. The rate and mode of forgetting narrative material. *J. Nerv. Ment. Dis.*, 1959, **129**: 391-404.

45. THOMAS, G. J., and OTIS, L. S., Effects of rhinencephalic lesions on conditioning of avoidance responses in the rat. *J. Comp. Physiol. Psychol.*, 1958, **51**: 130-134.

46. THOMPSON, R., and HAWKINS, W. F., Memory unaffected by mammillary body lesions in the rat. *Exp. Neurol.*, 1961, **3**: 189-196.

47. THOMPSON, R., and MASSOPUST, JR., L. C., The effect of subcortical lesions on retention of a brightness discrimination in rats. *J. Comp. Physiol. Psychol.*, 1960, **53**: 488-496.

48. THOMPSON, R., and RICH, I., Transitory behavioral effects of interpeduncular nucleus damage. *Exp. Neurol.*, 1961, **4**: 310-316.

49. Uchimura, Zur Pathogenese der örtlich elektiven Ammonshörnerkrankung. *Z. ges. Neurol. Psychiat.*, 1928, **114**: 567-601.

50. Van der Horst, L., Über die Psychologie des Korsakowsyndroms. *Mschr. Psychiat. Neurol.*, 1932, **83**: 65-84.

51. Victor, M., and Adams, R. D., The effect of alcohol on the nervous system. *Proc. Ass. Res. Nerv. Ment. Dis.*, 1953, **32**: 526-573.

52. Victor, M., Angevine, J. B., Mancall, E. L., and Fisher, C. M., Memory loss with lesions of hippocampal formation. *Arch. Neurol.*, 1961, **5**: 244-263.

53. Victor, M., Herman, K., and White, E. E., A psychological study of the Wernicke-Korsakoff syndrome. Results of Wechsler-Bellevue intelligence scale and Wechsler memory scale testing at different stages in the disease. *Quart. J. Stud. Alcohol.*, 1959, **20**: 467-479.

54. Victor, M., Hope, J. M., and Adams, R. D., A clinical study of Wernicke's disease. *Trans. Am. Neurol. Ass.*, 1952, **77**: 178-181.

55. Victor, M., Talland, G. A., and Adams, R. D., Psychological studies of Korsakoff's psychosis: I. General intellectual functions. *J. Nerv. Ment. Dis.*, 1959, **128**: 528-537.

56. Walker, A. E., Recent memory impairment in unilateral temporal lesions. *A.M.A. Arch. Neurol. Psychiat.*, 1957, **78**: 543-552.

57. Wechsler, D., A study of retention in Korsakoff psychosis. *Psychiat. Bull. New York State Hosp.*, 1917, **2**: 403-451.

58. ——, *The Measurement of Adult Intelligence*, 3rd ed. Williams & Wilkins, Baltimore, 1944.

59. ——, A standardized memory scale for clinical use. *J. Psychol.*, 1945, **19**: 87-95.

60. White, J. C., and Cobb, S., Psychological changes associated with giant pituitary neoplasms. *A.M.A. Arch. Neurol. Psychiat.*, 1955, **74**: 383-396.

61. Williams, M., and Pennybacker, J., Memory disturbances in third ventricle tumours. *J. Neurol. Neurosurg. Psychiat.*, 1954, **17**: 115-123.

RELEVANCE OF BASIC RESEARCH TO THE SPACE PROGRAM

ORR E. REYNOLDS
Bioscience Programs
National Aeronautics and Space Administration
Washington, D.C.

My assignment for this conference was to review its presentations in the light of their relevance to the space program.

The motives of the space program in biology can be divided rather readily into two categories. One motive is the opportunity that space transportation gives for studying biological phenomena which cannot be studied, or, at least, cannot as readily be studied on earth. The other motive is the importance of biological knowledge in application to space travel itself, as in the solution of physiological and psychological problems related to manned space travel. I might say this conference has contributed thoughts that relate to both these goals.

In the first category, of the opportunities offered by space travel for biological research, there are two major areas. One is the ability to escape from terrestrial influence and study phenomena foreign to life on earth. A typical example of this is the investigation of the role of gravity in a variety of organisms at different biological levels. Such study, in turn, may fit into the second category, because it may turn out to have some application to manned space flight.

Second, there is the opportunity that space travel in the future will (hopefully) afford us to look for life outside the earth. Both of these areas, it seems to me (the environment biology and the exobiology, as the two have grown to be called) provide a very strong basis for fundamental research and illustrate a great need for better conceptualization in biology. One of the reasons for this is the fact that opportunities for doing research in extraterrestrial environments are rare and expensive.

Whether or not one considers an orbiting satellite, a space probe or a planetary probe as a means of producing weightlessness or of escaping from the earth's diurnal influence, almost the only way to assure greater success of experiments (and greater economy) is to formulate specific hypotheses, thereby reducing the necessity for relying solely on empirical data. It seems to me that the content of the early part of this conference, largely work at the molecular level, has a very important role to play in this matter.

341

I would like to call attention to Dr. Fox's brief presentation, in which there was a primary point that I wish to emphasize. But let me first quote from Dr. Calvin's article in a recent issue of the *AIBS Bulletin*. He has the following paragraphs in an article entitled "Communication: from Molecules to Mars" (1).

Rather than try to define that particular concatenation of properties of a molecular system which might be acceptable to everyone as living, I would rather recognize the difficulty of satisfying everyone and simply take two of the qualities which everyone will agree are certainly basic attributes of a living system, and try to describe the sequence of events which might have produced them from nonliving origins.

These two processes which I think most, if not all, of us would agree upon as being prerequisites of present-day living systems are 1) their ability to transfer and transform energy in a directed way and 2) their ability to remember how to do this, once having learned it, and to transfer or communicate that information to another system like itself which it can construct.

Then he restates this: ". . . 1) the transfer and transformation of energy and 2) the communication and transformation of information."

I think this article is very significant because it has a bearing on the very central point of our problems discussed here.

Dr. Fox's presentation has a very optimistic note, and it is this: in looking for extraterrestrial life, it might be that one could no more expect life to be constructed of carbon compounds than of anything else, and hence one could hardly know what to look for. In other words, some kind of generalization is needed in order to know what to search for.

The fact that there is such a likelihood of natural compounds, which we associate with life, forming in the absence of living material, gives us some confidence in the hypothesis that there is, at least, a high probability that extraterrestrial life, if encountered, would involve some of the same molecular species with which we are familiar on earth. And, if that proves to be the case, then there also seems to be a probability that evolutionary processes, once life had arisen from this "preliving" stage would proceed along lines somewhat analogous to those it has followed on earth. That fact would make the job not less difficult but would make us more optimistic. In other words, it is not a hopeless thing to look for living organisms that are related, at least biochemically, in a very fundamental way to those we know on earth.

Now, another point about the evolutionary problem: evolution becomes both prebiological and biological, a very important key in our preparation for the day soon to come when we will look for and study life on other planets.

Common mechanisms, at the molecular level, appear to occur throughout the phyletic scale in our earth organisms. Therefore, those processes that we know in the lowest form such as bacteria, those processes concerned with deoxyribonucleic acid, ribonucleic acid and protein fulfilling the roles of genetic information storage and messenger or release mechanisms, and protein in the role of effector, might be very significant to consider in terms of the nervous system.

Dr. Hydén, I think, was one who earlier in this conference mentioned the fact that the protein production of nerves is at an extremely high level. It would seem to me worthwhile to think about the information processes in nerve being analogous to those found in lower systems. More discussion of the possible role of protein in this process might have been valuable.

I will turn now to the problem of manned space travel, and the discussions we have had here in application to that problem. It occurs to me that there are three ways in which our discussions relate to the problem of manned space flight.

The first is in the training of those chosen to visit other planets. With space in these vehicles at such a premium, we are going to need people with multidisciplinary talents, people who can adequately serve the roles of pilot and of scientist competent in all the necessary disciplines. This is a very specific problem, being discussed right now in the National Aeronautics and Space Administration and elsewhere. It seems to me that anything that can be done to effect a real increase in our ability to educate people significantly is essential.

The second is what you might call human engineering; it is the need to know enough about human functional processes and about man's ability to absorb and convey information, to be able to gear men to the vehicles that they must handle.

The third, the one that is most intriguing to me, concerns the long duration of space travel and the great distances involved. For example, a very simple difficulty is that, in a manned flight to Mars, about the minimal time in which a return could be expected would be four years. It is difficult to conceive of proceeding from the earth to Mars at any time other than during opposition, and there is a two-year wait between oppositions. The rate at which scientific and technical information accumulates on earth, and the rate at which an observer on Mars will be able to accumulate information are clearly important. So, too, are the techniques of communication between those on Mars and those on earth or in transit.

We obviously have several problems: How do we select the kind of information that we want to transmit to the traveler? How do we arrange for him to absorb it in a utilizable way? And in reverse, how do we get back information from him of the most valuable kind?

I think there is a real hazard that the transportation capabilities in space travel are going to outstrip rapidly our abilities to use these vehicles and their crews to conduct good scientific work.

In short, these are a few of the instances in which I think the subject matters that this conference has dealt with are of crucial importance to progress in the space program.

Hetherington: In speaking of the data storage and selection problems and the transmission power requirements involved, Dr. Reynolds pointed out the difficulties of communication. I wonder if he might not agree that the crewman in the capsule has at least as difficult a problem, in terms of his own personal information storage and retrieval system. As one obvious example, what about the landing skills he may not have a chance to practice for extended periods, since he may be in transit for years? When he comes back to Earth he may or may not have had the practice furnished by landing on Mars (under very different conditions of re-entry), and in this case some types of psychomotor "information" may have had little or no chance to be retrieved and re-lived for some years. This may turn into a very difficult information processing and retrieval problem for him, one which may have to be solved by means of in-flight simulation of some sort, or vicarious practice and prompting obtained by watching another pilot on a TV loop, or something else I cannot at the moment imagine. This problem, though allied to the communication difficulties Dr. Reynolds mentioned, may turn out to be even more crucial.

Reynolds: I think this is a case in which the proof of the pudding will be in the eating. Speaking personally, I believe the requirement for better conceptualization is so great that we ought to support research at the most fundamental level we can reach.

REFERENCE

1. Calvin, M., Communication: from molecules to Mars. *AIBS Bull.*, 1962, **12** (5): 29-44.

Professor Kogan was an invited speaker at the Conference but was unfortunately unable to be present. He has kindly sent the following short summary of the paper he wished to present.

ELECTRICAL ACTIVITY AND RNA OF BRAIN CELLS

A. B. KOGAN

Chair of Human and Animal Physiology

The Rostov State University

Rostov-on-Don, USSR

The study of the physicochemical nature of the processes of nervous activity demands the complex application of electrophysiological, cytochemical and microstructural methods. We have worked out some techniques that permit the simultaneous registration of the evoked potentials and the cytochemical and structural changes of brain cells in a definite functional state of unrestrained animals (4, 5; Figure 132).

Cortical neurons were studied in the cat with chronically implanted electrodes. A hollow capsule was fastened in the skull, the thin metallic lower surface of the capsule being shaped to fit the form of the brain hemisphere. The stainless steel electrodes with plexiglass insulation passed through the capsule at several points. In preliminary experiments the functional role of the cortical cell structures under the electrodes was defined by determining their electrical responses to light, sound, etc., and their reactions to direct brain stimulation. In the final experiment the specific functional state, so determined, of the brain structures under the electrode was evoked under electrophysiological control. At the same moment the metabolism in this cortical area was stopped by means of cold introduced by a carrier passing through the capsule (Figure 133). After the guillotining of the cat, this area underwent cytochemical, histological and electron-microscopic investigation.

Among the other cytochemical reactions carried out by us, RNA, as used in functional biochemistry (1, 2, 6, 7, 8) was determined by the methods of Brachet, Einarson and Shabadash. For the quantitative evaluation of the results microphotometry was applied. For this purpose, the reflection of a neuron was projected on the screen of a slot photometer and the absorption of light at different sites on the surface of the neuron was measured.

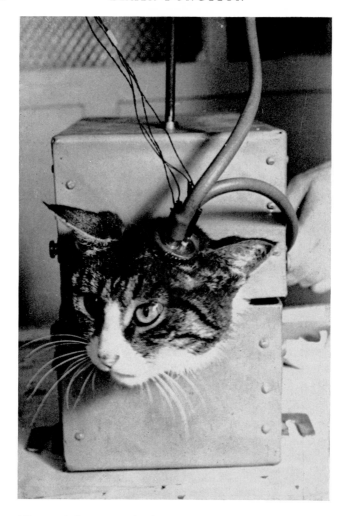

Figure 132. Cat with the chronically implanted device
during the final experiment.

In the pyramidal cells of the visual cortex in unrestrained cats, potentials evoked by light flashes were followed by a rise of the RNA content (Figure 134). This was often accompanied by redistribution of the RNA in the neuron, namely from apical to basal dendrites. Those cells which did not respond to light flashes did not show any rise of RNA.

Table 20 illustrates the results of those experiments in which the most evident changes of RNA contents were found. Only in a few experiments, however, was it possible to get statistically reliable average values for each of the neurons and for all neurons in the zone of excitation.

In many cases the photometric indices made it possible only to estimate the type of redistribution of RNA in the parts of the neuron. Frequently, the RNA content was markedly different even in neighboring cells. This variability may reflect the presence of both excited and inhibited neurons in

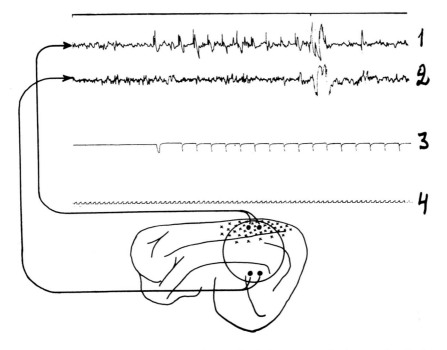

Figure 133. Schema showing leading off of the potentials during the final experiment. Nos. 1, 2: potential traces; 3: light flashes; 4: time, 0.25 sec. Note artifacts on trace 1, caused by the cold-carrier entering the capsule, after which the evoked potential disappeared.

TABLE 20

Pyramidal cells in the area giving electrical responses to light stimulation		Pyramidal cells in the area not responding to light stimulation	
Cell number	Average absorption of light by cytoplasm	Cell number	Average absorption of light by cytoplasm
1	61	1	60
2	48	2	69
3	43	3	72
4	56	4	47
5	38	5	64
6	42	6	66
7	53	7	54
8	63	8	58
9	44	9	63
10	57	10	55
		11	66
Average	50.7	Average	61.3
$t_{m1} = 19.5$ $(t_{N1} = 3.3)$		$t_{m2} = 26.9$ $(t_{N2} = 3.2)$	

Reliability of the average values comparison $-t_2 = 3.07$ $(t_{N1,2} = 2.8)$

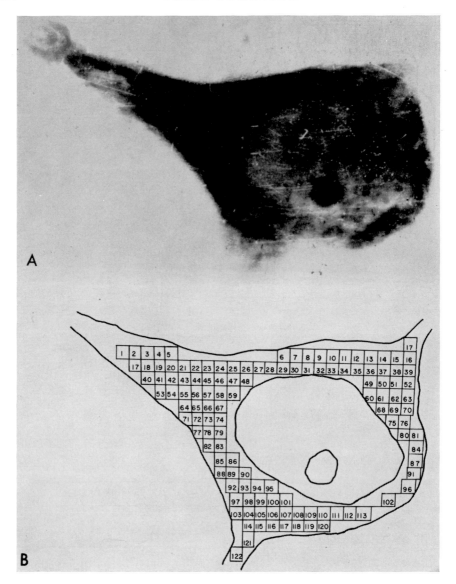

Figure 134. The pyramidal cell in which RNA was shown according to Brachet
(A) and the plan of its fractional photometering (B).

the active point of the cortex under observation (3). Some correlation between the amplitude of evoked potentials and RNA contents in cells was
observed.

REFERENCES

1. BRODSKY, W. Y., In: *First Conference on Nucleic Acids.* Moscow, 1959: 204-
    208 (in Russian).
2. HYDÉN, H., Cytophysiological aspects of the nucleic acids and proteins of

nervous tissue. In: *Neurochemistry* (K. A. C. Elliott, I. H. Page and J. H. Quastel, Eds.). Thomas, Springfield, 1955: 331-375.

3. JASPER, H., RICCI, G., and DOANE, B., Patterns of cortical neuronal discharge during conditioned responses in monkeys. In: *The Neurological Basis of Behaviour* (G. E. W. Wolstenholme and C. M. O'Connor, Eds.). Churchill, London, 1958: 277-294.

4. KOGAN, A. B., A complex investigation of the electrical, structural and cyto-chemical manifestations of the brain neurones activity. In: *Conference on the Electrophysiology of the Nervous System.* Kiev, 1960: 205-206 (in Russian).

5. ———, Some correlations between electrophysiological and structural chemi-cal manifestations of excitation in the nerve cell. In: *XXII International Congress of Physiological Sciences*, Vol. II (Abstracts of Communica-tions). Excerpta Medica, Amsterdam, 1962: No. 1054.

6. LEVINSON, L. B., In: *Lomonosov Lectures in Moscow University.* Moscow, 1957: 32-37 (in Russian).

7. PORTUGALOV, W. W., In: *II Conference on the Biochemistry of the Central Nervous System.* Kiev, 1957: 62-64 (in Russian).

8. WINNIKOV, Y. A., In: *Cytology*, Vol. I. Moscow, 1959: 141-152 (in Russian).

INDEXES

INDEX OF NAMES

INDEX OF SUBJECTS